DYNAMIC ASPECTS OF BIOCHEMISTRY

DYNAMIC ASPECTS OF BIOCHEMISTRY

BY

ERNEST BALDWIN, B.A., Ph.D.

*Professor of Biochemistry at University College in the
University of London, formerly Fellow of
St John's College, Cambridge*

SECOND EDITION

CAMBRIDGE
AT THE UNIVERSITY PRESS
1952

PUBLISHED BY
THE SYNDICS OF THE CAMBRIDGE UNIVERSITY PRESS

London Office: Bentley House, N.W. I
American Branch: New York

Agents for Canada, India, and Pakistan: Macmillan

First Edition   1947
Reprinted   1948
„   1949
Italian translation 1951
Second Edition   1952

Printed in Great Britain at the University Press, Cambridge
(Brooke Crutchley, University Printer)

'The difference between a piece of stone and an atom is that an atom is highly organised, whereas the stone is not. The atom is a pattern, and the molecule is a pattern, and the crystal is a pattern; but the stone, although it is made up of these patterns, is just a mere confusion. It's only when life appears that you begin to get organisation on a larger scale. Life takes the atoms and molecules and crystals; but, instead of making a mess of them like the stone, it combines them into new and more elaborate patterns of its own.'

ALDOUS HUXLEY, *Time must have a Stop*

CONTENTS

PART I. ENZYMES

CHAPTER I. THE GENERAL BEHAVIOUR AND PROPERTIES OF ENZYMES

CHAPTER II. THE NATURE OF THE CATALYTIC PROCESS

CHAPTER III. BIOLOGICAL ENERGETICS

CHAPTER IV. HYDROLASES AND ADDING ENZYMES

CHAPTER V. TRANSFERRING AND ISOMERIZING ENZYMES

CHAPTER VI. OXIDIZING ENZYMES

CHAPTER VII. DEHYDROGENASE SYSTEMS

PART II. METABOLISM

CHAPTER VIII. METHODS EMPLOYED IN THE INVESTIGATION OF INTERMEDIARY METABOLISM

CHAPTER IX. FOOD, DIGESTION AND ABSORPTION

CHAPTER X. GENERAL METABOLISM OF PROTEINS AND AMINO-ACIDS

CHAPTER XI. SPECIAL METABOLISM
OF THE AMINO-ACIDS

CHAPTER XII. EXCRETORY METABOLISM
OF PROTEINS AND AMINO-ACIDS

CHAPTER XIII. SOME SPECIAL ASPECTS
OF NITROGEN METABOLISM

CHAPTER XIV. METABOLISM OF PURINE
DERIVATIVES

TABLES

FIGURES AND DIAGRAMS

PREFACE TO THE SECOND EDITION

THE death of Frederick Gowland Hopkins shortly after the first edition of this book appeared was not only a great loss to biochemistry but also a grievous personal loss to his many pupils, colleagues and friends. I have not, however, altered the dedication in any way, for his spirit lives still in the essentially dynamic habit of thought that he himself did so much to develop and foster during his fifty years of service to biochemistry.

In preparing this second edition I have tried to bring it as nearly up to date as possible without increasing its size. This has necessitated a good deal of rewriting and rearrangement, and the text has therefore been completely re-set. No attempt has been made to enlarge the field which the book attempts to cover, but a few new explanatory sections have been introduced and also a chapter in which I have brought together and tried to unify the ideas on biological energetics which were scattered throughout the text of the first edition.

Many of those who reviewed the first edition and many of my colleagues and friends have encouraged me to believe that the book has had a real value in the dissemination of dynamic habits of thought, and it is my earnest hope that the new edition will prove as acceptable as the old and that I may be forgiven for any errors and shortcomings that have escaped me. I have also received much useful criticism, and this I have endeavoured to meet here. The problem of bibliography has given me particular concern. To give chapter and verse for every statement between these covers would be a formidable task indeed, while references to only the most recent papers would serve little useful purpose at a time when progress is as rapid as it is at present. This is essentially an elementary book, and I have therefore adhered to the policy adopted in the first edition and given only a list of review articles and books, mostly of recent date; these, I believe, can serve either to expand the general reader's horizons or provide starting points for a more intensive study of particular fields.

Once again I must express gratitude to the *Annual Review of Biochemistry*, and in particular to Dr J. Murray Luck, its Editor-in-Chief, who allowed me to see proof of the 1951 volume some months before its actual publication. This enabled me to find many papers missed in the course of routine reading. From the numerous friends and colleagues who have helped in one way or another in the preparation of the new edition and to whom my thanks are due, I must single out my wife for special mention. She has given me, as always, immeasurable assistance in proof reading, preparing the index, and carrying out many others of the often tedious tasks attached to the preparation of any book. My thanks are also due to the Cambridge University Press, not only for the excellence of their craftsmanship, which speaks for itself in these pages, but also for their wholehearted co-operation in every way and at every stage of the production of this new edition.

E. B.

PORTHLEVEN
August 1951

PREFACE TO THE FIRST EDITION

In spite of war-time difficulties and restrictions, Biochemistry has continued to expand more and more rapidly each year, in stature as well as in scope. It has been impossible for many years past for any one worker to read more than a small fraction of the new output, even when foreign journals were available. Without the invaluable aid of the *Annual Reviews of Biochemistry*, to whose authors and editors I and every other biochemist must pay high tribute, the preparation of this new book would have been impossible. Even with their help, some sections of the book will probably be out of date by the time it appears in print, and may well be out of date already in certain respects. But the last few decades have seen the establishment of a considerable body of information which, though it may change considerably in detail, will perhaps not change significantly in substance during the next few years. I venture to hope that a new edition may be called for before the present contents have become wholly archaic, so that there will be opportunity to correct the many faults which have doubtless escaped notice and to bring the whole volume up to date.

The subject-matter of biological chemistry, like that of biology itself, can be roughly divided into two parts; the static, or morphological, and the dynamic, or physiological. Knowledge of the latter demands as an essential pre-requisite a knowledge of the former, and it is therefore a matter for rejoicing that many organic chemists of the present day are devoting their attention to the chemical constitution and configuration of the organic *Bausteine* that form the material basis of living cells. In some fields, notably in that of protein chemistry, the interdependence and collaboration between the organic and the biochemist are so intimate that it is impossible to say which is the organic chemist and which the biochemist. If any differentiation were necessary it could best be made, probably, in terms of their respective attitudes towards the *Bausteine*. For the organic chemist the main focus of attention is the structure and configuration of these materials while, for the biochemist, the main problems are those of the behaviour and function of these substances in organized, biological systems.

The more static aspects of these *Bausteine* are already fairly well covered by monographs and review articles, some of which I have indicated in the bibliography; the essentially dynamic aspects, on the other hand, have hitherto been but inadequately described and, in view of their wide importance and interest, I believe that a real demand exists at the present time for a book of this kind.

Elementary Biochemistry is taught in this University in two courses. The first and older of these, Chemical Physiology, forms part of the course in mammalian Physiology, and caters primarily for the needs of medical and veterinary students. For these there already exists a wealth of text-books, which the present volume neither hopes nor desires to supplant. In the second course, much more recently introduced, Biochemistry is taught as an independent scientific discipline, and without that emphasis on clinical problems with which it has usually been associated in the past, and which properly finds a place in Chemical Physiology. For students taking this second course there exists no suitable text-book, and it is primarily with their needs in mind that the present book has been written. I hope, however, that it will also help to open up new horizons to those whose interest in Biochemistry is primarily that of the organic chemist or the clinician in training. Perhaps it will serve too as an introduction to others who, wishing to take an advanced degree course here or elsewhere, find it difficult at the present time to discover suitable elementary reading. With the needs of such students as these in mind I have included a short bibliography of review articles and books, mostly of recent date and written by experts in their respective fields.

In Biochemistry, as in any young but rapidly expanding branch of science, there are fields in which facts are scanty, evidence contradictory and speculation rife. I have tried to avoid such topics, but where this has not been possible I have attempted to give a critical account of the facts but, at the same time, to speculate a little. I cannot wholly subscribe to the doctrine that speculation is out of place in an elementary text-book, for there are many gaps in the subject, and unless these can in some way be bridged it is difficult or impossible to give a coherent account. My experience as a teacher has been that coherence is essential in an elementary exposition. Speculation plays and has always played an important part in the advance-ment of scientific knowledge, for no research worker gropes blindly after he knows not what; he invariably begins with certain reasonable possibilities in mind. In short, he speculates. To speculate unreasonably is worse than not to speculate at all, but providing certain tests of reasonableness and compatibility are applied beforehand, speculation is a valuable tool, and one which finds a place in every scientific workshop. The danger is that speculation is not always recognized as what it is, and I have, therefore, tried to distinguish clearly between fact and fantasy, hoping in this way to steer a middle course between unbridled imagination on the one hand, and an equally undesirable hypertrophy of the critical faculty on the other.

A word of explanation is perhaps necessary for the use in these pages of somewhat novel and certainly unorthodox methods of writing the equations of certain chemical reactions and groups or sequences of reactions. I have adopted them only after a long period of trial. They give a distinctively pictorial representation of chemical events, and many students find such a picture more easily comprehended and remembered than the more formal representations usually adopted. I trust that the reader will exercise the little patience necessary to become familiar with these 'whirligigs', for they have great advantages in cases where a long chain of successive chemical events has to be described briefly and as a whole.

The writing of this book has been largely a spare-time occupa-tion, and there has been little enough spare time during the war years. Progress has often been slow, therefore, and the task has nearly been abandoned more than once. I owe the fact of its eventual completion to the kind encouragement given to me by my friends and colleagues. Particular thanks are due to Dr D. J. Bell and Dr E. Watchorn, who have read the whole of the manuscript, and to Prof. A. C. Chibnall, who read the proofs. I am glad also to acknowledge the help I have had from Miss V. Moyle. These, and others who have read particular sections and chapters, have all given precious advice and valuable criticisms. My task has been simplified in many ways by Prof. J. B. S. Haldane's *Enzymes* and by Dr D. E. Green's *Mechanisms of Biological Oxidations*, and particular thanks are due to Dr Malcolm Dixon, who has given me much from his great personal store of information.

I should also like to record my thanks to Dr J. C. Boursnell, who heroically undertook the preparation of the index, to Mr H. Mowl, who prepared the drawings for Fig. 14, and to members of the Cambridge Part I Biochemistry Class of 1945–6, who have allowed me to make use of some of their experimental data in the preparation of Figs. 1, 3 and 7.

To my wife, who prepared the work for publication, and to all departments of the Cambridge University Press I wish to express my humble and hearty thanks for their patience, consideration and expert workmanship.

E. B.

CAMBRIDGE
January 1946

ACKNOWLEDGEMENTS

The author's thanks are due to the following for permission to reproduce figures: the Cambridge University Press for Figs. 2, 3C, and 24; Dr H. Fraenkel-Conrat and the *Journal of Biological Chemistry* for Fig. 3B; Drs F. Schlenk and F. Lipmann and the University of Wisconsin Press for Figs. 21, 22 and 31; Messrs Longmans Green & Co., Ltd., for Figs. 4, 5, 9, and 13; and Messrs W. Heffer & Co. Ltd. for Fig. 12.

PART I

ENZYMES

CHAPTER I

THE GENERAL BEHAVIOUR AND PROPERTIES OF ENZYMES

INTRODUCTION

WHEREVER we turn in the world of living things we find chemical changes taking place. Green plants, together with certain bacteria, are capable of fixing solar energy and synthesizing complex organic substances of high-energy content from very simple starting materials, namely, water, carbon dioxide and small amounts of inorganic substances such as nitrates and phosphates. Other living organisms possess the ability to decompose these complex materials and to exploit for their own purposes the energy that is locked up within them, and it is in this way that animals, for instance, obtain the energy they expend in the discharge of their bodily functions; reproduction, growth, locomotion and so on. Now it is a significant fact that nearly all the chemical changes that go on in living tissues are changes which, in themselves, proceed too slowly to be measurable or even, in many cases, detectable. How, then, does it happen that living animals can obtain energy and expend it as fast as they do? The answer is that living organisms possess numerous catalysts which speed up chemical reactions to the rates achieved in biological systems. Whether we consider digestion, metabolism, locomotion, fermentation or putrefaction, chemical changes are going on, and these chemical changes are catalysed. It is the purpose of this book to give some account of these changes and of the various mechanisms at present known to participate in their catalysis.

A catalyst, in the classical definition of Ostwald, is 'an agent which affects the velocity of a chemical reaction without appearing in the final products of the reaction'. Examples of catalysts are familiar to every student of chemistry, and perhaps the most striking is that commonest of all chemical reagents, water. As is well known, hydrogen and chlorine react together with explosive violence if exposed to sunlight, and yet, as Baker showed, perfectly dry hydrogen and perfectly dry chlorine fail to react together at all. Baker found that numerous familiar reactions do not proceed except in the presence of traces of water, and that water is, in fact, a very important catalyst. Finely-divided metals, such as platinum, nickel and palladium, also are capable of catalysing a wide range of reactions, and Wieland, for instance, found that on the addition of colloidal palladium to aqueous solutions of various simple organic compounds, a catalytic oxidation (dehydrogenation) of the compounds ensues. Many more examples could be cited. Thus the hydrolysis of esters is a process that goes on very slowly in neutral solutions but is greatly accelerated by traces of strong acids or alkalis. Again, chemical reactions as a whole proceed more rapidly at higher than at lower temperatures. But living organisms do not have at their disposal the strong acids and alkalis, the high temperatures and the other artifices which are available to a chemist working in a laboratory, yet the synthetic ability of living cells and tissues far surpasses that of the chemist.

We must know something about simple catalysts and their mode of action before turning to the more complex catalysts and catalytic systems that we find in living tissues. There are many resemblances between catalysis as effected by more or less complex chemical reagents on the one hand and by biological systems on the other, but differences also exist. In the first place, a catalyst, of whatever kind, only affects the *rate* of the reaction which it catalyses. This fact is particularly well illustrated in the case of a reaction such as the hydrolysis of an ester, which is reversible. If we take ethyl acetate, for example, and heat it with water, the ester is slowly hydrolysed, but the reaction stops before the hydrolysis is complete. On the other hand, if we start with equivalent proportions of ethyl alcohol and acetic acid and heat these together, we find that they react to form ethyl acetate, but once again the reaction stops before reaching completion. Indeed, from whichever side we start, the composition of the final reaction-mixture is always the same, the system attaining a state which can be represented by the following equilibrium:

$$C_2H_5OH + CH_3COOH \rightleftharpoons CH_3COO.C_2H_5 + H_2O.$$

If we employ dilute mineral acid as a catalyst we again obtain a reaction-mixture of the same composition, while if a biological catalyst such as liver esterase is used, the final composition is the same once more. These facts point to several important conclusions: first, that only the reaction velocity, and not the extent to which the reaction proceeds, is affected by the catalyst, and secondly, that in the case of a reversible reaction (and on theoretical grounds it is usual to assume that all reactions are reversible) the catalyst influences the reaction velocity equally in both directions. The direction in which such a reaction will proceed is determined, of course, by mass-law considerations and by the availability of free energy. We must therefore suppose that a catalyst which accelerates the decomposition of a given substance must also be capable of catalysing its synthesis. But it does not by any means follow that the necessary conditions can be experimentally realized.

A second important feature of the phenomenon of catalysis is that the effect of the catalyst is normally out of all proportion to the amount used. A minute quantity of colloidal platinum is sufficient to catalyse the decomposition of an unlimited amount of hydrogen peroxide, provided nothing happens to interfere with its catalytic properties. In practice, however, it frequently happens that catalysts are inhibited ('poisoned') by the presence of extraneous material. Thus, in the example just given, minute quantities of hydrocyanic acid, mercuric chloride or certain other substances suffice to destroy the catalytic properties of the platinum. This 'poisoning' is often a serious nuisance in commercial processes, but in many cases the catalytic activity can be recovered relatively easily. In biological systems, too, we find that a comparatively small concentration of the catalytic material is all that is necessary, and that the catalysts are easily inhibited in a variety of ways which we shall discuss in later sections.

According to Ostwald's definition, the amount and chemical composition of a catalyst is the same at the end of its period of activity as it was at the beginning, though it is frequently found that its physical properties have been changed. Here is what at first sight appears to be a fundamental difference between catalysts such as colloidal metals and the catalytic agents we find in living tissues, but the difference is more apparent than real. Biological catalysts commonly lose much of their activity as the reactions which they catalyse proceed, but in such cases it usually appears that the catalyst has undergone inhibition by the products of its own activity, or else that its physical state has been modified in such a way that its catalytic properties have been destroyed.

Another apparent difference between the two types of catalysts is that whereas a catalyst such as platinum black does not initiate a reaction but only accelerates one which already proceeds, albeit very slowly, in its absence, biological systems do in certain cases give the appearance of initiating new processes. For example, living yeast cells catalyse an almost quantitative conversion of glucose into ethyl alcohol and carbon dioxide according to the well-known equation:

$$C_6H_{12}O_6 = 2C_2H_5OH + 2CO_2.$$

By contrast, certain bacteria, e.g. *Streptococcus faecalis*, catalyse the conversion of glucose into lactic acid:

$$C_6H_{12}O_6 = 2CH_3CH(OH)COOH.$$

Other organisms again yield yet other products. Now glucose itself does not show any propensity to decompose spontaneously into either alcohol or lactic acid. Nevertheless, there is no real theoretical difficulty here. As is well known, it is the rule rather than the exception in organic chemistry that side-reactions take place, indicating that organic substances tend to decompose or react in more ways than one. Let us suppose, therefore, that glucose can decompose into a series of different products, A, B, C, D and so on, each product arising by its own series of reactions. Under ordinary conditions the conversion of glucose into A, B, C, etc., proceeds only at imperceptible speed, but, under the influence of the catalysts of yeast, one of the possible modes of breakdown is selectively accelerated to such an extent that it is followed almost quantitatively. The catalysts of *S. faecalis*, by contrast, selectively accelerate another and a different mode.

This last case serves to illustrate what is perhaps the most striking feature of biological catalysis. Whereas a catalyst such as platinum black can catalyse any of a rather wide range of reactions, it is characteristic of biological catalysts that they catalyse only one kind of reaction and even, more often than not, one particular reaction and one only. But this is a difference only in their degree of specificity, or exclusiveness, and cannot be reckoned as evidence that biological catalysts differ essentially or fundamentally from catalysts of other kinds.

Although the effects of biological catalysts have long been familiar, and although they have been deliberately used by mankind since the dawn of history for the production of cheese, alcoholic beverages and the like, it is only in comparatively recent years that we have acquired any knowledge or understanding of their mode of action. The celebrated Italian physiologist, Spallanzani, was perhaps the first to make a deliberate study of one of these catalysts, and this he did by feeding hawks with pieces of meat enclosed in wire cages, which were later regurgitated. In this way he demonstrated that the gastric juice of hawks contains something which brings about the liquefaction of meat. But as yet the nature of the responsible agent, which we now know under the name of pepsin, could not even be guessed.

It was Louis Pasteur who laid the foundations of our present knowledge. In the course of his famous researches on fermentation he demonstrated that solutions of organic materials such as glucose are perfectly stable if carefully sterilized and stored in sealed vessels. If, however, air was allowed to gain access to the solutions, fermentation set in, and this, Pasteur showed, was due to contamination with living yeast cells which came in with the air. So long as these micro-organisms were carefully excluded, no fermentation took place. Similarly, Pasteur showed that the souring of wine, a troublesome phenomenon which he was commissioned by the then government of France to investigate, was attributable to the presence of certain other micro-organisms. These and other observations of a like kind led Pasteur to conclude that processes such as alcoholic fermentation, the souring of wine and milk are due to, and inseparable from, the vital activities of certain particular micro-organisms, which he accordingly named 'ferments'.

Pasteur's views received a severe blow when it was discovered by the brothers Buchner that if yeast is macerated with sand and submitted to high pressures, a juice can be expressed from it which contains no living cells whatever, but is nevertheless capable of fermenting sugar with the production of alcohol and carbon dioxide. The Buchners, in fact, succeeded in demonstrating what Pasteur regarded as an impossibility, the fermentation of sugar in the complete absence of living cells. Yeast juice clearly contains the catalyst or catalysts by means of which living yeast accomplishes the alcoholic fermentation of sugar, and to describe this catalytic agent the term 'enzyme' was coined, from the Greek ἐν ζύμῃ, literally 'in yeast'. When other similar catalysts were later discovered and studied, the term enzyme was taken over as a collective title and the yeast-juice enzyme received the distinguishing name of zymase.

The discovery of zymase was a fundamental advance. It had hitherto been possible to study fermentation and kindred processes only in the presence of living cells, but living cells multiply, die off, use up some chemical substances and excrete others so that, superimposed on fermentation proper, there are many other chemical processes. With the newly discovered yeast juice, however, the chemistry of fermentation could be studied in isolation, quite apart from all the other chemical operations carried out by the intact organism. As we now know, 'zymase' is not a single enzyme or catalyst, but rather a complex system of catalysts, and similar juices can be prepared from many kinds of cells. The Buchners made their fundamental discovery as recently as 1897, and progress thereafter was rapid. The first enzyme to be obtained in the pure, crystalline state was obtained only some 30 years later, in 1926, and since that time numerous others have been purified and isolated.

Certain important discoveries were made comparatively early in the rather meteoric history of enzyme chemistry. Thus it was found that zymase loses its activity completely if boiled, and that if it is dialysed its activity is similarly lost. After dialysis, though not after boiling, activity could be restored by adding the dialysate, i.e. the small-molecular materials removed in the process of dialysis, or by the addition of a little boiled yeast juice. These observations show that, in addition to the thermolabile, non-dialysable enzymes, yeast juice also contains thermostable, dialysable factors in the absence of which fermentation cannot go forward. Thus there arose the conception of enzymes as thermolabile substances of high molecular weight, and of a second group of catalytic materials, called co-enzymes, which consist of small, thermostable molecules. Both are necessary if fermentation is to take place. Just as we know that zymase is in reality a complex mixture of enzymes, so, too, the dialysable complement is known to contain more than one co-enzyme, and we shall have a great deal to say about this particular case in a later chapter.

Even this brief review has revealed a number of the most important properties which characterize enzymes. *They are colloidal materials of high molecular weight, are thermolabile and highly specific, and can usually be extracted from the cells in which they are produced.*

NOMENCLATURE AND CLASSIFICATION OF ENZYMES

Enzymes may be classified in any of several ways. All enzymes, so far as we know, are produced inside living cells, and the majority of them do their work inside the cells which produce them, though they can usually be extracted and their activity studied independently. In simple animal organisms such as *Amoeba* the processes of digestion are preceded by the phagocytic ingestion of food particles, which then undergo intracellular digestion, but in more highly organized forms of animal life it is commonly found that digestive enzymes are secreted into the digestive cavity, so that digestion is extracellular, at any rate in part. Thus we can distinguish between intracellular and extracellular enzymes. This mode of classification is often useful and is likely to be considerably extended in the future as more information is gained about the precise localization of enzymes within the cell, e.g. in the nucleus, mitochondria, cytoplasm and so on.

More usually, enzymes are named and classified in terms of the reaction or reactions which they catalyse, though no practicable system of rigid nomenclature has yet been devised. We can distinguish, for example, a large and important group of enzymes which catalyse the hydrolysis of their substrates, i.e. the substances upon which their catalytic influence is exerted, and these enzymes are accordingly termed *hydrolases*. This group includes all the extracellular enzymes concerned with digestion, and many intracellular enzymes besides. Individual enzymes are usually named by adding -*ase* to the names of their respective substrates; for example, enzymes which catalyse the hydrolysis of starch are collectively called amylases (*amylum* = starch, Latin), and different individual amylases are distinguished by reference to the sources from which they are obtained. Thus we find a salivary and a pancreatic amylase among the digestive enzymes of mammals. Similarly, enzymes which catalyse the hydrolysis of proteins are known as proteinases, and those which act upon fats as lipases. The group of hydrolases also includes many non-digestive enzymes, such, for instance, as urease, which catalyses the hydrolytic breakdown of urea into ammonia and carbon dioxide; and arginase, which catalyses the hydrolysis of the amino-acid arginine into ornithine and urea.

A second large and important group of enzymes comprises those which catalyse biological oxidations and reductions. Most biological oxidations, as we shall see, involve the removal of hydrogen from the substrate undergoing oxidation, and most of the oxidizing enzymes are accordingly known as *dehydrogenases*. Some of these differ from the rest in certain respects and are called *oxidases*, though this must not be supposed to imply that they catalyse the addition of oxygen to their substrates.

In addition to these two large groups we know of a number of other types including *adding*, *transferring* and *isomerizing* *enzymes*.

Specificity

One of the most striking properties of enzymes is their specificity. By this we mean that a given enzyme can catalyse only a comparatively small range of reactions, and even, in many cases, one reaction and one only. It is possible to distinguish fairly sharply between a number of different degrees and types of specificity, and to make this clear we may consider first of all what is known as optical, or better, as *stereochemical specificity*.

The majority of chemical substances formed and broken down in metabolic processes are optically active and, of the two possible stereo-isomeric forms in which such substances can exist, only one is usually found on any large scale in natural materials and processes. Of the sugars, for example, we normally find only the D-isomers, though it is true that their enantiomorphs are occasionally found. Thus L-galactose has been isolated from various plant materials and from the molluscan polysaccharide, galactogen. None the less, it remains a fact that there is an overwhelming preponderance of D-sugars in nature. Similarly, of the α-amino-acids only the L-members occur extensively in nature: cases of the occurrence of D-amino-acids have been reported, but are relatively rare. Perhaps, therefore, it is not surprising to find, as we do, that most enzymes show a strong and usually a complete selectivity for one member of a pair of optical isomerides, and are therefore said to exhibit stereochemical specificity.

The phenomenon of stereochemical specificity is well illustrated in the case of the hydrolytic enzyme arginase. This enzyme acts upon L- but not upon D-arginine, producing L-ornithine and urea:

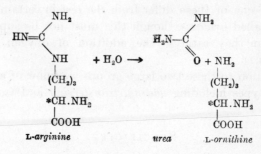

L-arginine   urea   L-ornithine

Similarly, the lactic dehydrogenase of muscle can catalyse the dehydrogenation of L-(+)- but not that of D-(−)-lactic acid to yield pyruvic acid:

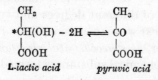

L-lactic acid   pyruvic acid

The same enzyme can also work in the reverse manner, acting upon the optically inactive pyruvic acid (asymmetric carbon atoms are marked with asterisks) and catalysing its reduction to yield L-lactic acid only. D-Lactic acid is never formed by this enzyme. In many micro-organisms, however, we find a lactic dehydrogenase which is specific for the D-form of lactic acid, and this is true, for example, of *Bacillus delbrückii*, an organism that is employed for the commercial production of lactic acid.

Stereochemical specificity of another kind is also known. The enzyme succinic dehydrogenase, for example, catalyses the oxidation of succinate to fumarate but never yields its geometrical isomer, maleic acid. Again, aconitase acts upon *cis*-aconitic acid, converting it into either citric or *iso*-citric acid, but has no action upon the *trans*- form of its substrate, by which it is actually inhibited.

Over and above the stereochemical specificity which is to be observed in the majority of enzymes, other types of specificity can be recognized. These other types differ mainly in the degree of exclusiveness. If, for the sake of simplicity, we consider only hydrolytic enzymes for the moment, the reaction catalysed by any given enzyme can be represented thus:

$$A—B + H_2O \rightleftharpoons A.OH + B.H.$$

The molecule of the substrate can be considered as consisting of three characteristic fragments, the two parts of the molecule itself, A and B, and the linkage which joins them. Three main types of specificity can be described with reference to these constitutional fragments. In the first type only the nature of the linkage is important, in the second the linkage and one-half of the molecule must be 'right', while in the third type all three fragments must be 'right'.

In the first type the precise nature of A and B is relatively unimportant, except that, if they are derived from optically active compounds they must have the appropriate stereochemical configuration, a condition which is already imposed by the stereochemical requirements of the enzyme. What is important, however, is that the linkage joining A to B shall be of the right kind, i.e. it must be an ester linkage in the case of a lipase or an esterase, a peptide link in the case of a peptidase, or a glycosidic link in the case of a glycosidase. If an enzyme is specific only towards the nature of the linkage bond it is said to exhibit *low specificity*. This type of specificity is less common than was once believed, for a number of enzymes of low specificity have proved to be mixtures of enzymes, each component of which is more specific than the original complex. It is found, however, among the lipases, which have so far defied all attempts to fractionate them.

The second type of specificity is more exclusive, for here the enzyme can only act upon substances in which the right chemical linkage is present and in which one of the two parts, A and B, is also of the right kind. As an example we may consider the case of the digestive enzyme usually called 'maltase', since it catalyses the hydrolysis of maltose (glucose-4-α-glucoside). Maltase obtained from the intestinal juices of a mammal will catalyse other reactions however; its action upon maltose is only one example of its catalytic action upon α-glucosides in general, which may be expressed in the following manner:

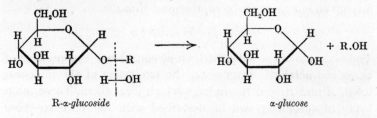

R-α-glucoside α-glucose

The specificity requirements of this particular enzyme are as follows. An α-glycosidic link is required in the substrate; compounds containing a β-glycosidic linkage are not attacked. Furthermore, the α-glycosidic radical must be derived from D-glucose, and replacement of the glucose unit by one derived from another sugar yields a product which is resistant to this particular enzyme. Thus the nature of the linkage *and* that of one-half of the molecule must be 'right' in every detail, though the nature of the 'R' group is a matter of relative indifference. An enzyme of this kind may be said to show *group specificity*, to indicate that it can act upon a group of closely related substrates, in this case a group of α-glucosides. Strictly speaking, therefore, this particular enzyme ought not to be called 'maltase', since its action is not uniquely confined to maltose; it is, in fact, an α-glucosidase. This kind of specificity is common among carbohydrases, for there also exist β-glucosidases, β-galactosidases and so on, each demanding its own particular kind of glycosidic linkage, together with a sugar radical of the appropriate type.

The third and commonest kind of specificity is the most exclusive of all. It is well illustrated by a maltase found in germinating barley (malt). Unlike the so-called 'gut maltase', this maltase acts only upon maltose itself, and is without action where other α-glucosides are concerned, so that in this case the title of maltase is strictly applicable. Here *both parts* of the substrate molecule must be 'right', together with the linkage bond, and the enzyme is therefore said to show *absolute specificity*. To take another example we may consider arginase again. This enzyme requires for its action that the substrate shall consist of unmodified L-arginine (I). Many substances derived from and closely related to L-arginine have been prepared and submitted to the action of this enzyme, but it fails always to act. Thus α-*N*-methyl arginine (II), δ-*N*-methyl arginine (III) and agmatine (IV) are all unaffected by arginase. Urease similarly requires that the structure of its substrate, urea, shall be intact and unsubstituted, and none of the considerable number of derived ureas that have been tested has been found to undergo hydrolysis under its influence.

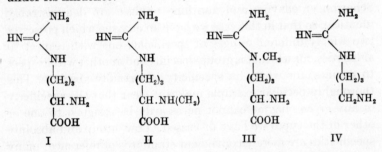

I   II   III   IV

Most of the examples so far mentioned have been chosen from the group of hydrolytic enzymes, but similar phenomena are to be seen in other groups. Thus succinic dehydrogenase acts only upon succinic acid (V) and is without action upon the closely related malonic acid (VI) by which, indeed, it is strongly inhibited. Succinic dehydrogenase is therefore absolutely specific, like malt maltase and arginase. Some oxidizing enzymes, however, are group-specific, and as an example we may take the case of the aldehyde oxidase of liver. Given suitable conditions, this enzyme can catalyse the dehydrogenation of many different aldehydes, but its action does not extend to other groups of compounds such, for instance, as the alcohols.

$$
\begin{array}{cc}
\text{COOH} & \text{COOH} \\
| & | \\
\text{CH}_2 & \text{CH}_2 \\
| & | \\
\text{CH}_2 & \text{COOH} \\
| & \\
\text{COOH} & \\
\text{V} & \text{VI}
\end{array}
$$

In conclusion we may consider a very unusual case. Milk contains the so-called Schardinger enzyme, which catalyses the oxidation of a very large number of different aldehydes to yield the corresponding acids, and is therefore group-specific. But milk also contains a factor which catalyses the oxidation of hypoxanthine and xanthine to uric acid, and this factor has received the name of xanthine oxidase. Many purines other than hypoxanthine and xanthine have been submitted to its action and found not to be attacked, so that the specificity of xanthine oxidase is very nearly absolute. The curious fact is that the Schardinger enzyme and xanthine oxidase are demonstrably identical, so that in this case we have an enzyme which possesses two widely different ranges of specificity, one with respect to aldehydes, for which it is group-specific, and another with respect to purines, for which its specificity is virtually absolute. This thoroughly peculiar example makes it clear that the specificity of any given enzyme cannot necessarily be assigned to one or other of the types we have discussed. Low, group and absolute specificities are merely convenient standards of reference; many intermediate grades exist, just as, in the solar spectrum, we can distinguish between red, orange, yellow, green, blue and violet, although the colours themselves merge into one another and form a continuous whole.

Finally, and most important of all, there is the fact that specificity is in reality a measure of the structural specialization that an enzyme requires in its substrate, and this must probably argue a corresponding degree of structural specialization in the enzyme itself.

THE CHEMICAL NATURE OF ENZYMES

The fact that enzymes are not dialysable long ago suggested that they might be related to substances of high molecular weight such as the polysaccharides and proteins, and even before any enzyme had been obtained in the pure state there was a considerable mass of evidence that they are proteinaceous in nature.

In recent years many enzymes have been concentrated, purified, and finally isolated in pure, crystalline form, and in every case the product has proved to be a protein. Many enzymes, such as pepsin, trypsin and a number of other hydrolytic enzymes, consist wholly of protein, but in other cases, notably among oxidizing enzymes, there is attached to the protein part of the molecule a non-protein fragment, known as a prosthetic group, so that the enzyme is a conjugated protein. While there is no doubt that every enzyme so far isolated is a protein of some kind, we cannot state categorically that all enzymes are proteins, if only because relatively few have so far been isolated. But even in other cases there is a good deal of indirect evidence to point to the proteinaceous nature of enzymes in general, and some of this we must consider here. Information regarding the chemical nature of enzymes has been obtained in many different ways, and most of it from considerations of the influence upon enzymic activity of environmental conditions such as temperature, pH and the presence of foreign materials of various kinds.

(i) *The Measurement of Enzymic Activity.* The activity of an enzyme can be determined by measuring the amount of chemical change it catalyses under any given set of conditions. If we incubate an enzyme together with its substrate under suitable conditions of temperature, pH and so on, we can withdraw samples of the reaction mixture from time to time and follow the course of the reaction by analysing the samples. Thus, if we choose yeast saccharase as our enzyme and sucrose as the substrate, we can measure the amount of chemical change at any given moment in terms of the amount of reducing sugars (glucose and fructose) that has been formed from the original non-reducing sucrose. It is usually necessary at the same time to carry out a 'control' experiment in which the enzyme is replaced by a previously boiled sample of enzyme; in this way we can correct our experimental results for any changes that are due to spontaneous transformation of the substrate or to any other process that is not catalysed by the enzyme. Similar methods can be devised and used for the study of other enzymes, and the results of a typical experiment are shown in Fig. 1.

It will be observed that the reaction velocity soon begins to decrease and eventually the process stops altogether. Now while the reaction is proceeding, changes are taking place in the reaction mixture. Substrate is disappearing, the products of the reaction are being formed, and the forward reaction may be opposed by a reverse process. In some cases other factors too may be at work, such, for instance, as changes of pH due to the formation or utilization of acid or alkali. All enzymes are sensitive to changes of pH in their immediate environment, all enzymes are influenced by the concentration of substrate available to them, and many are actually inhibited by the products of their own activity. If, therefore, we wish to obtain a reliable measure of the activity of an enzyme under any given set of conditions, it will be necessary either to avoid these changes in the reaction mixture or else to make some suitable allowance for them.

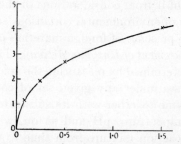

Fig. 1. A typical 'progress curve'; tryptic digestion of casein; data from a class experiment. Ordinate: increase in formol titre (ml. NaOH). Abscissa: time (hr.).

Two main procedures are available. In the first place we can measure the *length of time required to produce a given amount of chemical change*. In this case the amount of substrate used up, the amounts of products formed, the change of pH if any, and the extent of other changes likely to interfere with the enzyme will be the same in every experiment, so that different experiments will be comparable one with another, *always provided that the enzyme is stable under the conditions selected*. In such cases we can use time as a measure of the activity of the enzyme: actually, of course, the reciprocal of the time will be proportional to the activity of the catalyst, since an enzyme preparation that is half as active will take twice as long to produce the same amount of chemical change.

The second method is usually preferred, and consists in measuring the *amount of chemical change taking place over a very short interval of time from the start of the reaction*. Provided that the time interval can be made short enough, the changes in the composition of the reaction mixture will be small enough to be neglected. Ideally we should measure the *instantaneous initial velocity*, which is not a practicable proposition, but many excellent micro-methods are now available by the use of which we can obtain very good approximations to the instantaneous initial reaction velocity, and hence to the activity of an enzyme under any given set of conditions.

(ii) *The Influence of Temperature.* Most chemical reactions are influenced by temperature, the reaction velocity increasing with rising and decreasing with falling temperature. Enzyme-catalysed reactions are no exception to this general rule, but, because enzymes are very susceptible to thermal inactivation, the higher the temperature becomes, the more rapidly are the catalytic properties of the enzyme destroyed. For any given set of experimental conditions, therefore, it is possible to find what is called an *optimum temperature*, i.e. a temperature at which the greatest amount of chemical change is catalysed under that particular set of conditions. At suboptimal temperatures the enzyme is relatively more stable and therefore lasts longer, but the reaction which it catalyses proceeds more slowly. At temperatures above the optimum, on the other hand, the reaction takes place more rapidly but the catalyst is more rapidly destroyed.

There has been a good deal of misunderstanding on this subject in the past, for many biologists have supposed that the optimum temperature of an enzyme is a fixed and unalterable characteristic. A rise of temperature has a dual effect upon an enzyme-catalysed process: it increases the rate of the reaction, but it also increases the rate of thermal inactivation of the catalyst itself. Consequently, if we work over a period of a few seconds the optimum temperature may be very high indeed, because the catalytic properties of the enzyme do not need to be long lived. If, on the other hand, we choose to work over a period of a few days, a much lower optimum will be found since the enzyme must now last for a much longer period. It follows, therefore, that the time factor must be taken into account when we seek to determine the optimum temperature of any given enzyme, and that time and temperature are interdependent variables. The relationship between time and the optimum temperature of the digestive proteinase of an ascidian (sea squirt), *Tethyum*, is shown in Fig. 2.

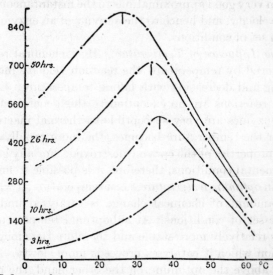

Fig. 2. Influence of temperature on digestive proteinase of *Tethyum*. Ordinate: mgm. amino-acid nitrogen per litre. (Substrate, gelatin: after Berrill 1929.)

With crude enzyme preparations such as were used in the earlier work on enzymes, the activity was usually of a rather low order, and it was therefore necessary to incubate the enzyme with its substrate for an hour or more in order to get a reasonable amount of chemical change. Under conditions of this kind most enzymes show an optimum temperature of about 30–40° C. This has led to the suggestion that, when animals became homoiothermic, they settled on a body temperature of the order of 35° C. because their enzymes would 'work better' in that neighbourhood than in any other. But consider the case of *Tethyum*.

Over a period of 2 hr. the optimum temperature of this digestive proteinase is of the order of 50° C., which is well above the thermal death-point of this species. *Tethyum* normally lives at temperatures in the neighbourhood of 15° C., and the digestion of its food takes about 50–60 hr. under natural conditions. If the optimum temperature is determined for a period of 55 hr. the value found is about 20° C., so that there is, after all, a nice adjustment of the enzyme to the biological requirements of the animal. This seems fairly generally the case, for 'there is evidence that the time taken for the passage of food through the gut at any normal temperature corresponds to the period which is optimal for enzymatic action at that temperature' (Yonge).

The thermal inactivation of enzymes is interesting from the physico-chemical viewpoint as well as from that of the biological behaviour of enzymes, for it yields important clues to the chemical nature of enzymes themselves. For most chemical reactions we find a temperature coefficient, represented by Q_{10}, of approximately 2; i.e. the rate of the reaction is approximately doubled for a rise in temperature of 10° C. If we determine the rate of thermal inactivation of enzymes in the neighbourhood of 70–80° C. we find Q_{10} values of the order of several hundreds. Temperature coefficients of this order are known for reactions of only two kinds; for the thermal inactivation of enzymes on the one hand, and for the thermal denaturation of proteins on the other. There is here, therefore, a striking indication that enzymes may be of protein nature, and that the process of thermal inactivation is analogous to, if it does not actually consist of, denaturation.

This latter point is stressed somewhat by the fact that enzymes are much less susceptible to thermal inactivation in the dry than they are in the wet state, while proteins appear to be more resistant to denaturation in the dry condition than they are in solution.

(iii)   *The Influence of* pH. The catalytic powers of an enzyme are, as a rule, exercised only over a somewhat restricted range of pH. Within this range the activity passes through a maximum at some particular pH, known as the *optimum* pH, and then falls off again. Fig. 3 illustrates the activity/pH relationships of several enzymes.

Generally speaking, the optimum pH is characteristic of a given enzyme, though under certain special conditions and in certain groups of enzymes the optimum pH may vary. This is true of the proteolytic enzymes, for example, and pepsin has an optimum pH that varies between 1·5 and 2·5 or thereabouts, different optima being found with different protein substrates. A given carbohydrase, on the other hand, shows always the same optimum pH, even when acting upon different substrates.

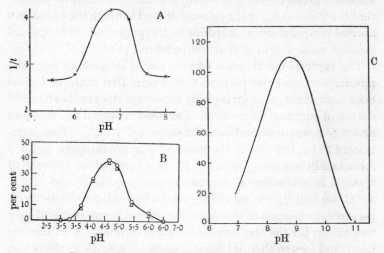

Fig. 3. Influence of pH on the activity of some enzymes.
A. *Salivary amylase* (substrate starch + NaCl). Ordinate: reciprocal of time taken to reach the achromic point. Results of a class experiment. B. *Papain-cysteine* (synthesis of carbobenzoxy-glycylanilide). Ordinate: yields as % of theoretical maximum, estimated by isolation (○) and titration (△). After Bergmann & Fraenkel-Conrat (1937). C. D-*Amino-acid oxidase* (substrate DL-alanine). Ordinate: oxygen uptake in 10 min. (μl.). Results of Krebs (1935), after Green.

In its general form the pH/activity curve of a typical enzyme closely resembles that obtained by plotting the degree of ionization of a simple ampholyte such as glycine against pH. It will be recalled that most of the properties of solutions of ampholytes such as proteins and amino-acids—such properties as solubility, osmotic pressure, conductivity, viscosity and so on—pass through either a maximum or a minimum at some particular pH, the so-called isoelectric pH. These changes are attributable to changes in the ionic condition of the ampholytes themselves. Being a zwitterion, any given protein can exist in a number of different ionic forms, and one of these, the isoelectric form, possesses a number of special and peculiar properties. It is therefore tempting to suggest that an enzyme may be regarded as a protein, and that of all the ionic forms in which it can therefore exist, only one particular ionic species possesses catalytic properties, this being the species which preponderates at the optimum pH. This may or may not be identical with the isoelectric form, and we shall have a little more evidence on this point later on (p. 47).

A further indication of the proteinaceous nature of enzymes is that extremes of acidity and alkalinity, which lead to the irreversible denaturation of proteins, lead also to the inactivation of the majority of enzymes. Moreover, these are irreversible changes, unlike those which are observed in the immediate vicinity of the optimum pH and which are for the most part reversible.

Generally speaking, enzymes are most stable in the neighbourhood of the optimum pH, so that the observed optimum does not vary with time. The optimum pH of an enzyme is therefore a more characteristic feature than its optimum temperature. But if, as is sometimes the case, the enzyme is one which is very unstable at or near its pH optimum, the value observed will, of course, vary with the duration of the experiment. Accurate determinations of the optimum pH can only be made in such cases by working over very short intervals of time. In the case of arginase, for example, the optimum pH is about 7–8 for a period of an hour or so, but the true optimum lies at about 10, a pH at which arginase is very unstable indeed. The case of arginase, however, is an unusual one: most enzymes have their pH optimum not very far from neutrality, most commonly between pH 5 and 7. Pepsin, however, has its optimum at the unusually acid value of 1·5–2·5, the precise figure depending upon the identity of its substrate.

(iv) *The Influence of Protein Precipitants.* Enzymes are inhibited by many different groups of chemical reagents, as well as by such physical factors as high temperatures, violent mechanical agitation, ultra-violet radiation and so on, all of which lead to the denaturation of proteins. Many protein precipitants also lead to the inactivation of enzymes. In this section special attention may be drawn to the effects of two groups of enzyme inhibitors which act also as precipitants for proteins, viz. the salts of heavy metals on the one hand and, on the other, the so-called 'alkaloidal reagents'. The former precipitate proteins by virtue of the heavy, positively charged ions to which they give rise in solution, and the alkaloidal reagents, which include such substances as trichloracetic acid, tannic acid and phosphotungstic acid, act by virtue of their heavy, negatively charged ions. That all these agents are powerful inhibitors of enzymic activity strongly suggests that enzymes are proteinaceous in composition.

More precise indications to the same effect are to be had by studying the effects of small concentrations of inhibitors of this kind. If it is indeed true that enzymes are proteins, we should expect to find that, in common with the proteins, they will be positively charged in acid solutions and therefore susceptible to the action of the negatively charged ions of phosphotungstic acid, for example. In alkaline solutions, on the other hand, they would be expected to be negatively charged and susceptible therefore to the action of positively charged ions, for example, Ag^+. This problem has been carefully investigated for a few enzymes, and the results obtained in the case of yeast saccharase are shown in Fig. 4. It will be seen that the effects of gradually increasing concentrations of silver ions are most marked on the alkaline side of the optimum pH. Phosphotungstic acid produces similar effects on the acid side.

These results show that the behaviour of yeast saccharase with respect to these inhibitors is consistent with the view that this enzyme is a protein. In practice, however, the concentration of silver ions required to produce complete inhibition of yeast saccharase is much smaller than that needed actually to precipitate proteins, and this suggests that the effect of Ag^+ is not a general one upon *all* the negatively charged centres of the protein molecule, but a localized and very specific one upon particular centres which are responsible for the catalytic properties of the presumptive saccharase protein. There thus emerges the notion that enzymic activity is not a property of the protein molecule as a whole, but rather that it is associated with certain special 'active' groups or centres.

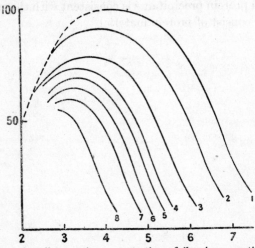

Fig. 4. Influence of small, increasing concentrations of silver ions on activity of yeast saccharase. Ordinate: initial velocities of hydrolysis of sucrose. Abscissa: pH. (After Haldane, from Myrbäck, 1926.)

Curve	Conc. Ag+	Curve	Conc. Ag+
1	0	5	4×10^{-6} M
2	5×10^{-7} M	6	10^{-5} M
3	10^{-6} M	7	2×10^{-5} M
4	2×10^{-6} M	8	10^{-4} M

Summary

1. Enzymes are complex, organic catalysts of high molecular weight, produced by living cells but capable of acting independently of the cells that produce them. They are characteristically thermolabile and highly specific.

2. Several kinds and degrees of catalytic specificity can be recognized. The majority of enzymes show stereochemical specificity, but, in addition, their specificity may be low or very high with reference to the chemical constitution of their substrates.

3. Enzymes are profoundly affected by many physical and chemical factors, and determinations of their activity therefore require to be made under very closely controlled conditions.

4. Enzymes are in all probability of protein nature. Every enzyme so far isolated has proved to be either a simple or a conjugated protein. The behaviour of enzymes towards heat, changes of pH and protein precipitants is consistent with the supposition that they consist of protein material.

CHAPTER II

THE NATURE OF THE CATALYTIC PROCESS

The Union of the Enzyme with its Substrate

It is difficult to imagine how a catalyst of any kind can influence the rate of a chemical reaction unless it actually participates in that reaction. Most authorities agree that catalysts do in some manner combine with the substance or substances upon which their catalytic influence is exerted, but there has been much difference of opinion as to whether the union is of a 'physical' or adsorptive kind, or whether it is to be regarded as 'chemical'. But it is difficult to maintain that there is any fundamental difference between these types of unions: rather must they be regarded as two extremes of one and the same phenomenon. In so far as it is possible to distinguish between adsorption and chemical combination it may be said that adsorption is, on the whole, a less specific and more freely reversible process than chemical combination. Calcium carbonate is a good example of what we should call a chemical compound, formed by the chemical union of carbon dioxide and calcium oxide. Yet at high enough temperatures the product dissociates freely, as though, by raising the temperature, we had converted a chemical into an adsorptive union.

While it is true that adsorption is often relatively unspecific, there is evidence in plenty that it can be very specific indeed. Thus we find that a positively charged material such as magnesium oxide will adsorb negatively charged dyes like eosin from aqueous solution, but fails to take up a positively charged dye such as methylene blue. Similarly, a protein will take up negatively charged dyes in solutions acid to its isoelectric pH, in which it is positively charged, while on the alkaline side it takes up positively but not negatively charged dyes. At or very near the isoelectric pH it will usually take up a little of both, since, being a zwitterion, it carries an equal number of positive and negative charges at one and the same pH.

Clearly, therefore, several factors have to be taken into account when we are considering adsorption. The nature of the surface at which the adsorption takes place is certainly of importance. Carotenoid pigments, for example, are adsorbed at a magnesium oxide/petrol ether interface but not at a magnesium oxide/alcohol interface. Charcoal can be used to adsorb coloured impurities of many kinds from aqueous solution, but is relatively useless in chloroform, and so on. The second important factor is, of course, the chemical nature of the material being adsorbed. It is not difficult to understand that a given surface may be so specialized, whether by virtue of its charge or for some other reason, as to be capable of taking up, i.e. reacting with, substances of one particular kind. Nor, if we allow for its possible topographical specialization, is it difficult to imagine that a particular surface may be capable of reacting with one particular substance and one only.

There is nothing inherently improbable in the idea that an enzyme actually unites with its substrate, and it is difficult, indeed, to imagine how the facts of enzyme specificity could otherwise be accounted for. Until recent years there has been no direct evidence that an enzyme enters into combination with its substrate, but studies of the kinetics of enzyme-catalysed reactions had already made it clear that the assumption of such a union is in fact warranted.

Keilin has provided direct evidence for the formation of an enzyme-substrate complex between peroxidase and hydrogen peroxide. If peroxidase is added to its substrate in the presence of a suitable hydrogen donator such as pyrogallol, a vigorous reaction ensues, in which the pyrogallol is oxidized and the hydrogen peroxide reduced. In the absence of any hydrogen donator, however, the hydrogen peroxide does not undergo reduction. Now peroxidase is an iron-porphyrin derivative and as such has a strong absorption spectrum, displaying four bands at 645, 583, 548 and 498 mμ respectively. If hydrogen peroxide is added to a strong solution of the enzyme there is a sharp change in colour and the spectrum changes completely. Only two bands at 561 and 530·5 mμ respectively can now be seen.

This can only mean that some kind of reaction has taken place between the enzyme and its substrate. Moreover, the amount of hydrogen peroxide required just to convert the whole of the enzyme into the new compound is equivalent to exactly one molecule of hydrogen peroxide for each atom of peroxidase-iron. Another compound, with bands at 583 and 545·5 mμ, is formed when the amount of hydrogen peroxide is increased to about 100 molecules per atom of peroxidase-iron.

Somewhat similar observations have been made with catalase. If hydrogen peroxide is added to catalase a violent reaction takes place, the substrate being converted into water and molecular oxygen. If, however, the enzyme is first treated with sodium azide, which inhibits its activity, there is only a slow reaction when hydrogen peroxide is added. The catalase-azide complex has a strong absorption spectrum with bands at 624, 544 and 506·5 mμ, changing on addition of hydrogen peroxide to a spectrum with two bands at 588 and 547 mμ. The original spectrum reappears when all the hydrogen peroxide has been decomposed, but the addition of more substrate then restores the two-banded spectrum. These observations show that the (inhibited) enzyme reacts in some way with its substrate.

INFLUENCE OF CONCENTRATIONS OF THE ENZYME AND ITS SUBSTRATE

The rate of any enzyme-catalysed process depends, other things being equal, upon the concentrations of the enzyme and of its substrate, and an examination of the effects of these and other factors is very important for any understanding of enzymic catalysis. In the vast majority of cases we find that, with a fixed quantity of enzyme, the initial reaction velocity increases with increasing substrate concentration until a limiting value is reached. Fig. 5 shows the results of a typical experiment carried out along these lines. The magnitude of the limiting velocity finally attained depends upon the concentration of the enzyme used and is, in fact, proportional to that concentration. These observations can be accounted for in terms of the theory brought forward by Michaelis.

For the purposes of the argument it is assumed that the enzyme and its substrate react together in some way to form an unstable complex, which then breaks down to yield the reaction

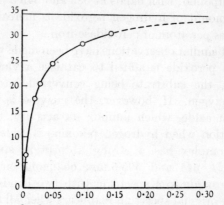

Fig. 5. Influence of substrate concentration on activity of yeast saccharase. Ordinate: initial velocity of hydrolysis. Abscissa: molar concentration of sucrose. (After Haldane, from Kuhn's data, 1923.)

products. If we choose a case such as the hydrolysis of sucrose by saccharase, these assumptions can be expressed in the following equations:

$$\text{(i)}\quad E + S \rightleftharpoons ES,$$
$$\quad\ (e-p)\quad (x)\quad\ (p)$$

$$\text{(ii)}\quad ES + H_2O \to E + P + Q.$$
$$\qquad\ (p)$$

The enzyme is represented here by E, the substrate by S and the intermediate enzyme/substrate complex by ES, while P and Q are the products of the process.

If we represent the *total* enzyme concentration as e it follows that, since an amount p is bound up in the form of ES, the concentration of free enzyme will be equal to $(e-p)$. The reaction velocity, which we will call v, is the rate at which the products are formed, and this will clearly be proportional to the concentration, p, of the unstable complex ES. We are now in a position to apply the principles of the mass law to our equations and in this way to make predictions which, if they prove to be in accordance with experimental observations, will provide evidence of the soundness of the assumptions epitomized in equations (i) and (ii).

It is necessary, before going further, to realize clearly that the concentrations represented by e, p, x and $(e-p)$ must, if we are to apply the mass law, be expressed as molecular and not as percentage concentrations. This fact is doubly important here because we are dealing with enzymes, which are colloidal materials, having very great molecular weights. Let us for a moment consider the enzyme E as a protein with the comparatively modest molecular weight of about 60,000, and compare it with a substrate such as urea with a molecular weight of 60. If we were to prepare 1 % solutions of the pure enzyme and of the substrate, the *molar* concentration of the substrate solution would be no less than 1000 times that of the solution of enzyme. This point is of considerable theoretical importance, as we shall see, but it serves also to emphasize the relatively enormous activity of enzymes. They occur in living cells and tissues in amounts so small that their molecular concentrations are infinitesimal, yet it is upon their catalytic activity that the life of the cells depends.

Returning now to Michaelis's theory we see that the following statements can be made:

For equation (i) rate of forward reaction $= x(e-p) \, k_1$,
$$\text{rate of reverse reaction} = pk_2,$$

where k_1 and k_2 are the velocity constants of the forward and backward reactions respectively. Hence, when the system is in equilibrium,
$$x(e-p) \, k_1 = pk_2;$$

therefore
$$\frac{x(e-p)}{p} = \frac{k_2}{k_1} = K_m. \tag{A}$$

Here K_m, the ratio of two constants, is itself a constant. It is, of course, the equilibrium constant of reaction (i) and is called the Michaelis constant. Its particular significance will be considered later.

We are very seldom in a position to evaluate either e or p, since even if we had a perfectly pure enzyme at our disposal its molecular weight would probably be unknown. These terms, e and p, must therefore be eliminated from our equations, and this can be done through the following considerations.

The reaction velocity, v, for the decomposition of ES (equation (ii)) will be proportional to p and also to the concentration of water, but since the concentration of water in the system does not change appreciably we can write

$$v = kp, \tag{B}$$

where k is a constant. By combining this with equation (A) we could eliminate p, but the term e would still remain, and this, like p itself, we are usually unable to evaluate. But let us consider a special case in which there is a large excess of substrate. This case is not a fictional invention since, on account of the great disparity of molecular weight between E and S, x will usually be much greater than e. In the presence of a large excess of substrate, therefore, $[S]$ will be very much greater than $[E]$ so that virtually all the enzyme will be converted into ES, when $p = e$. Now we have just seen (equation (B)) that the reaction velocity is proportional to p, and in the presence of a large excess of substrate p attains the value of e. Consequently, in the presence of a large excess of the substrate, the reaction velocity will attain a limiting value which may be called V. We thus have, for this special case, a third equation:

$$V = ke. \tag{C}$$

Dividing (B) by (C) we get

$$\frac{v}{V} = \frac{p}{e}. \tag{D}$$

It is now possible to get rid of the unwanted terms from equation (A). We can rewrite (A) as follows:

$$x(e - p) = pK_m;$$

therefore

$$ex - px = pK_m,$$

$$ex = px + pK_m = p(x + K_m),$$

and dividing by e $\qquad x = \dfrac{p}{e}(x + K_m).$

Substituting for p/e from equation (D) we get the Michaelis equation:

$$x = \frac{v}{V}(x + K_m),$$

and hence $\qquad v = \dfrac{Vx}{x + K_m}.$

This equation allows us to predict the manner in which the reaction velocity should be influenced by substrate concentration. It is, in fact, the equation of a rectangular hyperbola with the following properties (see Fig. 6):

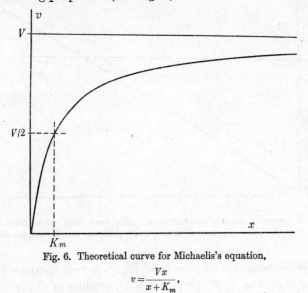

Fig. 6. Theoretical curve for Michaelis's equation,

$$v = \frac{Vx}{x + K_m},$$

where v = initial reaction velocity, x = concentration of substrate.

(a) the limiting velocity V, is the asymptotic value to which the reaction velocity tends as the concentration of the substrate is increased, and

(b) the Michaelis constant (K_m) corresponds to that substrate concentration at which half the limiting velocity is developed.

This fact is readily understood if we substitute $V/2$ for v in the Michaelis equation itself:

$$\frac{V}{2} = \frac{Vx}{x + K_m};$$

therefore

$$\frac{1}{2} = \frac{x}{x + K_m},$$

$$2x = x + K_m,$$

and

$$x = K_m,$$

when the reaction velocity is one-half the limiting velocity.

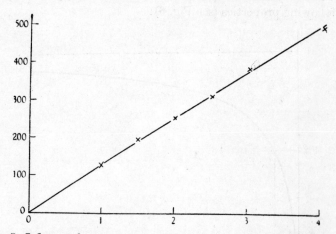

Fig. 7. Influence of enzyme concentration; yeast saccharase. Data from a class experiment. Ordinate: mg. invert sugar formed. Abscissa: ml. saccharase solution.

If the rectangular hyperbola of Fig. 6 is now compared with the curve of Fig. 5, which portrays the results of experimental observations, there can be no doubt that Michaelis's theory is in excellent agreement with the experimental results. Moreover, we have seen (equation (C)) that, according to this theory, the limiting velocity attained in the presence of an excess of substrate should be proportional to the concentration of enzyme, and this also is in agreement with the results of experimental enquiry (see Fig. 7).

Atypical results are not infrequently obtained in experiments designed to test the validity of Michaelis's predictions, but these are usually due to interference by some factor or other, e.g. inhibition of the enzyme by the products of its own activity. When due allowance is made for this interference the corrected results are found to agree with theoretical prediction.

The agreement between theoretical requirements and experimental observation goes far towards justifying the assumption upon which the theory was originally based, namely, that the enzyme actually combines with its substrate to form an unstable and correspondingly reactive complex. It may, of course, be argued that the same theoretical equation might be derived equally on the basis of different assumptions, but there is other and more direct evidence for the formation of enzyme/substrate compounds to which we have already referred (p. 26).

The Michaelis constant deserves a little further consideration. Let us suppose that we have an enzyme of low or of group specificity, and let us consider its activity towards two different substates, a and b. If the relationships between reaction velocity and substrate concentration are experimentally determined for both substrates we get a pair of hyperbolic curves like those of Fig. 8. For each of the two substrates there is a K_m value, and in the figure it will be observed that for b the value (K'_m) is greater than for a (K_m). This means that in order to get the same velocity out of a given concentration of enzyme, b must be taken at a higher concentration than must a. This must mean that the enzyme has a smaller affinity for b than for a: in other words a high K_m is indicative of a low enzyme-substrate affinity, and vice versa. Thus, not only does Michaelis's theory furnish us with evidence that the production of an enzyme-substrate compound is an essential part of the catalytic process: it provides at the same time a means whereby the affinity of an enzyme for its substrate can be numerically evaluated.

As we go on we shall see that the behaviour of enzymes is best explained on the supposition that they react with their respective substrates to form reactive complexes. In addition to the indirect evidence afforded by the applicability of Michaelis's theory there is a considerable mass of indirect evidence from other sources, as well as the recent direct evidence to which we have already referred.

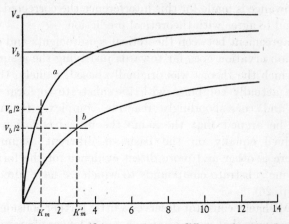

Fig. 8. Action of a group-specific enzyme upon two different substrates; for explanation see text. Reaction velocity in arbitrary units. Ordinate: reaction velocity. Abscissa: molarity of substrate.

COMPETITIVE INHIBITION

A great deal of information regarding the nature of enzymes and their mode of action has been gained by considering their inhibition, and studies of this kind have, as we have seen, done much to confirm the view that enzymes are made up essentially of protein material. Many enzymes are inhibited by the products of their own activity, and many more by substances which are structurally related to their substrates. In many such cases the inhibition is of what is known as the competitive type. A well-known and very important case is found in the competitive inhibition of succinic dehydrogenase by malonate.

If we take succinate together with succinic dehydrogenase we have a system in which, under suitable conditions, it is easy enough to measure the reaction velocity in terms of the rate of oxidation of the succinate. If now malonate is added the rate of oxidation promptly diminishes, but increases again if more succinate is added. Malonic acid is a dicarboxylic acid, the structure of which is closely related to that of succinic acid itself:

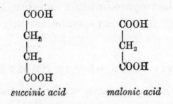

succinic acid   *malonic acid*

Malonate is able to combine with the enzyme, just as does the substrate, succinate. But whereas the enzyme-succinate complex breaks down to yield the reaction products, the enzyme-malonate complex contributes nothing to the reaction velocity. In consequence, a part of the enzyme is held in the form of enzyme-inhibitor complex, and so is not available for the catalysis of succinate oxidation, and the reaction velocity accordingly diminishes when the inhibitor is added.

This system may be more precisely described in the following manner. We have the following equilibria and reactions to consider:

$$E + S \rightleftharpoons ES \rightarrow E + F + G,$$

$$E + M \rightleftharpoons EM.$$

The rate of oxidation of the succinate is determined by $[ES]$, and this can be increased *either* by increasing $[S]$ *or* by decreasing $[M]$, which indicates that these two substances 'compete' for possession of the enzyme.

Now if the two compounds reacted at different points on the enzyme molecule there is no reason why they should not both be accommodated at the same time, each independently of the other. The fact that they do however compete shows that both unite with the enzyme molecule at precisely the same point.

Many other cases of the same kind are known. Thus yeast saccharase is competitively inhibited by fructose, and xanthine oxidase by adenine. That competitive inhibition exists at all is an indication that the substrate does not unite at arbitrary groups on the enzyme molecule, but *only at certain particular groups, and not elsewhere*. Thus these considerations not only confirm the view that a union is set up between an enzyme and its substrate when the two are brought together: they go further, by showing that the union is very specific not only in nature but also in locality.

ACTIVATION OF THE SUBSTRATE

The combination of an enzyme with its substrate seems to be the fundamental and essential step in the catalytic process, for it is as a result of this union, apparently, that the substrate molecule becomes more chemically reactive than it was in the free, uncombined state, and is more easily split, oxidized, reduced or whatever the case may be. We refer to this increase in chemical reactivity by saying that the enzyme has 'activated' its substrate, or that the substrate has undergone 'activation'. We do not know what precise intramolecular changes underlie activation, but we do know of other cases in which something of the same sort takes place.

Let us consider the behaviour of haemoglobin. This compound consists of a protein, globin, to which is attached a complex, tetra-pyrrollic ring-structure containing an atom of ferrous iron. The special and peculiar property of haemoglobin is its ability to react reversibly with oxygen, taking it up when the partial pressure is high and giving it off again at low partial pressures. It is particularly noteworthy that this performance involves no change in the valency of the iron, a fact which is implied by speaking of the 'oxygenation' as opposed to the 'oxidation' of haemoglobin. The important point for our present argument is that haem, by itself, does not possess this property. It acquires this property when, and only when, it is combined with the appropriate protein, globin. Free haem is very insoluble in water, and reacts spontaneously with oxygen to undergo oxidation to the ferric compound, haematin. Globin, by combining with haem, confers upon it a large measure of solubility in water, together with the new-found property of reacting reversibly with oxygen, without at the same time undergoing any change in the valency of the iron.

In addition to haemoglobin a number of other haem and haematin compounds with very special and peculiar properties are known, such, for example, as cytochrome, catalase and peroxidase. In each of these the haem or haematin system is present, but in none do we find the ability to combine reversibly with oxygen. The haem, presumably, is all right, but the protein is wrong. Thus the haem of haemoglobin possesses certain special properties which only become apparent when the haem nucleus is combined with the right kind of protein. While few, probably, would venture to assert that globin 'activates' haem in the sense that an enzyme activates its substrate, this case does show how the properties of a given substance can be profoundly and very specifically modified when the substance concerned enters into combination with the 'right' kind of protein.

We know too little about the phenomenon of activation to be able to make any clear picture of the changes which underlie it, but it is an interesting and highly significant fact that the hydrolytic processes catalysed by enzymes can as a rule be imitated by means of dilute acids, alkalis, or both, and sometimes merely by boiling water. Whether we treat sucrose, for example, with hot, dilute mineral acid or with saccharase prepared from yeast, we get precisely the same products, viz. glucose and fructose in equimolecular proportions. Saccharase, therefore, does not induce any new kind of reactivity in its substrate, but only exaggerates a tendency to react that is already inherent in the sucrose molecule.

ACTIVATORS AND COENZYMES

Activation of the substrate is an indispensable part of the chemical process catalysed by any enzyme, but it can take place without necessarily being followed by the hydrolysis, oxidation or other chemical modification of the substrate. Thus if we add peroxidase to a solution of hydrogen peroxide, the two unite to form an addition compound, as is shown by the resulting change in the absorption spectrum (p. 26). But, in the absence of other materials, there the matter ends. If some substance capable of being oxidized is also added, AH_2 say, there begins a rapid transference of H atoms to the activated hydrogen peroxide so that AH_2 is oxidized and the peroxide reduced, thus:

$$A\begin{matrix} H \\ \\ H \end{matrix} + \begin{matrix} O-H \\ | \\ O-H \end{matrix} = A + 2H-O-H.$$

This example suffices to show that, while activation is an essential part of the process of enzymic catalysis, activation only makes it *possible* for the reaction to take place: whether or not the reaction actually occurs often depends upon the presence of other materials, over and above the substrate and its activating protein, the enzyme. It is, in fact, true that in the vast majority of enzyme-catalysed reactions, substances other than the substrate and its activating enzyme-protein must also be present before any chemical change can be brought about. In processes of hydrolysis, for instance, water molecules form an indispensable part of the reaction system. The enzyme must therefore be considered as only a part, albeit the most important part from the biological point of view, of the whole reacting system. Similarly, in oxidation and reduction reactions, the majority of which are accomplished by the transference of pairs of hydrogen atoms from the substance being oxidized (the 'hydrogen donator') to the substance being reduced (the 'hydrogen acceptor'), we find that both substances must be present, together with the appropriate enzyme.

It has been known for many years that a considerable number of enzymes are unable to exert their catalytic influence except in the presence of certain appropriate materials which have become known as 'coenzymes' or 'activators'. It will be remembered that zymase, for instance, loses its activity if dialysed, and that this loss of activity is attributable to the removal from the juice of certain small, thermostable molecules in the absence of which fermentation cannot proceed. Recent work has shown that even such seemingly innocent substances as the ions of potassium, calcium, magnesium, chloride, phosphate and the like play indispensable parts in certain enzyme-catalysed processes. In such cases it is clear that the inability of the enzyme to act in the usual way might be due to one or other of two causes. Either (a) the enzyme cannot activate its substrate because some accessory part of the enzyme itself has been removed, or (b) by contrast, the enzyme is capable of activating its substrate but no reaction takes place because some substance with which the substrate ordinarily reacts has been removed. It is possible to distinguish more or less sharply therefore between two groups of accessory substances, those which are *parts of the activating system* on the one hand, and on the other those which are a *part of the reaction system* but play no part in activation. Although it is difficult to justify any distinction in many cases, the tendency at the present time is to refer to accessory substances which are in effect a part of the activating system and are required before the enzyme can activate its substrate, as 'activators'. The term 'coenzyme', on the other hand, tends to be reserved for substances which play some part in the reaction catalysed by the enzyme, but not in the activation of the substrate. We shall follow this practice here. It must, however, be remembered that the *activation of an enzyme* by the appropriate 'activator' is quite distinct from the *activation of the substrate* that takes place as a result of its union with the specific activating protein or enzyme.

It is sometimes found that enzymes are secreted in a form in which they have no catalytic activity whatever, i.e. in the form of enzyme-precursors, or 'pro-enzymes'. The classical case to consider here is that of trypsinogen. The juice secreted by the pancreas of vertebrates contains a pro-enzyme, trypsinogen, which is devoid of action upon proteins, but when the pancreatic juice enters the small intestine, trypsinogen is converted into the active proteolytic enzyme, trypsin. The change is attributed to the presence of an enzyme or enzyme-like factor present in the intestinal juice to which the name of enterokinase has been given. The change from trypsinogen to trypsin appears to be due to the removal from the pro-enzyme of a substance which acts, so to speak, as a 'mask' covering the reactive centres of trypsin itself. This 'mask' appears to be a polypeptide, and its removal is presumably due to proteolytic action on the part of enterokinase. This kind of activation, which for want of a better term we may refer to as '*unmasking*', is now known to occur in several proteolytic enzymes, and will be dealt with at greater length when we come to consider them in more detail.

A second kind of activation, and one which is commonly encountered, might similarly be referred to as '*de-inhibition*'. Many enzymes are readily inhibited by mild oxidizing agents, and it frequently happens in the course of attempts to isolate a given enzyme that much of its activity is lost in the process as the result of oxidation by atmospheric oxygen, catalysed as a rule by traces of heavy metals present in the material, or derived from mincing machines or other metallic devices used in the preparation. In such cases the activity can very often be recovered by adding reducing agents such as cysteine or reduced glutathione. It has been shown by Hopkins that in the case of succinic dehydrogenase, though the same is not true of the lactic enzyme, any treatment tending to oxidize the —SH groups of the enzyme-protein, so that —S—S— cross-linkages are formed between adjacent molecules of the enzyme, results in the loss of dehydrogenase activity. These —S—S— linkages can be reduced again by means of —SH compounds, e.g. reduced glutathione, and the dehydrogenase activity of the enzyme returns therewith.

Activation by de-inhibition is a common process and may often be accomplished merely by removing inhibitory material. Cytochrome oxidase, an enzyme of central importance in respiratory metabolism, is powerfully inhibited by cyanide, but regains its activity if the cyanide is removed. Cytochrome oxidase is also powerfully inhibited by carbon monoxide in the dark, and a very striking case of activation by de-inhibition can be demonstrated in this case by exposing the preparation to strong light, which causes the carbon monoxide-oxidase compound to dissociate. Many other examples might be quoted.

Activation by unmasking or de-inhibition is due, apparently, to the removal of material that inhibits by blocking the active parts of the enzyme. In other cases, however, it is less clear how the activator functions. Many enzymes concerned with phosphorylation, for example, require the presence of magnesium ions, but we do not know for certain what part these play. It is widely believed that the magnesium furnishes a means whereby the enzyme and its substrate can combine, i.e. that the enzyme-protein and the substrate react together through the magnesium ion. If this is the case, it follows that the enzyme-protein alone is unable to activate its substrate and that the magnesium must be regarded as a part of the activating machine. That this is so seems very probable, since one such enzyme, enolase, has been crystallized in the form of a magnesium-containing protein.

Many different metallic ions are now known to function as activators of one enzyme or another and, as a general rule, the relationship between the enzyme and the metallic ion is very specific. As is well known, minute quantities of numerous 'trace elements', including Mn, Mo, Zn and Co for example, are indispensable nutritional factors for living organisms, ranging from bacteria to mammals. It is becoming increasingly clear that they play the part of specific activators for particular enzymes. In general they appear to be parts of the activating system, i.e. the enzyme protein fails to activate the substrate unless the appropriate metallic ion is also present.

Another much-quoted case is that of salivary and similar amylases. If a preparation of salivary amylase is dialysed it loses its power to digest starch at pH 6·8, which is the optimal value under normal conditions. Activity is regained by the addition of chloride ions, but the effect is not specific, and chloride may be replaced by other univalent anions, though these are less effective (Fig. 9). Here, again, there is reason to suspect that the ionic activator is *a part of the activating machine*, and that in its absence the enzyme-protein cannot activate its substrate in the normal manner.

We have so far considered three main types of activators, those which act by unmasking the active groups of the enzyme, those which remove extraneous inhibitory material, and those which perhaps act because they are, in effect, a part of the enzyme. Other cases will be dealt with later when we consider individual enzymes in greater detail. We must turn now to consider accessory substances which confer activity upon inert systems because they *play a part in the chemical reaction which follows upon the successful activation of the substrate.* Substances of this kind are usually spoken of as coenzymes.

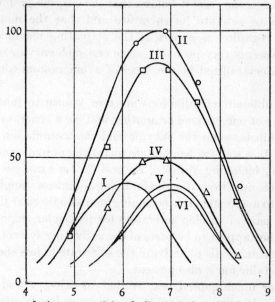

Fig. 9. Influence of anions upon activity of salivary amylase. Ordinate: initial velocity of hydrolysis. Abscissa: pH. (Substrate, soluble starch: after Myrbäck, 1926.)

Curve	Salt
I	Traces of NaCl
II	NaCl
III	NaBr
IV	KI
V	$NaNO_3$
VI	$KClO_3$

Of these the longest known, perhaps, is the co-carboxylase of yeast. Yeast, and the juice expressed from it by the Buchner technique, contain an enzyme known as carboxylase which, in the presence of co-carboxylase though not in its absence, catalyses the decomposition of pyruvic acid into acetaldehyde and carbon dioxide:

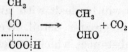

$$\begin{array}{c} CH_3 \\ | \\ CO \\ | \\ COOH \end{array} \longrightarrow \begin{array}{c} CH_3 \\ | \\ CHO \end{array} + CO_2$$

Co-carboxylase enters in some way into this reaction, which is
called decarboxylation, though how it does so is still unknown.
It is essential also for a more complex process known as oxidative
decarboxylation, a reaction that takes place on a large scale in
animal tissues and in which decarboxylation is attended by
a simultaneous oxidative change:

$$R.CO.\overset{.........}{[COO]}H \xrightarrow{+\frac{1}{2}O_2} R.COOH + CO_2.$$

This reaction, which is a good deal more complex than the
'straight' decarboxylation observed in yeast juice, is believed to
be responsible for the production of a very large part of the carbon
dioxide formed in respiration, just as the straight decarboxylation catalysed by yeast juice is the source of the carbon dioxide
produced in alcoholic fermentation. In both cases we find the
same substance, co-carboxylase, as an essential part of the
reacting system, and in both cases decarboxylation takes place.
The coenzyme must therefore play some specific part in the
decarboxylation reaction, though we do not at present know
exactly what its role may be.

We are on surer ground when we consider the coenzymes
involved in many oxidative processes. The majority of biological
oxidations are carried out by the transference of hydrogen
atoms from the substance undergoing oxidation, the 'hydrogen
donator', to another substance, the 'hydrogen acceptor'. The
dehydrogenases which catalyse reactions of this kind are not
only specific to the hydrogen donator but to the hydrogen
acceptor as well. It follows, therefore, that in the absence of the
appropriate hydrogen acceptor any given dehydrogenase, capable
though it probably is of activating the hydrogen donator, cannot
lead to any chemical change. This is true, for example, of the
lactic dehydrogenase of muscle and of the alcohol dehydrogenase
of yeast. In neither case does the substrate undergo oxidation
unless the proper, i.e. specific, hydrogen acceptor is present. In
these two systems the hydrogen acceptor is a substance known
as coenzyme I or, less appropriately perhaps, as cozymase. This
compound is able to take up a pair of hydrogen atoms from

a suitably activated molecule of lactic acid or of alcohol, and the resulting reaction may be pictured as follows, e.g.

$$CH_3CH(OH)COOH + Co\ I \rightleftharpoons CH_3COCOOH + Co\ I.2H.$$

Of the dehydrogenases at present known, the majority require Co I as hydrogen acceptor and cannot use any other known, naturally-occurring substance in its place. Even the closely related Co II, which differs from Co I only in that it contains three instead of two phosphate radicals per molecule, cannot replace Co I. Nor can Co I replace the Co II which is required as hydrogen acceptor by a smaller group of dehydrogenases, of which hexosemonophosphate dehydrogenase may be cited as an example.

Co I and Co II are not by any means the only compounds which can act specifically as donators and acceptors of particular radicals or groupings. Indeed, during recent years, numerous reactions have been discovered in which particular radicals or groups are transferred from one molecule to another, and in every case it appears that a donator or acceptor substance is involved, over and above the enzyme which catalyses the transfer. These we need not discuss in any detail here since we shall refer to them frequently when we deal with intermediary metabolism, but a brief reference to one such system is desirable by way of example.

Muscle itself, and extracts prepared from it under suitable conditions, contain an important compound known as adenosine triphosphate. It also contains an important guanidine base, creatine. Under the influence of the muscle enzymes a phosphate radical can be transferred from adenosine triphosphate to creatine, and the process, which is reversible, can be represented thus:

adenosine triphosphate + creatine $\rightleftharpoons$ adenosine diphosphate + creatine phosphate.

The enzyme catalysing this transfer is specific both for the phosphate donator, adenosine triphosphate, and for the acceptor, creatine. But just as there are many dehydrogenases that can use Co I as a common hydrogen acceptor for different substrates, so too there are a number of transphosphorylating enzymes which use adenosine triphosphate as a common phosphate donator with respect to their different substrates. We are probably justified, therefore, in regarding adenosine triphosphate as the coenzyme of all those phosphorylating enzymes which require its collaboration.

Co I and Co II, adenosine triphosphate and certain other compounds discharging comparable 'carrier' functions play a vital part in metabolism. Normally they occur only in very small concentrations in living tissues—Warburg and Christian, for example, could isolate only about 20 mg. of Co II from the red blood corpuscles of some 250 l. of horse blood—but the reactions in which they participate are very rapid indeed. Since these co-substances are essential for the occurrence of these reactions, and since they are present in such small amounts, it is clear that we must regard them as true catalysts. Their catalytic influence is, in fact, no whit less important than that of the enzymes with which they collaborate.

PROSTHETIC GROUPS

In recent years a considerable number of enzymes have been greatly concentrated and finally obtained in crystalline form, and in many cases, notably among enzymes concerned with processes of oxidation and reduction, the enzyme molecule has been found to contain a non-protein moiety in addition to its protein component. Enzymes of this kind, therefore, are conjugated proteins, and the non-protein fragment is called the prosthetic group in each case.

The question arises whether or not there is any essential resemblance between the functional behaviour of a substrate, a coenzyme and a prosthetic group. In substances such as haemoglobin, haemocyanin and the like it has long been known that the non-protein part of the molecule is firmly attached to the protein component, and the special name of prosthetic group was coined to describe it. All the conjugated proteins, to which class haemoglobin and haemocyanin belong, were regarded as consisting of a protein portion to which there was firmly attached a prosthetic group of some kind. In more recent times we have made the acquaintance of conjugated proteins of which the prosthetic groups are relatively much more loosely attached. Thus there exists in the eggs of the lobster a green chromoprotein, ovoverdin, the prosthetic group of which can be removed by heating to about 60° C., but reunites with the protein on cooling. Still more striking, perhaps, are the visual chromoproteins, rhodopsin and porphyropsin, which dissociate on exposure to light, but reunite in the dark. Many such cases are now known, and the notion that a prosthetic group is necessarily firmly attached or screwed down to its protein partner has been abandoned.

If we import the same notions into the field of biological catalysis we find that, in the main, it is possible to distinguish between substrates and coenzymes, which are only loosely and temporarily attached to the catalytic proteins with which they react, and prosthetic groups, which are relatively firmly fixed to their protein partners. The part played by the prosthetic group is precisely known in some cases. Certain oxidizing enzymes have a prosthetic group which functions as a 'built-in' hydrogen acceptor, taking over a pair of hydrogen atoms from the activated substrate and subsequently passing them on to another acceptor. In such cases the enzyme behaves as an activating protein and hydrogen acceptor rolled into one, and the functional behaviour of the prosthetic group in such a case is therefore analogous to that of the coenzyme of a typical dehydrogenase. The essential difference is that, whereas the partnership set up between the activating protein and the prosthetic group of an enzyme such as catalase is a relatively permanent affair, the partnership between, say, lactic dehydrogenase and lactic acid, or between the dehydrogenase and Co I, is only a loose and a temporary one on account of the relatively slight affinity between the partners.

The difference between coenzymes, substrates and prosthetic groups is therefore one of degree rather than of kind. Whether we consider Co I as a temporary prosthetic group of lactic dehydrogenase, or haematin as a permanent or built-in coenzyme of peroxidase, matters little so long as the functional significance of the various parts of the system is clear. What does matter is that we shall realize that the old, sharp distinction that seemed to exist between enzymes and carriers, and between substrates, coenzymes and prosthetic groups cannot now be justified, a fact which brings a new unifying influence to bear on our knowledge of biological catalysis.

Quantitative Characterization of Enzymes

Certain features of enzymic catalysis already alluded to in the first chapter of this book may now be considered in more detail. Enzymes in general may be considered under two headings, according as their substrates do or do not ionize. As examples of the former type we may consider the proteinases, and of the latter type the carbohydrases. In all these cases the activity of the enzyme is profoundly affected by pH, and since the substrates of the carbohydrases, for example, do not ionize, the influence of pH upon these enzymes must be entirely due to its influence upon the catalytic proteins.

Knowing that enzymes are proteins, we may infer that they carry numerous ionizable groups, the ionic state of which depends upon the pH of the surrounding medium. Since there is some particular pH at which the enzyme is more active than at any other, we may suppose that, of all the possible ionic forms in which the enzyme-protein can exist, only one possesses catalytic properties, and that it is this form that predominates at the optimum pH. Michaelis and Davidson suggested that, since a change of pH in either direction away from the optimum leads to a diminution of catalytic activity, two kinds of groups must be involved in determining activity, the one kind being acidic and the other basic in nature. The enzyme, like any other protein, must be considered as an ampholyte, and in view of the close resemblance that exists between the dissociation curve of a simple ampholyte such as alanine on the one hand, and the pH/activity curve of a typical enzyme on the other, Michaelis and Davidson went on to suggest that the two halves of the pH/activity curve must correspond to the dissociation curves of the two particular groups or sets of groups upon the ionic condition of which the catalytic activity of the protein depends. For any given enzyme, therefore, the form and position of the pH/activity curve should be constant, even if the enzyme acts upon several different substrates, always provided that the substrates themselves do not ionize. This seems generally to be true.

TABLE 1. pH OPTIMA OF SOME ENZYMES
(*From* Haldane's Tables)

Enzyme	Source	Substrate	Optimum pH
Pepsin	Stomach	Various proteins	1·5–2·5
Trypsin	Pancreas	"	8–11
Amylase	Saliva	Starch (+ chloride)	6·7–6·8
"	Pancreas	" "	6·7–6·8
"	Malt	Starch	5·2
α-Glucosidase	Gut	Maltose	6·1
"	Yeast	"	6·6
"	"	α-Methylglucoside	6·2
β-Glucosidase	Almond	Various β-glucosides	4·1–4·5
"	Malt	Cellobiose	5·1
Saccharase	Gut	Sucrose	6·2
"	Yeast	"	4·6–5·0
Lipase	Liver	Ethyl butyrate	8·3
"	Pancreas	"	7
"	*Ricinus*	Tributyrin	5
Succinic dehydrogenase	Muscle	Succinate	9
" "	*Bact. coli*	"	8–10
Xanthine oxidase	Milk	Xanthine	5·5–8·5
Arginase	Liver	L-Arginine	9·8
Carboxylase	Yeast	Pyruvate	4·8
D-Amino-acid oxidase	Liver; kidney	DL-Alanine	9

If, therefore, we determine the pK values for the dissociation of the two sets of ionizable groups, which we can do by carefully plotting the pH/activity curve, we shall have determined in quantitative terms two constants that are characteristic of the enzyme. This has been done in only a few cases. It is considerably easier to determine the maximum of the resultant of the two dissociation curves, i.e. the optimum pH; a number of pH optima for various enzymes are listed in Table 1.

In the case of enzymes that act upon ionizable substrates, the position is complicated by the fact that changes of pH will influence the ionic conditions both of the enzyme and of its substrate. Further, if we change the substrate, the shape and position of the pH/activity curve will be expected to change too, and we do in fact find that enzymes such as pepsin and trypsin show different pH optima when acting upon different proteins. Nevertheless, if we stipulate some particular substrate in any particular case we can determine the optimum pH or the two pK values for that particular enzyme/substrate pair.

TABLE 2. MICHAELIS CONSTANTS OF SOME ENZYMES
(*From* Haldane's Tables)

Enzyme	Source	Substrate	K_m
Pepsin	Stomach	Egg albumin	4·5%
Trypsin	Pancreas	Casein	2%
Amylase	Saliva	Starch (+chloride)	0·4%
	Pancreas	,, ,,	0·25%
α-Glucosidase	Yeast	α-Methylglucoside	0·037–0·075 M
,,	,,	α-Phenylglucoside	0·021–0·050 M
β-Glucosidase	Almond	β-Methylglucoside	0·060–1·12 M
,,	,,	β-Phenylglucoside	0·040–0·065 M
Saccharase	Yeast	Sucrose	0·016–0·04 M
,,	,,	Raffinose	0·24–0·66 M
,,	Gut	Sucrose	0·02 M
Lipase	Pancreas	Ethyl butyrate	>0·03 M
,,	Liver	Ethyl-(+)-mandelate	0·0007 M
,,	,,	Ethyl-(−)-mandelate	0·0017 M
Succinic dehydrogenase	Muscle	Succinate	0·001 M
Xanthine oxidase	Milk	Xanthine; hypoxanthine	$<3 \times 10^{-5}$ M
,,	,,	Acetaldehyde	>1 M
D-Amino-acid oxidase	Liver; kidney	DL-Alanine	5×10^{-3} M
Carboxylase	Yeast	Pyruvate	0·01 M
Catalase	Liver	Hydrogen peroxide	0·025 M

An interesting example of the usefulness of these ideas is found in connexion with the effect of chloride ions upon the activity of salivary and pancreatic amylases. If chlorides are removed, the more alkaline of the two pK values shifts from about 8 to 6·7, so that the pH/activity curve, which is the resultant of the two dissociation curves, becomes shifted over towards the left and loses height at the same time (see Fig. 9, p. 42). Presumably, therefore, one of the active groups of the enzyme ionizes differently according as chloride is or is not present.

Another characteristic property of enzymes that can be measured and expressed in quantitative terms is the Michaelis constant K_m. This, it will be remembered, is that concentration of substrate at which, in the presence of a given amount of enzyme, the reaction velocity attains half its limiting value. A list of some K_m values is given in Table 2. The Michaelis constant differs from enzyme to enzyme, and varies also from substrate to substrate when the enzyme's specificity is not absolute. If we have an enzyme preparation that acts upon several glycosides, for example, we commonly find a different K_m for each substrate, but this does not tell us whether two or more different enzymes are concerned, or whether a single enzyme of group-specificity is at work. Preparations of yeast saccharase, for example, act upon both sucrose and raffinose, and the question arises whether yeast contains a raffinase as well as a saccharase. The K_m value for sucrose is about one-sixteenth as great as that for raffinose, but the ratio is always the same, no matter how the enzyme preparation may be prepared or purified. If two enzymes were concerned we should expect them to be present in different proportions in different preparations made by different procedures, and it therefore follows that probably only one enzyme is concerned, a conclusion which is confirmed by the fact that the pH/activity curve has the same pK values and the same optimum pH whether sucrose or raffinose is the substrate.

A fourth characteristic constant can be determined in certain cases. It will be remembered that in the presence of a large excess of substrate, the reaction velocity of an enzyme-catalysed reaction reaches a limiting value V. If the (molar) concentration of the enzyme is known and is equal to e, then

$$V = k.e,$$

where k is the velocity constant of the reaction. In general we cannot evaluate e, since the molecular weight of the enzyme must be known if this is to be calculated and, moreover, the enzyme must be available in a chemically pure form. These requirements are seldom fulfilled. Nevertheless, the value of k would be characteristic for a given enzyme acting upon a given substrate if we could but determine it. The best we can do in most cases is to determine V in the presence of an arbitrarily defined concentration of the enzyme. If the enzyme is one that acts upon more than one substrate, say on two compounds a and b, the ratio V_a/V_b will be constant if the enzyme concentration is the same in both cases. Even this second-best determination has proved itself valuable in deciding the identity of pairs of enzymes. Consider once more the case of yeast saccharase. This enzyme attacks sucrose twice as fast as raffinose, and the ratio remains the same from one preparation to another. If two enzymes were concerned we should expect the ratio to vary from case to case, but this does not happen, thus adding still more evidence of the identity of the presumptive raffinase with saccharase.

To establish the identity of one enzyme with another, even in relatively crude extracts, a number of ways are thus open. We can see whether the two behave in the same manner with respect to inhibitors and activators, and we can find out whether their specificities are similar or different. These, however, are properties that cannot be exactly defined or numerically expressed, but further evidence of a perfectly quantitative nature can be obtained by measuring (a) the two pK values, given by the positions of the points of inflexion of the pH/activity curve, or in default of these, the optimum pH. In addition (b) the Michaelis constant may be determined for one or more different substrates, and (c) we may determine the limiting velocities corresponding to known or arbitrarily defined concentrations of the two enzymes.

Summary

Summarizing our conclusions as to the nature of the enzyme-substrate union it may be said first of all that there is every reason to believe that such a union does in fact take place. The union is a very specific one; a given enzyme can combine with and activate only a limited number of substrates and, often enough, only one substrate. There is reason to think that the reaction takes place at certain definite points on the surface of the enzyme, rather than at any arbitrary point or points, and it seems that the specificity of an enzyme is really a measure of the extent to which the enzyme and the substrate 'fit' at the points through which they unite.

Even when the activating protein fits the substrate well enough to allow union to take place between them, the 'fit' may be thought to be still slightly imperfect, so that the substrate molecule is subjected to some kind of internal strain which results in the increase of chemical reactivity to which we refer as activation.

The essential function of an enzyme is that of activating its substrate. It may lose the power to do this for any of a large number of reasons, but in many cases the lost activity can be recovered. But even when activation has been accomplished, the substrate does not necessarily undergo any chemical change, since substances other than the substrate and its activating protein may also be required. We have considered ways in which the power of activation may be restored to an enzyme that has lost it, and we have considered some cases in which accessory substances or coenzymes enter into the reactions taking place after the substrate has been successfully activated.

Finally, we have seen that it is possible to obtain quantitative data which are characteristic of individual enzymes.

CHAPTER III

BIOLOGICAL ENERGETICS

The Concept of Free Energy

BEFORE going further it is necessary to know something about the conditions which determine whether or not any given chemical reaction can take place, whether it be catalysed or uncatalysed. To analyse these conditions completely would require somewhat lengthy thermodynamic arguments, but for present purposes use may be made of a simple mechanical analogy.

Let us consider a perfectly smooth body standing on a perfectly smooth plane. This body has a certain amount of gravitational potential energy, but this energy is not available for the performance of work of any kind unless the plane is tilted. Suppose now that the plane is slightly inclined. The body begins to slide downwards because some of its potential energy has become available to push it down the plane. When the body slips, work can be done (e.g. if the body is attached by means of a string to some suitable motor), and the amount of work done will be thermodynamically equivalent to the amount of gravitational potential energy lost by the body. How much work can be done by this system depends upon the system itself, for while it is theoretically possible for the body to go on sliding down an inclined plane of indefinite length until the whole of its potential energy has been converted into work, this is not a case of much practical interest. Generally speaking *the properties of natural systems are such that only a part of their total potential energy is available for the performance of work*. A larger or smaller part of the total energy is always unavailable except in theoretical cases. Hence we must distinguish between the 'free' or available energy and the total energy of the system.

Now we know as a matter of practical experience that a body will never move *up* the plane so long as the system is left to itself; an upward movement can only be accomplished by supplying energy to the system from an external source. The body will always slide *down* an inclined plane if left to its own devices, provided that the frictional forces opposing the tendency to slip are not too great. If these forces are reduced to zero the body will certainly slip, and work can be done by the system. It is in fact true that, in any self-operating system, the *free energy always tends to decrease* and, provided that frictional forces do not oppose it, the whole of the free energy lost to the system can be converted into an equivalent amount of work.

We can express these ideas more precisely with reference to heat engines. Let us consider a heat engine supplied with an amount of energy equal to Q. This energy is supplied at a high temperature T_1 (measured on the absolute scale), and conducted to a lower temperature T_2. It can be shown on theoretical grounds that the amount of work done by such an engine cannot exceed an amount W, where

$$W = Q\,\frac{T_1 - T_2}{T_1}.$$

This equation can be transformed to give

$$W = Q - \left(\frac{Q}{T_1}\right) T_2.$$

Thus the maximum available work will always be less than the total possible work by an amount given by $(Q/T_1)\,T_2$. It follows that no work can be done by an engine of this kind *unless the heat can be conducted from a higher to a lower temperature* since, if $T_1 = T_2$, the second term becomes arithmetically equal to Q but opposite in sign. This point is of great importance for biochemical reactions, which usually take place at virtually constant temperature. Furthermore, an engine of this kind can only convert its *total* energy into useful work if $(Q/T_1)\,T_2 = 0$, i.e. when $T_2 = 0$, and the 'exhaust' or condenser of the engine is maintained at the absolute zero of temperature. At all other temperatures a part of the total energy will be unavailable, and the magnitude of the unavailable energy at any temperature T is determined by the product of that temperature and the factor (Q/T_1). The latter is known as the entropy of the system and is usually represented by S. Entropy measures the extent to which the total energy of a system is unavailable for the performance of useful work.

Similar considerations apply to systems other than heat engines and, in fact, for any self-operating system working at a temperature T we can write the following general equation:

$$F = H - T.S,$$

where F represents the free energy of the system (sometimes represented by G), i.e. the amount of energy available for the performance of useful work, H is the total heat energy of the system and S is its entropy. It is not possible to determine the absolute values of these variables apart, of course, from the temperature. We can, however, observe the changes that they undergo when the system passes from its original state into a new condition represented by

$$F' = H' - T.S'.$$

Subtracting from the former equation we get

$$(F - F') = (H - H') - T(S - S'),$$

or, in the usual terminology,

$$\Delta F = \Delta H - T.\Delta S.$$

In a chemical as in any other kind of system *there is always a tendency for free energy to escape* when any change takes place in the system. A chemical change that is accompanied by a loss of free energy can therefore proceed without external assistance. On the other hand, a reaction involving a gain of free energy can only proceed if it is in some way coupled to a suitable source of free energy, which may itself be another chemical reaction. Now chemical changes as a whole are accompanied by thermal changes, and are most commonly exothermic. But the heat evolved during an exothermic process does not correspond to the change of free energy, for the change of entropy has also to be reckoned with. In an ordinary chemical reaction, therefore, all we can measure directly is ΔH, the change in total heat energy; ΔF can only be arrived at indirectly. This is not the place to deal with the procedures whereby values for ΔF can be determined or calculated, but one method of particular importance may be mentioned in passing. It applies only to reversible reactions and depends upon accurate measurements of the equilibrium constant, K, of the reaction. Thus, for a reaction

$$A + B \rightleftharpoons C + D,$$

K is defined by the equation

$$K = \frac{[A]\,[B]}{[C]\,[D]}.$$

In such a case, $\qquad \Delta F = -RT \log_e K,$

where R is the gas constant and T the absolute temperature.

Sometimes the change of entropy is small, so that ΔF is approximately equal to ΔH, but it is equally possible to have a reaction in which the change of entropy is very large indeed, so that the reaction is actually endothermic but results nevertheless in a loss of free energy. We see then, that the total heat change of an exothermic or endothermic reaction gives no indication as to whether or not that reaction can take place under its own power or must be assisted by other processes going on in the environment; the only reliable guide is a knowledge of ΔF.

If ΔF is zero the system is in chemical equilibrium: if it is positive (i.e. free energy goes into the system) the reaction cannot take place except with external aid: but if it is negative (i.e. free energy comes out of the system) the reaction can proceed of its own accord. Processes which are attended by a loss of free energy (i.e. $\Delta F < 0$) are said to be *exergonic*, while those which involve an uptake of free energy (i.e. $\Delta F > 0$) are known as *endergonic* changes.

A chemical reaction is thermodynamically possible, then, if it is exergonic, i.e. is attended by a loss of free energy. Whether or not it actually takes place, however, depends upon other factors. A body will not slide down a rough plane if the frictional forces are greater than the forces exerted by its free gravitational potential energy. Similarly, while a chemical reaction *can* take place if it entails a loss of free energy, it will not actually *do* so if the 'frictional forces' tending to oppose it are too large. In other words, *a chemical reaction requires for its accomplishment that the molecules shall be in a reactive state.* This requirement is taken care of in biological systems by the enzymes they contain. For example, we may keep a neutral, aqueous solution of sucrose almost indefinitely without appreciable hydrolysis, for although hydrolysis is thermodynamically possible, it does not actually take place because the molecules are not sufficiently reactive. If we add a small amount of saccharase or, alternatively, a little dilute mineral acid, the sugar is hydrolysed. By activating the molecules these catalysts overcome the 'frictional forces' opposing hydrolysis.

It follows from all this that no catalyst can initiate or accelerate a reaction that is not already possible on energetic grounds: all that it can do is to influence the velocity at which a thermodynamically possible reaction actually takes place.

BREAKDOWN AND SYNTHESIS IN BIOLOGICAL SYSTEMS

The numerous and diverse chemical processes which underlie the activities of a living organism collectively constitute its *metabolism*. For purposes of discussion the overall metabolism of a cell or tissue can be considered as consisting of two parts, *katabolism*, which involves the chemical degradation of complex materials into simpler products, and *anabolism*, which involves the elaboration of complex products from simpler starting materials. Katabolism and anabolism are usually defined in terms of chemical complexity, but this is a somewhat unsatisfactory variable because we have no quantitative means of measuring or expressing it. But, in a general kind of way, increases in chemical complexity are associated with increases of free energy, and for our present purposes we may conveniently define as katabolic those processes which involve a loss of free energy and are therefore exergonic, and as anabolic those in which free energy is gained and which are therefore endergonic.

Now, animal and plant tissues as a whole are known to contain intracellular enzymes which can be extracted and shown to catalyse the katabolic breakdown of proteins and other high-molecular materials into simpler units. It seems improbable that this can be their sole function in the cell. After death these enzymes do in fact lead to the digestion of much of the tissue substance, a process known as autolysis, and this is why game and certain kinds of meat are allowed to 'hang' before being cooked. This same process of autolysis is the first stage in the decomposition of dead organisms; bacteria and the biblical worms come into the picture considerably later.

During life, however, anabolic (i.e. synthetic) processes are numerous and of very great importance, especially during growth and in tissue repair after injury. They include the synthesis of catalytic and tissue proteins from amino-acids; polysaccharides from simple sugars; oils, fats and waxes from their constituent alcohols and fatty acids, to make no mention of the elaboration of other more or less highly specialized products such as hormones, pigments and so forth. But, in addition, we have good reason to believe that the tissue constituents themselves are not permanent, static structures, but rather that they are constantly in a state of breakdown balanced by synthesis.* This is true even of hard structures such as the bones and the teeth. It seems, therefore, that we must envisage the possibility that intracellular enzymes are concerned both with the breakdown and the synthesis of proteins, fats, carbohydrates and other cell constituents.

On theoretical grounds we must believe that an enzyme which can catalyse the hydrolysis of its substrate, for example, must also be capable of catalysing the condensation of its products, and in a number of instances such a reversibility of action can readily be demonstrated, e.g. among lipases and esterases (see p. 106; Fig. 12). In many other cases, however, attempts to

---

* In this connexion see Schoenheimer's *The Dynamic State of Body Constituents* (1942), London, which is already classical.

demonstrate synthesis by an enzyme known to catalyse the corresponding degradation have yielded only negative results. It must be remembered, however, that in order that a given chemical reaction shall take place it is not enough for the molecules concerned to be in a reactive state: *the energy conditions also must be favourable.* It is possible, therefore, that the failure of many experiments has been due only to inability to reproduce under experimental conditions the proper energetic circumstances, and does not necessarily mean that the enzymes concerned are inherently incapable of working in both directions. For these reasons we might assume that in the cell, if not in the laboratory, the right energetic conditions are attainable, and that, in the cell, the same enzymes can catalyse synthesis and breakdown alike. But their synthetic action would be expected to require the maintenance of normal physiological conditions inside the cell because, if these break down, the necessary provisions of energy would not be forthcoming and only the phase of degradation would be observed.

The function of the intracellular 'autolytic' enzymes might be regarded, then, as that of maintaining equilibrium between the complex materials of the cell substance and their simpler constituents, so that a balance is struck between synthesis and degradation. And we must not think of the equilibrium thus set up and maintained as in any sense a static affair but as an essentially dynamic system in which breakdown and re-synthesis are proceeding simultaneously at high but equal velocity. We should do well to recall Hopkins's celebrated aphorism, that *life is a dynamic equilibrium in a polyphasic system.*

In living cells, then, katabolism and anabolism proceed together. This raises several problems of the greatest energetic importance. First, what is the biological source of the free energy required for the essentially endergonic processes of anabolism; secondly, how is that free energy harnessed or 'captured' by the cell and, thirdly, how is it brought to bear upon the processes wherein it is consumed? And it should be borne in mind that free energy is expended not only in anabolic reactions, but in the performance of muscular and other kinds of biological work.

For many years these problems seemed so complex and so wholly baffling that many biologists were content to believe them unanswerable; that living organisms must in some way contrive to operate in defiance of the laws of thermodynamics. Although the most spectacular progress in the field of biological energetics has been made in comparatively recent years, the most fundamental experiments were undoubtedly those performed just before the end of the last century, by Rubner in Germany, and speedily confirmed in America by Atwater, Rosa and Benedict. These workers constructed animal calorimeters capable of containing dogs, and later even men, in conditions of comparative comfort for periods of days or even weeks. The apparatus, which will not be described here since there are admirable descriptions in many physiological and biochemical text-books, was constructed in such a way that the following measurements could be accurately and simultaneously carried out:

(a) Total energy output, measured as heat.
(b) Total oxygen consumption.
(c) Total carbon dioxide production.
(d) Total nitrogen excretion.

Numerous corrections had, of course, to be applied, e.g. for heat brought into the apparatus in hot food and for heat removed in the bodily excreta. And there were many engineering difficulties.

From (b), (c) and (d) it is possible to calculate the weights of carbohydrate, fat and protein oxidized in the course of an experiment and hence to arrive at the total yield of energy attributable to their metabolism, the calorific values of these metabolic substrates having previously been determined with a high degree of accuracy by combustion in the bomb calorimeter.

Of such fundamental importance is the outcome of these experiments that the reader is asked to examine with more than usual care the data of Table 3, which is compiled from the results of Rubner's experiments. These were followed up by experiments on human subjects in the Atwater-Rosa-Benedict calorimeter. Whether the subjects were resting, active or even taking fairly strenuous exercise, e.g. by riding stationary bicycles, the observed and calculated heat outputs agreed within limits even narrower than in Rubner's experiments. These results provided irrefutable proof that a living organism as exalted even as man himself cannot create energy out of nothingness, and no convincing evidence to the contrary has at any time been forthcoming. *Living organisms, like machines, conform to the law of the conservation of energy, and must pay for all their activities in the currency of metabolism.*

TABLE 3. CALCULATED AND OBSERVED HEAT OUTPUTS OF DOGS IN RUBNER'S EXPERIMENTS. (*After* Lusk)

(Kilo-cal. per sq.m. of body surface per 24 hr.)

Diet	Duration of exp. (days)	Heat output		Difference (%)
		Calculated	Determined	
None	5	1296·3	1305·2 }	−1·42
	2	1091·2	1056·6 }	
Fat	5	1510·1	1498·3	−0·97
Meat and fat	8	2492·4	2488·0 }	−0·42
	12	3985·4	3958·4 }	
Meat	6	2249·8	2276·9 }	+0·43
	7	4780·8	4769·3 }	

With these results before us it is clear that there can be but one answer to the most fundamental of our problems. *Energy used in anabolism must be drawn from katabolic processes : no other source is open.* This means that there must exist some kind of coupling between katabolism and anabolism; some kind of mechanism that allows the transference of free energy from one to the other. There then remains the problem of the manner in which the free energy to which the cell gains access in the course of its katabolic operations can be captured and utilized for anabolic and other purposes. In order to deal with these problems we must necessarily enquire into the mechanisms which underlie the synthetic reactions that make up anabolism and, in particular, we must consider the possibility that anabolic processes may be merely reversals of katabolic changes catalysed by the same enzymes.

Reversibility of Biological Reactions

All reactions are reversible in theory, but because they are reversible in theory it does not necessarily follow that they are reversible in actual practice, at any rate under biological conditions. The explosion of an atomic bomb is reversible in theory, but reversal of the explosive process is something that is not very likely to be accomplished, at any rate in the foreseeable future. Much the same is true of many enzyme-catalysed reactions under biological conditions; and, of course, it is with biological reactions that we are particularly concerned here. Now enzymes, in common with catalysts of other kinds, influence only the velocity and not the direction of the reactions they catalyse, and there are, as has been pointed out already, many enzyme-catalysed processes that go equally freely in either direction. But many others do not.

No chemical reaction is totally irreversible; on the contrary, every reaction tends towards an equilibrium, e.g.

$$A \rightleftharpoons B + C.$$

Equilibrium is rapidly reached in the presence of a suitable enzyme or other catalyst, and the composition of the equilibrated mixture is determined by the molar concentrations of the reactants and by the overall change of free energy. If the intrinsic free energy of A is very large compared with that of the products, decomposition of A will predominate over its synthesis and, if the degree of predominance is very large indeed, as it often is in practice, the process will be virtually unidirectional and may, for all practical purposes, be regarded as irreversible. In considering the conditions required to reverse the process and so bring about the synthesis of A, we have in fact to consider the conditions required to alter the final equilibrium in such a way that synthesis can become the predominant process.

Let us consider now a simple biological process of a virtually irreversible kind that can be represented as follows:

$$A \rightarrow B + C; \quad \Delta F = -\epsilon \text{ cal.}$$

Since the change of free energy associated with the process is less than zero ($\Delta F < 0$) the reaction is one that is thermodynamically possible and will therefore proceed spontaneously in the presence of an appropriate catalyst. When it takes place, ϵ cal. of free energy will become available for each g.mol. of substrate transformed, and, if some suitable device were present to trap it, this free energy could be converted into work of some kind. But in the absence of such a contrivance this free energy is merely dissipated in the form of heat, and the total output of heat can then be calculated from the usual equation:

$$\Delta H = \Delta F + T . \Delta S.$$

Since ϵ cal. of free energy are liberated when the reaction proceeds in the forward direction, it follows that it can be made to go backwards if, *and only if*, an amount of free energy equal to ϵ cal. is supplied in some way. It is useless merely to supply heat equal to ΔH to the system because, as we have seen, heat cannot do work unless it is conducted from a higher to a lower temperature, and biological processes usually take place at virtually constant temperature. Thus, although our reaction is theoretically reversible and although the enzyme concerned may be able to catalyse the forward and reverse processes alike, the backward reaction can only be realized if the requisite amount of free energy can be provided; and provided, moreover, *under biological conditions*.

In the laboratory the chemist, faced with the task of performing an energy-consuming synthesis will as a rule make use of high temperatures, strong acids, strong alkalis and similar 'powerful' reagents. But these are resources that are denied to biological systems. Even if they were available, these factors would destroy the indispensable catalytic properties of the enzymes and would lead, therefore, if they led to anything at all, to wholesale damage of the tissues and to gross disorganization of their metabolic systems. Living cells, by contrast, operate in the neighbourhood of pH 7 and at temperatures ranging roughly from zero to $40°$ on the centigrade scale, and even under these very 'mild' conditions their synthetic ability is vastly superior to that of the organic chemist.

ENERGETICS OF SYNTHETIC REACTIONS

Consider again the reaction

$$A \rightarrow B + C\,; \ \Delta F = -\epsilon \text{ cal.}$$

One way of achieving the reverse process would be in some way to incorporate into one of the reactants, B and C, an amount of free energy equal to or greater than ϵ cal. per g.mol. This, indeed, is the usual method in biological systems, and processes whereby this is accomplished have come to be known as *priming reactions*. The usual biological procedure is that some suitable additional grouping, very commonly a phosphate radical, is introduced into one of the reactants, say B, to give a product of higher free energy content, say B—R. In the presence of a suitable catalyst a reaction leading back to the original starting material is then possible:

$$B\text{—R} + C \rightarrow A + R\,; \ \Delta F \leqslant 0.$$

But B—R is not chemically identical with B; and so great is the specificity of enzymes in general that an enzyme capable of activating B would almost certainly be unable to activate B—R. In other words, although the breakdown of A is possible in the presence of a suitable enzyme, its *synthesis must follow a different chemical pathway and require the participation of other enzymes.* Moreover, the synthesis of A will involve a priming reaction whereby B or C can be raised to a higher energy-level.

A process of the kind usually represented by $X \rightleftharpoons Y$ will only be possible, then, if it entails little or no change of free energy: where there is any large change of free energy the inter-conversion can only be properly represented by some other kind of symbolism specially designed to emphasize the fact that the forward and backward pathways are totally different. No satis-factory symbolism for this purpose has yet been devised.

To make these notions clear we may take a specific example in which 'R' is a phosphate radical. The digestive hydrolysis of the polysaccharide glycogen is a 'downhill', i.e. an exergonic, reaction, and is irreversible. Now glycogen can also be broken down to glucose by intracellular enzymes present in the liver, and this process too is exergonic and irreversible. But certain other enzymes present in the liver can bring about the endergonic synthesis of glycogen from free glucose. The reactions involved may be diagrammatically summarized in the following manner

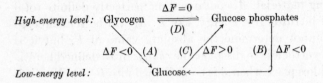

High-energy level :   Glycogen $\xrightleftharpoons[(D)]{\Delta F = 0}$ Glucose phosphates

$\Delta F < 0$ (A) (C) $\Delta F > 0$ (B) $\Delta F < 0$

Low-energy level :   Glucose

Whether glycogen is broken down to glucose by digestive enzymes (A) or by the liver enzymes $(D+B)$, there is a fall from a higher to a lower free-energy level, and in neither case can the pathway of breakdown be retraced. Synthesis can only proceed by a pathway involving a priming reaction (C) whereby the glucose is phosphorylated and thus raised to a higher free-energy level. Once this has been accomplished the phosphorylated sugar can polymerize (D) to form glycogen with little further change of free energy, so that an equilibrium is set up. We shall return presently to a more detailed examination of this process.

Endergonic or anabolic synthesis can be accomplished, then, through the *incorporation of free energy into the reactants* by means of priming reactions. Such a reaction is a necessary preliminary to the synthesis of glycogen from glucose, and similar priming reactions are now known to be involved at one or another stage in many biological syntheses, e.g. of glutamine, hippuric acid, urea and many other substances.

Bond Energy and the Biological Transfer of Energy

All priming reactions appear to follow a common pattern; all are 'transfer reactions', i.e. reactions in which a grouping or radical of some kind is transferred from one molecule to another. All are enzymatically catalysed and the radical most usually involved is that of phosphoric acid.

In order to gain some understanding of the mechanisms that underlie reactions of this kind let us consider once more the reaction

$$A \to B + C; \quad \Delta F = -\epsilon.$$

The starting material, A, contains some perfectly definite total amount of intrinsic free energy, say F. It will be remembered that we cannot determine the absolute value of F, but it is possible nevertheless to discover the *change* in F, defined here as $-\epsilon$, that takes place when A is transformed into $B + C$. Now it is quite certain that the intrinsic free energy of A is not uniformly spread out over the molecule and since A can be split into B and C we may think of A itself as consisting of two parts, B and C, linked together by a bond the rupture of which yields up ϵ cal. of free energy for each g.mol. of A disrupted. It is convenient to think of the free energy ϵ as being especially associated with the bond that links B with C, in other words as '*bond energy*'. If we represent this bond by a dotted instead of the usual full line our reaction can be rewritten as follows:

$$A = B \overset{\epsilon}{\cdots} C \to B + C; \quad \Delta F = -\epsilon \text{ cal.}$$

With this concept of bond energy in mind let us now consider a typical transfer reaction in which a radical R is transferred from one substance, say $X \cdots R$, to another, say Z:

$$X \overset{\epsilon}{\cdots} R + Z \rightleftharpoons X + R \overset{\epsilon}{\cdots} Z.$$

Many such reactions are known, some reversible and others irreversible and we shall consider first those which are reversible, since they entail changes of free energy small enough to be neglected.

If the bond linking X to R is associated with any significant amount of free energy, it follows that this bond cannot be ruptured in any simple, straightforward manner, for there is no overall change of free energy in the process as a whole. Consequently we may infer that not only the radical R but *the bond energy associated with it* can be transferred from the donator to the acceptor substance. It might be thought that the transfer proceeds in two stages, free energy being liberated in the first and quantitatively consumed in the second:

$$\text{(i)} \quad X \cdots^{\epsilon} R \rightarrow X + R — \epsilon,$$

$$\text{(ii)} \quad R + Z + \epsilon \rightarrow R \cdots^{\epsilon} Z.$$

This interpretation is almost certainly erroneous. The energy ϵ cannot have any free existence because, if it did, it would in all probability be dissipated as heat, most or all of which would be unavailable for the performance of useful work in a virtually thermostatic biological system. Some other interpretation must accordingly be sought.

The transference of the radical R from X to Z is evidently accomplished in some manner which does not entail the removal and subsequent reattachment of R, and the most likely way in which this could be done is by the formation of an intermediate reaction complex of some kind. Such a complex might be formed between the reactants themselves, or through the agency of a catalytic enzyme-protein to which both reactants can be attached. Such evidence as we have suggests that the first stage in the reaction often consists in union of the group donator, $X \cdots R$, with the enzyme, followed by removal of X and its replacement by Z. Finally the Z-R-enzyme complex dissociates, yielding $R \cdots Z$ and regenerating the enzyme, probably in the following manner:

(i) $X \cdots^{\epsilon} R + \boxed{\text{enzyme}} \rightleftharpoons X \cdots^{\epsilon} R—\boxed{\text{enzyme}} \rightleftharpoons X—R \cdots^{\epsilon} \boxed{\text{enzyme}} \rightleftharpoons X + R \cdots^{\epsilon} \boxed{\text{enzyme}}$.

(ii) $Z + R \cdots^{\epsilon} \boxed{\text{enzyme}} \rightleftharpoons Z—R \cdots^{\epsilon} \boxed{\text{enzyme}} \rightleftharpoons Z \cdots^{\epsilon} R—\boxed{\text{enzyme}} \rightleftharpoons Z \cdots^{\epsilon} R + \boxed{\text{enzyme}}$.

Here the radical R and the free energy with which it is associated is handed over to the enzyme, which then passes it on to the second reactant.

If the transfer process as a whole is reversible and if the intermediate stages postulated here correspond to reality, it follows that all the partial reactions must also be reversible. This could only be the case if the bond energy of $X \cdots R$ is conserved. We must therefore conclude that all the intermediates are tautomeric or resonating substances, so that the bond energy can be shifted from one bond to another in the way depicted here.

An alternative possibility is that both donor and acceptor might be simultaneously accommodated on the enzyme to form a tautomeric complex which then decomposes. This possibility may be expressed in the following manner, both reactants being linked to the enzyme throughout:

$$X \overset{\epsilon}{\cdots} R + Z \rightleftharpoons X \overset{\epsilon}{\cdots} R—Z \rightleftharpoons X—R \overset{\epsilon}{\cdots} Z \rightleftharpoons X + R \overset{\epsilon}{\cdots} Z.$$

We can account in either of these ways for the transference of the radical R from one to the other of the reactants without any actual liberation of the radical in question or the rupture of any energy-laden bond. These schemes also account for the free reversibility of the transfer process as a whole and for the complete efficiency of the transference of free energy from one molecule to another. Here, in fact, we have mechanisms whereby, at the expense of the 'katabolism' of $X \overset{\epsilon}{\cdots} R$ to yield X, a new compound $R \overset{\epsilon}{\cdots} Z$ can be 'anabolized', the free energy of the bond being quantitatively transferred from one molecule to the other with no 'spilling over' of free energy in the form of heat.

In addition to reversible reactions of this kind there are other transfer reactions which are irreversible. This happens in reactions where the bond energy of the donor substance (ϵ) is greater than that required to form the new bond (ϵ'): in such a reaction the excess balance of free energy ($\epsilon - \epsilon'$) is spilled out and dissipated as heat. Although they are wasteful of free energy, reactions of this kind are very important in metabolism.

These somewhat theoretical considerations may at first appear to be the products of an overheated imagination, but we shall shortly consider examples to show that, in point of fact, these 'model' reactions do have biological counterparts.

PROPERTIES AND FUNCTIONS OF ADENOSINE TRIPHOSPHATE

It will be helpful now to consider certain properties of the substance known as adenosine triphosphate. This compound, otherwise known as ATP, is apparently a universal constituent of living stuff and plays a part of fundamental importance in biological exchanges of energy. We shall consider its detailed structure later; for the moment it may be represented as A—Ⓟ—Ⓟ—Ⓟ, where A represents the nucleoside adenosine and Ⓟ stands for the radical of phosphoric acid.

The terminal phosphate radical of ATP can readily be removed by hydrolysis, either by dilute mineral acid or by an enzyme, and the process is attended by the liberation of about 12,000 cal. of heat, of which about 11,500 cal. correspond to free energy and the remainder to an increase of entropy. The reaction may therefore be written as follows:

$$A—Ⓟ—Ⓟ—Ⓟ + H_2O \rightarrow A—Ⓟ—Ⓟ + HO.Ⓟ; \quad \Delta F = -11,500 \text{ cal.}$$

The second phosphate radical can be similarly removed:

$$A—Ⓟ—Ⓟ + H_2O \rightarrow A—Ⓟ + HO.Ⓟ; \quad \Delta F = -11,500 \text{ cal.}$$

The third phosphate radical can also be removed, again by acid hydrolysis or under the influence of an enzyme, but with much more difficulty, and this time only some 2000–3000 cal. of heat are evolved, of which about 2000 cal. correspond to free energy:

$$A—Ⓟ + H_2O \rightarrow A + HO.Ⓟ; \quad \Delta F = -2000 \text{ cal.}$$

The yield of free energy in this last reaction is of the same order of magnitude as that found for the hydrolysis of most simple phosphate esters such, for example, as the glucose phosphates ($\Delta F = -3000$ to -4000 cal.) and phosphoglycerol ($\Delta F = -2200$ cal.).

Clearly, there is some far-reaching difference between the bonds through which the first two phosphate radicals are attached and that which binds the third: in fact there exist in the ATP molecule two specimens of what may be called 'high energy' or *'energy-rich' phosphate bonds* as distinct from the third 'energy-poor' or *'low energy' phosphate bond*, which resembles those found in most common phosphate esters. Thus, if we use the special symbol $\sim$ to represent an energy-rich bond, the structure of ATP can be more adequately represented thus:

$$A—Ⓟ \sim Ⓟ \sim Ⓟ.$$

We shall not trespass here into the fields of theoretical chemistry in search of reasons for these phenomena; it is sufficient for our immediate purposes to know that they exist. Similar high-energy bonds are now known to be present in a number of other compounds, including inorganic pyrophosphates, and a list of some of these, together with approximate data for the free energy of their respective hydrolyses, is shown in Table 4. The values for ΔF shown here must be regarded as approximate only; a high degree of accuracy is only obtainable under exceptionally favourable conditions and, as the table itself shows, different methods of estimation give rather different results. Energy-rich bonds are found in particular association with certain particular structures (see Table 5).

TABLE 4. APPROXIMATE FREE ENERGIES OF HYDROLYSIS OF SOME PHOSPHORIC ACID DERIVATIVES

(after Avison & Hawkins, 1951)

Compound	ΔF (cal.)	pH	° C.	Method of determination
Glycerol-1-phosphate	$-2,200$	8·5	38	Equilibrium measurements of enzymatic hydrolysis
Glucose-6-phosphate	$-3,000$	8·5	38	
Fructose-6-phosphate	$-3,350$	8·5	38	
	$-3,500$	8·5	38	Equilibria with glucose-6-phosphate
Glucose-1-phosphate	$-4,750$	8·5	38	
ATP (terminal group) ($\sim$)	$-11,500$	7·5	20	Calculation
1:3-Diphosphoglyceric acid ($\sim$)	$-16,250$	6·9	25	Enzymatic equilibria with ATP
Acetyl phosphate ($\sim$)	$-14,500$	6·3	37	
Phospho-*enol*-pyruvic acid ($\sim$)	$-15,900$	?	20	
	$-15,850$	?	20	Calculation
Phosphocreatine ($\sim$)	$-13,000$	7·7	?	Enzymatic equilibria with ATP
Phosphoarginine ($\sim$)	$-11,800$	7·7	20	

Adenosine triphosphate plays a central part in the energy transactions of many and perhaps all kinds of living tissues. It enters into numerous priming reactions, for example, and its importance lies in the ease with which its terminal phosphate radical can be transferred, *together with a part or all of the 11,500 cal. of free energy with which it is associated,* to other molecules. Two examples of this behaviour may be considered.

First we have the Lohmann reaction, so named after its discoverer. This, a freely reversible reaction, is catalysed by an enzyme that occurs in all kinds of vertebrate muscles and can be expressed as follows:

$$A—\text{\textcircled{P}}\sim\text{\textcircled{P}}\sim\text{\textcircled{P}} + C \rightleftharpoons A—\text{\textcircled{P}}\sim\text{\textcircled{P}} + C\sim\text{\textcircled{P}}$$

where C represents the guanidine derivative, creatine. When this reaction takes place there is only a small change of free energy. The whole 11,500 cal. of the terminal phosphate radical of the ATP are transferred, along with the phosphate radical itself, to the creatine, and the free energy of hydrolysis of the product, creatine phosphate, is about −13,000 cal. per g.mol., a difference of the order of only 1500 cal., and the transfer is readily reversible. A very convenient shorthand notation for reactions of this kind may be used and is frequently used throughout these pages:

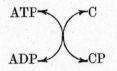

Double-ended arrows are used to indicate the free reversibility of the reaction. The mechanism of the reaction is presumably similar to one or other of those suggested on pp. 67, 68.

TABLE 5. PHOSPHATE DERIVATIVES
AND ENERGY-RICH BONDS

Type and identity of bond

Esters:

$\diagdown$C—O—Ⓟ   Glycerol-α-phosphate
$\diagup$ Glucose-6-phosphate

Carbonyl phosphates:

$\diagdown$C—O ~ Ⓟ   Phosphoacetic acid
$\diagup$ Phospho-*enol*-pyruvic acid
                  1:3-Diphosphoglyceric acid

Guanidine phosphates:

HN = C$\diagup$NH ~ Ⓟ
       $\diagdown$NH   Creatine phosphate
        | Arginine phosphate

Polyphosphates:

$$\underset{\underset{OH}{|}}{\overset{\overset{O}{\|}}{-P}}-O \sim \underset{\underset{OH}{|}}{\overset{\overset{O}{\|}}{P}}-OH \quad \text{ATP, ADP}$$

As a second example we may consider an irreversible transfer reaction that takes place between glucose and ATP in the presence of the very widely distributed enzyme, hexokinase,

The products are glucose-6-phosphate and adenosine diphosphate (ADP). The reaction may be written in the following manner:

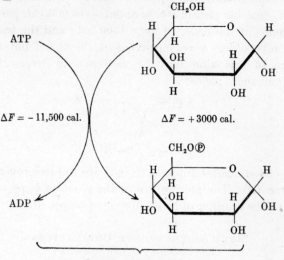

ATP

$\Delta F = -11,500$ cal. $\Delta F = +3000$ cal.

ADP

Overall: $\Delta F = -8500$ cal.

If we consider only the conversion of ATP to ADP we see that this part of the system suffers a loss of 11,500 cal. of free energy. The gain of free energy in the conversion of glucose to its phosphate amounts to only about 3000 cal., however, so that a balance of some 8500 cal. of free energy is left over and spilled out as heat. This reaction, unlike the Lohmann reaction, is therefore unidirectional and irreversible. Although so much free energy is wasted, this is a reaction of fundamental importance in carbohydrate metabolism because glucose can neither be stored nor metabolized unless it is first of all phosphorylated, and this, the *hexokinase reaction*, is the principal and perhaps the only mechanism through which this preliminary phosphorylation can be achieved; simple direct introduction of a phosphate radical is energetically impossible since $\Delta F > 0$ for such a reaction. The hexokinase reaction is typical of priming reactions as a whole and is, in fact, the first step in the synthesis of glycogen from glucose (see p. 65).

It will now be of interest to follow the rest of this process. The priming reaction raises the free energy of glucose sufficiently to allow the formation of a glucosidic bond, i.e. by about 3000–4000 cal. per g.mol. In the next reaction a glycosidic bond is formed by shifting the phosphate radical from the 6- to the 1-position:

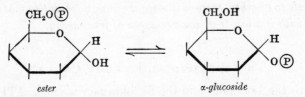

This reaction (catalysed by phosphoglucomutase) yields as its product α-glucose-1-phosphate, itself a glucoside. Finally the glucoside radical, *together with the free energy of its glucosidic bond*, is transferred from the phosphate radical to a partly formed α-glucosidic glycogen chain (under the influence of phosphorylase):

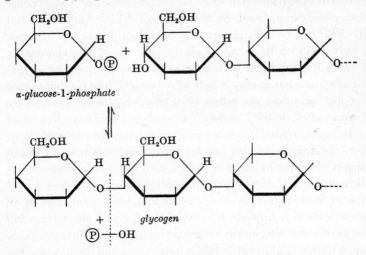

The final stage in this synthesis is instructive from our present point of view, since it shows that, in addition to 'high energy transfers' such as that which occurs in the Lohmann reaction and involves the participation of ATP, 'low energy transfers'

too are possible. Group transference is a common phenomenon in biochemistry. Enzymes are known that can catalyse the transference of methyl-, amino-, amidino- and a variety of other radicals, over and above the phosphatic and glycosidic groups that have provided our examples here, and it should be borne in mind that *whenever a group or radical is transferred from one molecule to another, there is always a strong probability that it will carry with it a larger or smaller quota of free energy.*

THE BIOLOGICAL ENERGY CYCLE

In both the Lohmann and the hexokinase reactions, ATP loses phosphate and energy in favour of its reaction partner and in both cases an endergonic reaction is achieved by coupling to one that is exergonic. This appears to be a fundamental operation in the synthesis of complex biological compounds from simpler starting materials, and, as far as we know at present, anabolic, synthetic operations can only be accomplished at the expense of an energy-rich bond, most usually of ATP. And this is not all. ATP can be split in any of a considerable variety of ways. It may yield up its terminal phosphate radical and the energy of the adjacent bond in a reaction of the kind we have just discussed, so that energy is as it were 'forced' into the phosphate acceptor, or, under the influence of an adenosine triphosphatase of some kind, it may undergo a catalysed hydrolysis to yield ADP together with free inorganic phosphate. In this case, however, the free energy of the terminal energy-rich bond is not conserved, either in whole or in part, as it is in a transfer reaction, but is liberated. If the reaction is allowed to proceed in a test-tube or flask this free energy is dissipated as heat, but in an intact muscle it appears largely in the form of the *mechanical energy* of the concomitant muscular contraction. It is probably not without significance, therefore, that the adenosine triphosphatase of muscle is identical with myosin, which is itself a constituent of the actual contractile machinery of the muscle cell and plays the part of a 'transformer' which converts chemical into mechanical energy.

In the electric organs of certain fishes, e.g. *Torpedo, Raia* spp., *Gymnotus, Malapterurus,* 'transformers' of a different kind are present, for myosin is lacking in the most highly developed of these organs, despite the fact that they arise by the morphological transformation of embryonic pre-muscular cells. The *electrical energy* dissipated when these organs discharge arises, according to present knowledge, from ATP once again. The *light energy* dissipated by bioluminescent organisms such as the fire-fly (*Photinus pyralis*) similarly has its origin in ATP according to recent reports, and energy drawn from ATP can also, it is believed, accomplish the performance of *osmotic work,* for example in the absorption of glucose from the small gut against large osmotic gradients.

Now the amounts of ATP present in most tissues are not very large, and are out of all proportion to the energy turnover of these tissues. It follows, therefore, that ATP must be used and reformed over and over again if the many and diverse activities of the tissues are to be maintained. But, as we know to-day, *new energy-rich bonds arise in the course of many katabolic transformations* and, indeed, it would appear that katabolism as a whole is directed above all to the generation of new energy-rich phosphate bonds. These can be transferred, together with the phosphate radicals with which they seem almost invariably to be associated, to ADP left after previous breakdown of ATP molecules. It is significant, however, that *newly generated energy-rich bonds cannot be utilized directly* for the performance of endergonic operations: *they can be put to service only through the intermediation of the ADP/ATP system.* No alternative system has so far been brought to light.

It would not be profitable to discuss the processes that lead to the generation of new energy-rich bonds until we have studied katabolic processes in some detail, but one simple example may not be out of place here. The synthesis of ATP from ADP calls for the provision of some 11,500 cal. of free energy per g.mol. This can be provided, for instance, by new energy-rich bonds generated in the course of the metabolic degradation of glucose or glycogen. One such bond appears when one of the numerous intermediate products, 2-phosphoglyceric acid, undergoes dehydration under the influence of the enzyme enolase to yield phospho-*enol*-pyruvate:

$$\begin{array}{ccc} CH_2OH & CH_2 & \\ | & \| & \\ CHO\textcircled{P} & \rightarrow & CO \sim \textcircled{P} + H_2O \\ | & | & \\ COOH & COOH & \end{array}$$

The removal of the elements of water from phosphoglyceric acid results in structural alterations within the molecule. These are attended by a redistribution of the intrinsic free energy of the system, leading to a 'concentration' of free energy in the neighbourhood of the phosphate radical; in other words to the generation of a new energy-rich bond. The free energy of this new bond has been estimated at about 16,000 cal., i.e. rather more than is required to forge a new bond in ATP. This new bond energy, together with the phosphate radical, is then transferred to ADP and a new molecule of ATP is thereby produced.

THE STORAGE OF PHOSPHATE BOND ENERGY

Energy-rich bonds can be transferred from ATP to creatine, arginine and probably certain other guanidine bases, by the Lohmann reaction, to form 'phosphagens' and, in certain tissues, energy-rich bonds are stored in the form of these substances. These stored bonds cannot be used directly, but only through the ADP/ATP system. They can, however, be transferred directly to ADP through the Lohmann reaction, and the transfer is freely reversible. When such a tissue enters into physiological activity, ATP is broken down and provides energy in the form characteristic of the particular organ. Unless or until new bonds are generated rapidly enough to resynthesize ATP as fast as it is used up, the tissue can draw on the energy-rich bonds of the phosphagen reserve, transferring these to ADP and thus regenerating ATP. Later, after activity has ceased, the metabolic generators continue to run for a short time, so that ATP continues to be produced and, reacting now with the free guanidine base, resynthesizes phosphagen and thus replenishes the store. These notions may be diagrammatically summarized in the so-called 'energy dynamo' of Fig. 10.

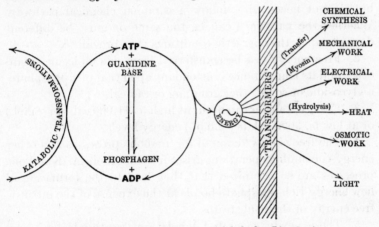

Fig. 10. The 'energy dynamo' (modified after Lipmann).

It is interesting and important to notice that the second energy-rich bond of ATP is not as a rule available as a direct source of energy for chemical synthesis, nor for the production of mechanical or electrical energy. It can, however, be rendered available through the activity of the peculiar enzyme, myokinase. Unlike enzymes in general, myokinase will tolerate prolonged heating to 100° C., precipitation with trichloracetic acid and other kinds of physico-chemical maltreatment. It has been prepared from muscle, and appears to be present in other tissues as well. This enzyme specifically catalyses the transference of the terminal phosphate radical from one molecule of ADP to a second molecule of the same substance, so that AMP (adenosine monophosphate) and ATP are produced:

$$2A—\textcircled{P}\sim\textcircled{P} \rightleftharpoons A—\textcircled{P} + A—\textcircled{P}\sim\textcircled{P}\sim\textcircled{P}.$$

The new molecule of ATP can then be utilized in the usual manner.

SUMMARY

1. The breakdown and synthesis of biological materials may, but do not necessarily, follow a common chemical pathway. Whether the pathways can be the same or must be different depends upon the energetic conditions that prevail.

2. Free energy can be transferred from one molecule to another and its transference is attendant upon that of a phosphate, a glycosidic or some other grouping or radical.

3. Energy transfer can occur at high (c. 11,000 cal. per g.mol.) or at low (c. 3000 cal. per g.mol.) energy levels.

4. The free energy required for anabolic processes and other energy-consuming operations arises from katabolism. Katabolic processes are so organized that they lead to the formation of new energy-rich phosphate bonds at the expense of the intrinsic free energy of their substrates.

5. These newly generated bonds are 'captured' by transference to ADP so that new molecules of ATP are formed, and it is only through the intermediation of the ADP/ATP system that their energy can be utilized for biological purposes.

6. Energy-rich bonds can be stored in certain tissues in the form of phosphagens.

7. The free energy of the terminal energy-rich bond of ATP can be utilized in one or another of the many energy-expending processes in which this remarkable substance participates. Among these are numerous 'priming' reactions which form essential steps in the biochemical synthesis of complex, high-energy products from simpler starting materials of lower free-energy content.

CHAPTER IV

HYDROLASES AND ADDING ENZYMES

GENERAL INTRODUCTION

THE classification of enzymes presents a good many problems and no entirely satisfactory system has yet been devised. Some kind of classification is desirable, however, for purposes of description and enzymes will here be arbitrarily divided into the following groups:

> Hydrolases,
> Adding enzymes,
> Transferring enzymes,
> Isomerases,
> Oxidizing enzymes.

Enzymes which catalyse a hydrolytic splitting of their substrates are known as *hydrolases*. All digestive enzymes, whether intracellular or extracellular, fall into this class, and digestion itself may be regarded as an organized, orderly series of hydrolytic reactions which result in the smooth, stepwise breakdown of large, complex molecules into smaller and simpler products. Hydrolytic enzymes are capable of carrying through the processes of digestion from beginning to end without the aid or intervention of enzymes of other kinds. Apart from the digestive hydrolases there are numerous intracellular hydrolases concerned with processes other than digestion.

A group of exceedingly important enzymes known as *phosphorylases* has been discovered in recent times: these catalyse the splitting of their substrates not by means of the elements of water but by those of phosphoric acid, a process known as phosphorolysis. This bears a close superficial resemblance to hydrolysis:

$$\text{Hydrolysis} \qquad \text{R}.\text{R}' + \text{H}.\text{OH} \rightleftharpoons \text{R}.\text{OH} + \text{H}.\text{R}',$$
$$\text{Phosphorolysis} \qquad \text{R}.\text{R}' + \text{H}.\text{O}\textcircled{P} \rightleftharpoons \text{R}.\text{O}\textcircled{P} + \text{H}.\text{R}'.$$

In spite of this resemblance the phosphorylases are better classified as transferring enzymes and will be so considered in the next chapter. Certain hydrolases also have been found to be capable of catalysing transfer reactions as well as hydrolysis, and this aspect of their activity will also be dealt with in the next chapter.

In addition to the hydrolases we shall consider in the present chapter another group of enzymes. These catalyse a simple, direct splitting of their substrates without the intervention of any other reactant:

$$R.R' \rightleftharpoons R + R'.$$

Enzymes of this type are best named with reference to the reverse aspect of the reactions they catalyse. Whereas hydrolytic enzymes catalyse processes of condensation when acting in reverse, members of this other group catalyse simple addition reactions and may therefore be called *adding enzymes*. They include enzymes which catalyse the addition of water, carbon dioxide and other substances to some second molecule.

Although reversibility signs are used in the generalized equations given here, there are many cases in which the reactions catalysed are, for energetic reasons, irreversible in practice, at any rate under biological conditions. The reader may be reminded of one of the cases considered in the preceding chapter. The digestive hydrolysis of glycogen is virtually irreversible because free energy is required for its reversal and cannot be directly supplied. The *intracellular* degradation and synthesis of glycogen proceed freely, however, but *by other enzymes and through different intermediates* from those involved in digestive hydrolysis. Glycogen, which yields maltose as the principal end-product of its digestive hydrolysis, cannot be synthesized directly from maltose nor even from free glucose. But α-glucose-1-phosphate, the first product of intracellular degradation, gives rise freely and reversibly to glycogen: it can do so because α-glucose-1-phosphate and glycogen have practically identical free-energy levels, significantly higher than that of free glucose. By undergoing phosphorylation the free sugar is *raised to a higher free-energy level* and only then can it give rise to glycogen.

In what follows we shall consider the properties of a number of the most widely distributed hydrolytic and adding enzymes. If the next few chapters savour somewhat of the catalogue it is because we must necessarily know a good deal about individual enzymes before we can attempt to see how, in the living cell, tissue or organism, they are organized into the catalytic systems that underlie the metabolic processes inseparable from life itself.

PEPTIDASES

Until comparatively recently it was usual to distinguish between two main groups of enzymes concerned with the hydrolysis and presumptive synthesis of proteins and their breakdown products. On the one hand were enzymes such as pepsin and trypsin, which were believed to act upon proteins but not upon smaller molecules such as those of the peptones and peptides. On the other hand was a group of so-called peptidases, known collectively as erepsin, and these were regarded as being devoid of action upon any but the relatively small molecules of polypeptides and, perhaps, peptones. Most of our earlier views have now been seriously modified or even abandoned. As is well known, the chemical synthesis of peptides was, until about 1932, a difficult undertaking, and of the enormous variety of possible peptides a mere handful was obtainable by synthetic chemistry. Our knowledge of the specificity of protein- and peptide-splitting enzymes was fragmentary in consequence. In recent years, thanks mainly to the ingenious methods introduced by Bergmann, peptides of many kinds hitherto unavailable have been produced and, in the meantime, a number of the enzymes themselves have been obtained in highly purified, crystalline form.

The older methods for the synthesis of peptides mostly involved covering the $-NH_2$ group of one amino-acid and condensing the acyl chloride of the protected product with a second amino-acid or its ester. A 'covered' dipeptide could thus be obtained from which, by removal of the covering group, the free dipeptide could theoretically be regenerated. The reactions involved may be written as follows, if we represent the covering group by X:

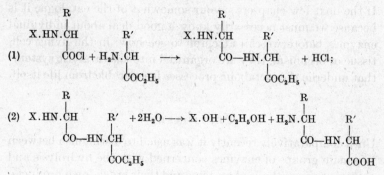

Tri- and higher peptides could be prepared by further reactions based on the same lines before removing the covering group. The use of the benzoyl radical, introduced by Curtius, made possible the synthetic production of numerous benzoylated peptides, but attempts to remove the benzoyl group by hydrolysis resulted in simultaneous hydrolysis of the peptide bonds, so that the yields of free peptides were negligible at best. The use of other substituent radicals had little better success, and numerous other methods of synthesis have been tried.

In Bergmann's method the covering group employed is one which can be removed by reduction, a treatment which does not at the same time open peptide links. Bergmann employed *benzyloxycarbonyl chloride*. This reagent is made by treating benzyl alcohol with phosgene in solution in toluene:

$$C_6H_5CH_2OH + COCl_2 = C_6H_5CH_2O . CO . Cl + HCl.$$

It reacts readily with the amino-group of an amino-acid to yield a *carbobenzoxy-derivative*, thus:

$$C_6H_5CH_2O . CO . Cl + H_2N . R = C_6H_5CH_2O . CO . HN . R + HCl.$$

Its subsequent removal is accomplished by catalytic reduction with hydrogen in the presence of colloidal palladium, a treatment that is without action upon peptide bonds:

$$C_6H_5CH_2 . O . CO . HN . R + H_2 = C_6H_5CH_3 + CO_2 + H_2N . R.$$
$$toluene$$

These carbobenzoxy-compounds are very stable, and can readily be converted into the corresponding acyl chlorides so as to facilitate condensation with a second amino-acid. There is, moreover, no racemization of the product under Bergmann's conditions.

As an example of a synthesis carried out by Bergmann's method we may take the relatively simple case of the preparation of glycylglycine. The reactions used are as follows:

(i) $C_6H_5CH_2O.CO.Cl + H_2N.CH_2COOH = C_6H_5CH_2O.CO—HN.CH_2COOH + HCl;$
$$carbobenzoxyglycine$$

(ii) $C_6H_5CH_2O.CO—HN.CH_2COOH \xrightarrow{PCl_5} C_6H_5CH_2O.CO—HN.CH_2COCl;$

(iii) $C_6H_5CH_2O.CO—HN.CH_2COCl + H_2N.CH_2COO.C_2H_5$
$$glycine\ ethyl\ ester$$
$= C_6H_5CH_2O.CO—HN.CH_2CO—HN.CH_2COO.C_2H_5 + HCl;$
$$carbobenzoxyglycylglycine\ ethyl\ ester$$

(iv) $C_6H_5CH_2O.CO-HN.CH_2CO—HN.CH_2COO.C_2H_5$

$\xrightarrow[\text{and reduction}]{\text{saponification}} C_6H_5CH_3 + CO_2 + H_2N.CH_2CO—HN.CH_2COOH + C_2H_5OH.$
$$glycylglycine$$

By taking suitable precautions it is possible to prepare peptides containing the dicarboxylic and dibasic amino-acids as well as mono-amino-mono-carboxylic acids by this method, and with its aid peptides of many different kinds have now been made available.

Digestive Peptidases. The proteolytic enzymes of vertebrates fall into two groups, the first of which is mainly concerned with the degradation of the large molecules of the food proteins to yield smaller fragments, the second group completing the process initiated by the first and leading eventually to the liberation of free amino-acids. It is worthy of note that denatured proteins are more readily attacked than the native materials. The first group includes *pepsin*, which arises from the gastric juice, and *trypsin* and *chymotrypsin*, formed from precursors present in the pancreatic juice. In the second group we have *carboxypeptidases*, contributed by the pancreatic juice, together with *aminopeptidases* and *dipeptidases*, which are present in the intestinal secretions, probably together with other carboxypeptidases. The

6-2

proteolytic ('peptolytic') enzymes of the intestinal juice were formerly regarded as one enzyme, to which the name *erepsin* was given, but it is now known that erepsin is, in fact, a very complex mixture of enzymes, each individual member of which is very much more specific than the original mixture.

Activation

Four of these enzymes are actually secreted in the form of enzymatically inactive precursors which undergo activation by 'unmasking'. Pepsin is secreted by the gastric mucosa in the form of *pepsinogen*, which is activated in the first instance by the hydrochloric acid of the gastric juice to yield pepsin itself. Pepsin, once formed, is capable of activating more pepsinogen, so that, once begun, the activation of pepsinogen is an autocatalytic process. Both pepsinogen and pepsin itself have been obtained in pure, crystalline form, and it has been shown that the conversion of the inert pro-enzyme into the active form is attended by a fall in molecular weight from some 42,000 to 38,000. A polypeptide of molecular weight 5000 or thereabouts is split off, and may be regarded as the 'masking' substance.

Trypsin and chymotrypsin are similarly secreted in the form of enzymatically inert precursors, *trypsinogen* and *chymotrypsinogen*. All four compounds have been crystallized. Trypsinogen is activated by an enzyme-like substance called *enterokinase*, which is present in the intestinal secretions and of which the precise nature is not yet known. Enterokinase acts upon trypsinogen to produce trypsin, which then activates more trypsinogen so that, as in the case of pepsinogen, activation is an autocatalytic process. In this case, however, there is no detectable change in molecular weight.

Chymotrypsinogen differs from trypsinogen in that it is not activated by enterokinase. It is, however, activated by trypsin. Chymotrypsin does not activate chymotrypsinogen, and in this case, therefore, activation is not autocatalytic. The activation of the enzyme precursors of pancreatic juice is thus started off by enterokinase, which activates trypsinogen with production of trypsin. The trypsin then activates more trypsinogen and chymotrypsinogen as well. The proteolytic enzymes of pancreatic juice do not therefore become active until they reach the small intestine and come into contact there with enterokinase.

Of the other pancreatic peptidases only carboxypeptidase requires this kind of activation: the pro-enzyme is activated by trypsin, but not by enterokinase or chymotrypsin. Aminopeptidases and dipeptidases are not activated in this way. They lose their activity if dialysed, but activity is specifically restored by the addition of traces of specific metals such as Mn, Zn, Mg and occasionally even Co, which appear to be the natural activators for these enzymes.

It is thought that these metallic activators behave as loosely bound prosthetic groups for the enzyme proteins with which they collaborate, and thus provide a means of attachment for the substrates by forming co-ordination compounds with them. In the case of one carboxypeptidase which has been isolated in the crystalline form, Mg appears to be the natural activator and the enzyme-substrate complex is believed to be of the following type:

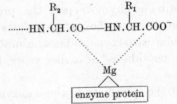

The presence of the chelation bonds (dotted lines) is thought to bring about an electronic distortion of the peptide link which they enclose, thereby weakening this already sensitive bond and facilitating its hydrolysis.

Specificity

Biologically speaking it is possible to draw some sort of distinction between pepsin and the trypsins on the one hand—the proteinases of the old nomenclature—and the group of peptidases on the other. The digestion of the food proteins is begun by the 'proteinases', and the fragmented products thus formed are further degraded by the 'peptidases' to yield in the end free amino-acids. It was formerly believed that pepsin and the trypsins are able to attack only large molecules of the same order of size as the protein molecules of the food, and that the peptidases are only able to deal with molecules of the order of size found among polypeptides and perhaps peptones. More recent work, which became possible only when Bergmann's method had made a wide variety of synthetic peptides available, has shown that pepsin, chymotrypsin and trypsin, as well as the peptidases, are able to act upon comparatively simple peptides, *always provided that peptide linkages of the right kind are present*. Bergmann therefore calls them all peptidases, but it is still possible to maintain a distinction between the two groups. The peptidases of the older nomenclature are able to split only those peptide links which join terminal amino-acid residues to the main chain. Pepsin and the trypsins, on the other hand, can act also upon peptide bonds remote from the terminal units and are accordingly called endopeptidases, by contrast with the exopeptidases, i.e. carboxy-, amino- and dipeptidases. Briefly, then, pepsin, trypsin and chymotrypsin, the 'proteinases' of the older classification, become the *endopeptidases* of Bergmann's nomenclature, while carboxypeptidases, aminopeptidases and dipeptidases, the 'peptidases' of earlier years, become the *exopeptidases*.

Our ideas about the specificity of these enzymes have undergone a drastic change in recent years. It was formerly held that pepsin, trypsin and chymotrypsin are able to attack peptide bonds at more or less any point in the chain. But if both pepsin and trypsin are allowed to act upon the same protein we find that both enzymes together open up more peptide linkages than either alone, and it follows that both enzymes do not act upon the same, but upon different linkages. Thanks to the brilliant work of Bergmann and his colleagues we now know a good deal about the nature of the particular bonds attacked by the various peptidases. One general fact may be emphasized at once: with certain exceptions, the peptidases as a whole act only upon normal peptide links, i.e. links formed between the α-amino-

and α-carboxyl radicals of L-amino-acids. Enzymes capable of attacking peptides containing amino-acids of the D-series have recently been described, but will not be considered here.

Pepsin can act only on peptide bonds of certain definite types. As Bergmann has shown, it can attack a peptide link lying between an L-dicarboxylic and an L-aromatic amino-acid, given certain conditions. These are, first, that the second carboxyl radical of the dicarboxylic acid residue must be free, and secondly, that there must not be a free amino-group in the immediate vicinity of the peptide linkage. Thus pepsin attacks carbobenzoxy-L-glutamyl-⦙-L-tyrosine, glycyl-L-glutamyl-⦙-L-tyrosine, carbobenzoxyglycyl-L-glutamyl-⦙-L-tyrosine and carbobenzoxy-L-glutamyl-⦙-L-phenylalanine. The influence of the free γ-carboxyl

TABLE 6. ACTION OF PEPSIN UPON SYNTHETIC PEPTIDES

Substrate	Action of pepsin
Carbobenzoxy-L-glutamyl-⦙-L-tyrosine	+
Glycyl-L-glutamyl-⦙-L-tyrosine	+
Carbobenzoxyglycyl-L-glutamyl-⦙-L-tyrosine	+
Carbobenzoxy-L-glutamyl-⦙-L-phenylalanine	+
L-Glutamyl-L-tyrosine	−
Carbobenzoxy-L-glutamyl-L-tyrosine amide	−
Carbobenzoxy-L-glutamyl-⦙-L-tyrosylglycine	+
Carbobenzoxy-D-glutamyl-L-tyrosine	−
Carbobenzoxy-L-glutamyl-D-phenylalanine	−

group of the glutamic acid residue is neutralized if there is a free amino-group nearby, for L-glutamyl-L-tyrosine and carbobenzoxy-L-glutamyl-L-tyrosine amide are resistant to pepsin. The resistance of carbobenzoxy-L-glutamyl-L-tyrosine amide is not due solely to the fact that the α-carboxyl group of the tyrosine is covered, for carbobenzoxy-L-glutamyl-⦙-L-tyrosyl-glycine is attacked, though more slowly than carbobenzoxy-L-glutamyl-⦙-L-tyrosine. Replacement of the L-acids by their D-isomers makes the peptides resistant to pepsin, for carbobenzoxy-D-glutamyl-L-tyrosine and carbobenzoxy-L-glutamyl-D-phenylalanine are not attacked. These results are summarized in Table 6.

Chymotrypsin resembles pepsin in attacking peptide links in which aromatic amino-acids are involved but, whereas pepsin attacks on the amino side of the aromatic acid, chymotrypsin acts on the carboxyl side. Thus both enzymes attack carbo-benzoxy-L-glutamyl-⁞-L-tyrosyl-⁞-glycine amide, but do so at different points, as follows:

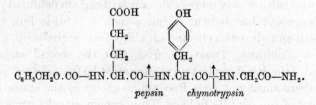

Chymotrypsin also attacks carbobenzoxy-L-tyrosyl-⁞-glycine amide and carbobenzoxy-L-phenylalanyl-⁞-glycine amide, for example, but its action is prevented by the presence of a free carboxyl radical in the immediate vicinity of the peptide link. Thus carbobenzoxy-L-glutamyl-L-tyrosyl-glycine, unlike its amide, is resistant to chymotrypsin, though acted upon by pepsin. On the other hand, L-glutamyl-L-tyrosyl-⁞-glycine amide is attacked by chymotrypsin and not by pepsin, since the effect of the free γ-carboxyl radical of the glutamyl unit, which is required for the activity of pepsin, is neutralized by the free α-amino-group of the same amino-acid unit. These results are summarized in Table 7.

TABLE 7. ACTION OF PEPSIN AND CHYMOTRYPSIN
UPON SYNTHETIC PEPTIDES

Substrate	Pepsin	Chymo-trypsin
Carbobenzoxy-L-glutamyl-⁞-L-tyrosyl-⁞-glycine amide	+	+
Carbobenzoxy-L-tyrosyl-⁞-glycine amide	−	+
Carbobenzoxy-L-phenylalanyl-⁞-glycine amide	−	+
Carbobenzoxy-L-glutamyl-⁞-L-tyrosyl-glycine	+	−
L-Glutamyl-L-tyrosyl-⁞-glycine amide	−	+

Trypsin can act at peptide linkages adjacent to either an arginine or a lysine unit and replacement of these basic amino-acid residues by others yields resistant products. The second amino-group of the dibasic amino-acid unit must be unsubsti-tuted, for trypsin acts upon α-benzoyl-L-arginine⁞amide and α-benzoylglycyl-L-lysine:amide, for example, but not upon α-benzoylglycyl-(ε-carbobenzoxy-)-L-lysine amide, in which both the amino-groups of the lysine unit are covered.

To sum up, we may say that *pepsin* can act at peptide links formed between the α-carboxyl group of a dicarboxylic amino-acid and the α-amino-radical of an aromatic amino-acid, but requires that the second acidic group of the dicarboxylic acid shall be free, and is inhibited if there is an amino-group nearby. *Chymotrypsin* can act upon peptide bonds formed from the α-carboxyl group of an aromatic amino-acid, but is inhibited if there is a carboxyl radical in the immediate vicinity, while *trypsin* can act upon peptide links formed from the carboxyl group either of arginine or of lysine, but requires that the second amino-group of the dibasic amino-acid unit shall be free. This enzyme appears to be inhibited by nearby α-amino or carboxyl radicals.

It must not be supposed, however, that these enzymes cannot attack peptide linkages other than those determined by Bergmann, for Harington has already shown that bonds of certain other types can be attacked by pepsin. In Harington's work it was found that an aromatic amino-acid is required, but that the free carboxyl grouping of glutamic acid can be replaced by the sulphydryl of cysteine. Both tyrosyl-cysteine and cysteinyl-tyrosine, for example, were attacked by pepsin, though more slowly than the corresponding *N*-carbobenzoxy derivatives. Even so, the fact remains that pepsin cannot act upon any arbitrary peptide linkage, but is restricted, probably, to linkages of only a few special types. Clearly, therefore, the endopeptidases are very exacting indeed and, contrary to earlier opinion, able to act only upon bonds of certain types. The specificity requirements established by Bergmann are summarized in Fig. 11.

By their concerted action the endopeptidases divide intact protein molecules into smaller fragments, and the stage is set for the action of members of the group of exopeptidases, viz. carboxypeptidases and aminopeptidases. These enzymes catalyse the splitting only of terminal peptide bonds, with consequent liberation of the terminal amino-acid units. *Carboxypeptidases* remove the terminal unit of which the carboxyl radical is free, *aminopeptidases* acting at the other end of the chain, where the

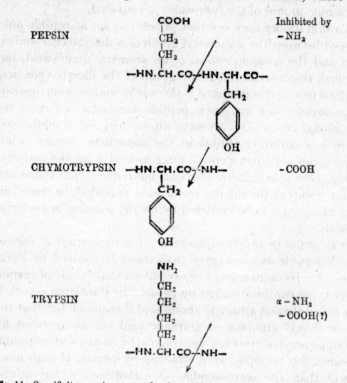

Fig. 11. Specificity requirements of endopeptidases. The essential requirements are printed in heavy type: the point of attack is indicated by an arrow in each case.

terminal unit has a free amino-group. Thus in L-leucyl-glycyl-L-tyrosine, for example, we have the following structural arrangement:

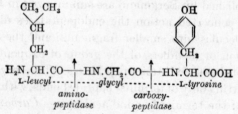

The appropriate carboxypeptidase acts upon this tripeptide to liberate tyrosine, and aminopeptidase to produce free leucine. Carboxypeptidases require a free carboxyl radical for their action to take effect, aminopeptidases requiring a free amino-group; but carboxypeptidases are unable to act if there is a free amino-group nearby, while aminopeptidases are similarly affected by a free carboxyl radical. Neither type of enzyme, therefore, attacks the dipeptide left after the other has attacked the original tripeptide, nor will either group attack peptides containing amino-acid residues of the D-series.

In these peptidases, then, we can recognize specificity requirements which include the presence of the right terminal radical, which must be unsubstituted, and the absence from the immediate vicinity of electrically opposite radicals, together with the usual stereochemical requirements. It is now certain, however, that the requirements of these peptidases are more exacting even than this, and that there exist more than one amino- and more than one carboxypeptidase, each with special requirements.

Whereas the endopeptidases split large protein units into smaller fragments and produce few free amino-acid molecules in the process, the amino- and carboxypeptidases liberate free terminal amino-acid units one by one until only dipeptides remain. These, as we have seen, are not further attacked by these enzymes, but are split in their turn by *dipeptidases*. Probably there are several of these enzymes, each specific for certain individual dipeptides or groups of dipeptides. For example, glycylglycine is hydrolysed by a specific dipeptidase which, in its turn, is rather specifically activated by Co; Mn can replace Co but is very much less efficient. Again, a specific prolidase has been described: this attacks the bond linking the imino-group of proline or hydroxyproline to an adjacent carboxyl radical. It is activated by Mn. Like most of the other digestive exopeptidases, dipeptidases are activated by metals and require that the constituent amino-acids of their substrates shall be members of the L-series, so that, of the four possible alanyl-leucines, the L-L-, L-D-, D-D- and D-L-, only one is attacked by a dipeptidase, namely L-alanyl-L-leucine.

In passing, the reader may be reminded that peptidases capable of attacking peptides containing amino-acids of the D-series are believed to exist, but the foregoing description of the digestive peptidases holds, even though it cannot be extended to cover all kinds of peptidases.

Finally, it is interesting that some peptidases have a weak esterase activity; this does not appear to be due to contamination, for esterase activity has been observed in highly purified, crystalline trypsin, chymotrypsin and carboxypeptidase.

Rennin. In the gastric juice of young mammals we find another proteolytic enzyme, rennin. Like pepsin, this enzyme is secreted in the form of an inactive precursor, pro-rennin, which is activated by hydrochloric acid. The optimum pH for activation is considerably less acid than that for pepsin. The most characteristic feature of rennin is its milk-clotting power, and it is, in fact, the active principle of commercial preparations of 'rennet'. It catalyses the conversion of the milk casein ('caseinogen') into another product, paracasein ('casein'), the calcium salt of which is insoluble so that, in the presence of the calcium of the milk, a firm clot or curd is formed. Rennin from the abomasum (fourth stomach) of the calf has been obtained in crystalline form, but little has as yet been discovered about its specificity requirements. Like pepsin, rennin has proteolytic properties, but with a more alkaline pH optimum: its optimal pH when acting upon haemoglobin, for example, is 3·7 as against about 2·0 for pepsin.

Intracellular Peptidases

The presence of intracellular enzymes capable of catalysing the hydrolysis of peptides of greater or less chemical complexity and molecular weight has been demonstrated in many animals and plants. In many cases these enzymes probably have digestive functions, especially among the lower animals, many of which produce no digestive secretions but take particulate food by phagocytosis and digest it intracellularly. There is a considerable literature on this subject, and it may be said that enzymes resembling pepsin and trypsin, at least in their general properties, are present in some cells, but not much is known about them.

Other intracellular proteolytic enzymes include such plant enzymes as papain, ficin and bromelin, obtained from the sap or latex of the paw-paw, fig and pineapple respectively. Probably all of these are complex mixtures. Much more is known about the intracellular, autolytic enzymes of animal tissues, known collectively as *kathepsin*. Kidney and spleen tissues offer good sources of kathepsin, but it is present in many other organs and also in tumours of various kinds. Most of our recent knowledge of the kathepsin group we owe to Bergmann and his collaborators, who have shown that kidney and spleen kathepsins comprise at least four components, the specificity of each of which has now been studied. Of these, kathepsin I is homospecific with pepsin, i.e. has the same specificity requirements as pepsin; kathepsin II is homospecific with trypsin, while components III and IV are homospecific with aminopeptidase and carboxypeptidase respectively. The existence of these homospecificities suggests that extracellular digestive peptidases may have had their evolutionary origin in intracellular, kathepsin-like enzymes.

Although a quantitative as well as a qualitative homospecificity has been demonstrated between the digestive peptidases and the components of kathepsin, the enzymes are not identical. The kathepsins are not activated by unmasking, as in the case of the digestive endopeptidases, nor yet by heavy metals such as manganese, as in the case of dipeptidase. On the contrary, the intracellular peptidases are inactivated by heavy metals, but can be activated by the addition of cyanide, hydrogen sulphide, cysteine, glutathione and sometimes by ascorbic acid. It is now widely believed that the active form of papain, for example, is a complex formed between the enzyme-protein and an —SH compound, probably papain-cysteine: the inhibitory action of heavy metals is probably due to their tendency to react with free —SH groups.

It has already been suggested that these intracellular peptidases most probably function to maintain a dynamic equilibrium between the cell proteins and simpler products present in the cell contents. We have seen that the extracellular, digestive peptidases constitute a set of tools whereby the proteins of the

food can be completely dismantled, and, if it could be shown that
the action of enzymes of this kind is reversible, we should feel
more confident that the kathepsins, with which they are homospecific, constitute an outfit capable of reconstituting as well as
degrading proteins. Bergmann has succeeded in demonstrating
synthetic activity on the part of several peptidases and has
shown, for example, that chymotrypsin catalyses the condensation of benzoyl-L-tyrosine with glycylanilide to yield benzoyl-L-
tyrosyl-glycylanilide. The product in this case is insoluble and
is precipitated, so that the hydrolytic action of the enzyme does
not seriously oppose its synthetic performance. Other syntheses
have been accomplished with, for example, papain-cysteine,
i.e. papain activated by the addition of cysteine, and an example
can be seen in Fig. 3 (p. 20).

Other Peptidases include *carnosinase*, a dipeptidase that can
be obtained from pig kidney. It acts upon the thoroughly
atypical dipeptide carnosine (β-alanyl histidine) and on a few
other peptides containing histidine. Of rather particular interest
is the κ-toxin of the gas gangrene organism, *Clostridium welchii*.
This toxin is a *collagenase* which, by digesting connective tissue,
enables the organism to spread rapidly and extensively into the
adjacent tissues. Apart from collagen this toxin is only known
to attack gelatin, which is itself derived from collagen. Similar
enzymic toxins are produced by other *Clostridia* also.

CARBOHYDRASES

Enzymes capable of catalysing the breakdown of carbohydrates
are very widely distributed indeed, and occur both in digestive
secretions and within the cells of animals, plants, and micro-
organisms of many and perhaps all kinds. They may be considered under two main headings, the *polysaccharases*, which act
upon the large molecules of polysaccharides such as starch and
glycogen, and the *glycosidases*, the substrates of which are small
molecules such as various di- and trisaccharides, in addition to
glycosides of other kinds.

Polysaccharases

Amylases

Most is known about the amylases, which act upon starch and glycogen but not upon cellulose. Plant amylases have been resolved into components known respectively as α- and β-amylases, and representatives of both types have been crystallized. In the ordinary course of events these enzymes act together upon starch and glycogen to catalyse a more or less quantitative conversion into the disaccharide, maltose. They act, however, in rather a different manner and in order to appreciate the differences it is necessary to have in mind a fairly clear picture of the probable structure of starch and glycogen. In considering the modes of action of the α- and β-amylases, however, it is important to realize that the use of the prefixes α- and β- is not meant to imply that these enzymes act upon α- and β-glucosidic links respectively. Recent work on the purification of these two amylases has shown that they are accompanied by other enzymes, which also play a part in the total digestion of starch, and their names are given in Table 8, together with the identities of the linkages upon which they are believed to act.

TABLE 8. LINKAGES ATTACKED BY AMYLOLYTIC ENZYMES

Enzyme	Linkages attacked
α-Amylase	$1:4\text{-}\alpha\text{-}$
β-Amylase	$1:4\text{-}\alpha\text{-}$
Z-enzyme	$1:3\text{-}\beta\text{-}$
Amylo-1:6-glucosidase ⎱ R-enzyme ⎰	$1:6\text{-}\alpha\text{-}$

Starch consists of a mixture of two main components, *amylose*, which accounts for 20–25 % of most vegetable starches, and *amylopectin*. Amylose, which gives a pure blue coloration with iodine, consists mainly of $1:4\text{-}\alpha$-linked glucose units and can be attacked either by α- or by β-amylase. Pure crystalline β-amylase catalyses a 70 % conversion of amylose into maltose, but complete conversion requires the assistance of another enzyme, the so-called *Z-enzyme*, which is usually found in association with the amylases. This Z-enzyme has no action upon $1:4\text{-}\alpha$-links but is known to act upon 1:3-β-glucoside links, from which it is concluded that amylose, while it consists mainly of 1:4-α-glucosidic units, contains a few 1:3-β-linkages as well. The whole molecule contains some 200–300 glucosidic units and is probably a long, coiled but unbranched or only slightly branched structure.

Amylopectin, on the other hand, is extensively branched and is built up from 'unit chains', each containing on the average 20 or 24 1:4-α-linked glucosidic units. An unknown number of these unit chains are joined together to make amylopectin. We cannot say at the present time exactly how the 'inter-unit chain' linkages are arranged, except that the terminal, reducing unit of one chain is united to a hydroxyl of a glucose unit in an adjacent chain, probably as a rule in the 6-position. The structure of amylopectin can be pictorially represented in the following manner:

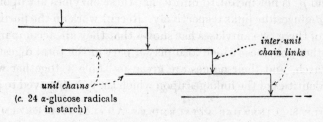

inter-unit chain links

unit chains
(c. 24 α-glucose radicals in starch)

The molecular structure in the neighbourhood of a branching point is thus probably as follows:

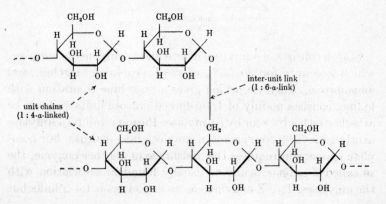

inter-unit link (1 : 6-α-link)

unit chains (1 : 4-α-linked)

Glycogen appears to contain no component analogous to amylose. It resembles amylopectin in structure except that the unit chains contain only about twelve, or sometimes eighteen, 1:4-α-linked glucosidic units. Amylopectin gives a purplish coloration with iodine. Different glycogens give different colorations; some give none at all, but the usual response to the iodine test is a reddish brown.

β-Amylase, more appropriately termed the *maltogenic amylase*, appears to be absolutely specific for 1:4-α-linkages and acts freely upon amylose until a 1:3-β-link is approached. Similarly, it acts upon the open chains of amylopectin until a branching link (1:6-α-link) is approached and in this way about 55 % of the amylopectin is converted into maltose (glucose-1:4-α-glucoside). The residual resistant product, the so-called α-amylodextrin or 'limit dextrin', gives a port-wine colour with iodine. This dextrin, which is resistant to the maltogenic amylase, can be further attacked by the *dextrinogenic* or α-amylase, which splits it into smaller fragments which are still of a dextrin-like nature but no longer give any colour with iodine.

α-Amylase received its alternative title of dextrinogenic amylase because, acting upon amylopectin, it yields only comparatively small dextrin-like products in the first instance, and these can then be further attacked by the maltogenic enzyme. But the activity of α-amylase is not much affected by the presence of linkages other than the 1:4- links to which, like β-amylase, it is specific: this α-enzyme can 'straddle' the branching linkages of amylopectin and, if allowed to act for long periods, degrades some 80–90 % of amylopectin. The main product is maltose but, since 1:6-linkages are not attacked by this enzyme, appreciable quantities of 1:6-linked sugars, especially *iso*maltose (glucose-1:6-α-glucoside) are also formed, the amounts depending on the degree of branching of the parent polysaccharide.

The fission of the 1:6-branching links requires the presence of a newly discovered hydrolytic enzyme, *amylo-1:6-glucosidase*. This enzyme has been obtained from muscle, and closely similar enzymes have been obtained from beans and potatoes (*R-enzyme*). The total breakdown of starch is thus a somewhat complex process in which four enzymes at least are usually involved, Z- and R-enzymes, together with the α- and β-amylases. The chief product, maltose, is accompanied by smaller amounts of glucose.

The digestive (salivary and pancreatic) amylases of animals have not been resolved into α- and β-components. They are apparently single enzymes which act in the same sort of way as the dextrinogenic α-amylases of plants. They can carry out an extensive conversion of amylose, amylopectin and glycogen into maltose, together with a certain amount of free glucose. Representatives of the group have now been crystallized and highly purified and, according to one report, purified salivary amylase catalyses a large-scale ($>90\%$) conversion of potato amylose into maltose and maltotriose in a ratio of $2\cdot3 : 1$, but stops acting when this has been achieved. Pancreatic amylase, however, can hydrolyse maltotriose to maltose and glucose and presumably contains other enzymic components. Thus although maltose is the main product of digestion by these two enzymes, some free glucose is also produced.

It has long been known that salivary and pancreatic amylases lose their activity if dialysed, and the case is often quoted in illustration of the importance of inorganic ions in the activation of certain enzymes. This, however, is not entirely a true bill, for while it is true enough that dialysed salivary amylase, for example, is no longer active under conditions which were formerly optimal, it is still weakly active at more acid pH values. There is, it is also true, a considerable loss of total activity, but the removal of chloride ions does not deprive the enzyme of its power to activate the substrate, but appears to alter its physical state in some way. In all probability the enzyme dissociates in a different manner in the absence of chloride ions (see p. 49) and, if this is so, it might perhaps be expected that the replacement of chloride by other ions would lead to a displacement of the optimum pH. This does in fact happen, as is shown by the curves of Fig. 9 (p. 42).

Although the enzymes that catalyse the digestive hydrolysis of starch and glycogen must, on theoretical grounds, be regarded as capable of working reversibly, it has not so far proved possible to synthesize polysaccharides with their aid because the synthesis is essentially an endergonic process.

Cellulase

Although cellulose forms a very large part of the food of herbivores, remarkably few animals of any kind possess any enzyme or enzymes capable of catalysing its hydrolysis. Cellulose-splitting enzymes have been described in the digestive secretions of a number of herbivorous gastropod snails, including terrestrial forms like *Helix* and aquatic species such as *Strombus*, *Pterocera* and *Aplysia*; cellulases appear to be present also in the digestive juices of a few wood-eating insects. The shipworm, *Teredo*, is an interesting creature from this point of view, for its digestive gland contains cells which appear to be specialized for the phagocytic ingestion and intracellular digestion of the fine particles of wood which the animal scrapes off as it bores. But in the vast majority of cases it is nevertheless true that animals do not produce cellulase, even when they depend largely upon cellulose as a primary source of food.

This paradox is due to the fact that most cellulose-eating animals do not digest cellulose for themselves, but maintain in their alimentary tracts large populations of symbiotic micro-organisms, including bacteria, protozoa and yeasts, which play a very important part in their nutrition. Indeed, it has been claimed that the snail's cellulase is not a product of the snail itself but is formed by symbiotic inhabitants of the crop and the intestine. Many intestinal micro-organisms are capable of degrading cellulose, and recent work on the processes of digestion in ruminants has shown that cellulose is broken down by the symbionts with production of large amounts of lower fatty acids. Acetic and propionic acids predominate, and are accompanied by formic, butyric and valeric acids, together with large volumes of carbon dioxide, methane and hydrogen. The ruminant thus obtains fatty acids rather than sugars from the cellulose it consumes, and has to repay the micro-organisms which carry out the conversion by providing them with *Lebensraum* in the form of a capacious caecum, a multiple stomach, or some other commodious dilatation of the alimentary canal. Similar processes are believed to take place in many wood-eating insects and other herbivores.

Little is known about the enzymes whereby these symbiotic organisms break down the cellulose. Presumably they must include a cellulase, and it has indeed been shown that the free-living protozoan, *Vampyrella*, secretes an extracellular cellulase which attacks the cellulose of the cell walls of the *Spirogyra* which furnishes its food. The secretion of extracellular cellulases must probably play an important part in the early stages of microbial attack upon cellulose, which is so insoluble as to require some extracellular comminution before it can be got into the cells for further chemical manipulation. Cellulose-splitting enzymes and enzymes capable of synthesizing cellulose certainly occur in plants and fungi, and must be of very great importance in plant economy, but we have very little information about them.

It is said that preparations containing cellulase will also act upon the animal polysaccharide, chitin, in which the β-linked glucose radicals of cellulose appear to be replaced by similarly linked units of N-acetyl glucosamine. Whether or not cellulase and chitinase are identical has not been determined.

Other polysaccharases include enzymes capable of splitting polyfructofuranosides, such as inulin and levan, and enzymes that act upon polysaccharides such as the mannans, pectins and so on, but we have only very scanty information about these.

Glycosidases

We know of many enzymes capable of splitting simple glycosides, all of which show a high order of specificity towards the glycosidic part of the substrate molecule. Of these the most important are the glucosidases and the saccharases. Some of these enzymes can catalyse transfer reactions as well as hydrolyses.

α-Glucosidases

α-Glucosidases of two types are known. The most specific of these are the '*true*' *maltases*, which act only upon a single α-glucoside, viz. maltose (glucose-4-∶-α-glucoside). Enzymes of this kind occur in malt and in *Aspergillus*. The more widely distributed digestive 'maltases' of animals, and the 'maltase' of yeast, are able to act upon α-glucosides other than maltose and should therefore be called *α-glucosidases* rather than maltases. These enzymes will act upon such substances as methyl-:-α-glucoside and sucrose (β-fructofuranosido-:-α-glucoside), though they are without action upon the α-glucosidic linkages of the large molecules of starch and glycogen.

The order of specificity of these α-glucosidases is very high, for a completely unmodified α-glucosido-radical is required in their substrates: β-glucosides, α-galactosides, α-xylosides and α-*iso*-rhamnosides are not attacked, in spite of their close structural resemblances to the α-glucosides:

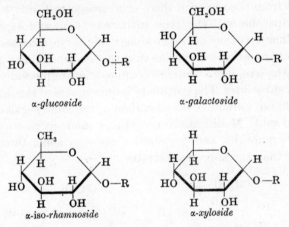

β-*Glucosidases*

Many cells and tissues have been shown to contain β-glucosidases. The classical source of such an enzyme is the 'emulsin' of bitter almonds. The latter contain amygdalin, a β-glucoside which, when attacked by the β-glycosidase component of emulsin, yields mandelonitrile, which is then attacked by another enzyme, mandelonitrilase, to give free hydrocyanic acid. Sweet almonds also contain these enzymes, but amygdalin is absent.

β-Glucosides are as common in nature, especially in plant materials, as their α-counterparts are rare, and among the more interesting of these we may mention salicin (salicyl-⋮-β-glucoside) and a β-glucoside of indoxyl which occurs in the indigo plant and gives rise, after hydrolysis and oxidation, to natural indigo. There are many others. In addition, a number of the simpler saccharides are β-glucosides, notably cellobiose (glucose-4-⋮-β-glucoside), which stands in the same relation to cellulose as maltose does to starch and glycogen, and gentiobiose (glucose-6-⋮-β-glucoside), which occurs naturally in combination with mandelonitrile in the form of amygdalin.

β-Glucosidases obtained from different plant and animal sources have much in common. In particular, it may be pointed out that their specificity, though high, is less marked than that of the α-glucosidases. Although 'cellobiases' have been described from time to time there is no reason to think that they are comparable with the 'true' maltases of malt and *Aspergillus*, but rather that they are all group-specific β-glucosidases. These enzymes are rather less specific than the corresponding α-glucosidases, which require a completely unmodified α-glucosidic radical in their substrates. The specificity requirements of the β-glucosidases do not extend as far as carbon 4, for some β-galactosides are also split. Modifications can also be made at position 6, for β-*iso*-rhamnosides and β-xylosides are also split, though less rapidly than the normal substrates:

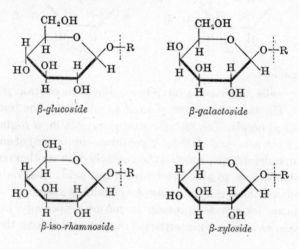

β-*glucoside*   β-*galactoside*

β-*iso-rhamnoside*   β-*xyloside*

Saccharases are very widely distributed indeed in the digestive secretions of animals, in plants and in many micro-organisms, though not, apparently, in the cell contents of animals. Two types can be distinguished, the *glucosaccharases* (in digestive secretions of animals and in *Aspergillus*) and the *fructosaccharases* (in yeast).

Sucrose itself is α-glucosido-$\vdots$-β-fructofuranoside, and the molecule may be attacked from either end. The glucosaccharases are competitively inhibited by glucose, which may therefore be presumed to compete with sucrose for possession of the combining groups of the saccharase molecule. The glucosaccharases are, in fact, α-glucosidases. Similarly, the fructosaccharases are competitively inhibited by fructose, and may therefore be supposed to act from the fructose end of the sucrose molecule. Highly purified yeast saccharase is able to attack methyl-$\vdots$-β-fructofuranoside and is thus a β-fructofuranosidase.

The differences in specificity between these types of saccharases are shown even more clearly by the fact that fructosaccharase attacks the trisaccharide raffinose (β-fructofuranosido-$\vdots$-α-glucosido-6-α-galactoside) while glucosaccharases do not. Another trisaccharide, melezitose (melicitose: α-glucosido-β-fructofuranosido-6-$\vdots$-α-glucoside) is split by glucosaccharase and not by fructosaccharase.

Other glycosidases are known. They include α-galactosidases, which attack compounds such as raffinose (β-fructofuranosido-α-glucosido-6-$\vdots$-α-galactoside), and β-galactosidases which act upon compounds such as lactose (glucose-4-$\vdots$-β-galactoside). Brewers' yeast, for example, contains an α-galactosidase ('mellibiase'), while bakers' yeast, *Aspergillus* and the digestive secretions of animals contain β-galactosidases ('lactases'). Mannosidases also are known.

Reversibility of the glycosidases

A number of β-glucosides have been synthesized enzymatically with the aid of emulsin, but to achieve such syntheses it is necessary to employ conditions which, from the biological point of view, are grossly artificial. Thus, in the synthesis of gentiobiose, for example, strong solutions of the reactants are taken in order to force the reaction backwards in accordance with the principle of the mass law. β-Methyl-D-glucoside, again, has been synthesized by emulsin acting in a non-aqueous medium (dioxane). Claims have been made for the synthesis of sucrose from strong solutions of glucose and fructose, but these seem to be less well supported by the experimental evidence. Whether or not they are true can only be finally decided when sucrose is actually isolated from the reaction mixtures.

Whereas the amounts of sugars such as gentiobiose are fairly large under equilibrium conditions, the amounts of sucrose present at equilibrium are certainly small, and it seems certain that the free-energy conditions favour the hydrolysis rather than the synthesis of sucrose, just as is the case in the breakdown and synthesis of starch and glycogen from glucose. Sucrose is, nevertheless, synthesized on a large scale by many plants, and as yet we have very little knowledge about the mechanisms involved. It does seem improbable that the process can be catalysed by saccharase with glucose and fructose as starting materials; an initial priming reaction is necessary as we shall see.

LIPASES AND ESTERASES

Under this heading we have to consider several distinct groups of enzymes. There are, first of all, the very widely distributed *lipases* and *esterases* which catalyse the hydrolysis of esters of alcohols with organic acids and, in addition, several groups which catalyse the hydrolysis of esters formed between alcohols and inorganic acids. Of these the *phosphatases* and *sulphatases* may be mentioned, phosphatases of various kinds being almost universally distributed and of enormous metabolic importance.

There are sharp differences of specificity with respect to the acidic component of the ester. Phosphatases are group-specific as a rule, and act only upon organic esters of phosphoric acid such, for example, as phosphoglycerol and hexosemonophosphate, and are without action upon organic sulphates or esters of organic acids. Lipases, on the other hand, are enzymes of low specificity.

They act only upon esters of organic acids, such as ethyl acetate and the fats, but provided that the acid is organic in nature its precise chemical identity, and that of the alcoholic radical, are matters of relative indifference.

Lipases

Lipases occur in the gastric, pancreatic and intestinal juices of vertebrates, and have been reported also in the digestive secretions of many invertebrates. They also occur in plants, especially in seeds, and have been found in other organisms such as *Aspergillus* as well. Their specificity is very low, and any lipase will split virtually any wholly organic ester. The acid component may be anything from acetic to palmitic, stearic, or even higher fatty acids, and may be saturated or unsaturated. Similarly, the alcohol may be a short-chain compound such as methyl or ethyl alcohol, or a long chain such as cetyl alcohol (C_{16}). It may be monohydric or, as in the case of glycerol, polyhydric, and esters even of complex alcohols such as cholesterol are also attacked. So low is the specificity of these enzymes that many attempts have been made to fractionate them, but without success. In certain other cases, notably that of 'erepsin', it has been found that enzymes of seemingly low specificity consist, in reality, of mixtures of enzymes, each individual catalyst being more specific than the mixture, but this has not so far been found to be true of the lipases.

Lipases from different sources split different esters at different relative rates. Apparently the liver enzyme 'prefers' esters of short-chain fatty acids, while the pancreatic enzyme prefers esters of long-chain acids. Gastric lipase and the lipase of the castor-oil bean (*Ricinus*) resemble the pancreatic enzyme in this respect. Enzymes of the type found in liver are usually called *esterases* to indicate their apparent preference for simple esters as opposed to fats.

Although their specificity towards the structure of the substrate is very low, the lipases show marked stereochemical specificity when allowed to act upon esters containing an asymmetric carbon atom, such, for example, as the ethyl esters of the mandelic acids, $C_6H_5\overset{*}{C}H(OH)COOH$. One isomer is always more rapidly attacked than the other in cases of this kind, whether the asymmetric carbon atom is situated in the alcoholic or in the acidic component of the ester.

Some authors have suggested that bile salts, which play an important part in the digestion and absorption of fatty substances, may function as activators for the digestive lipases, but this is open to doubt.

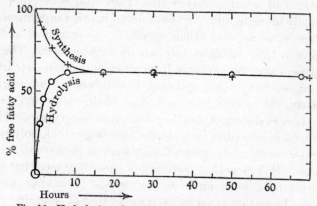

Fig. 12. Hydrolysis and synthesis of triolein by *Ricinus* lipase.
(After Parsons; data of Armstrong and Gosney.)

An important feature of the lipases is the readiness with which they will catalyse the synthesis as well as the hydrolysis of fats and esters. If a fat such as triolein is incubated under suitable conditions with, say, pancreatic lipase, the reaction does not go to completion. Instead, an equilibrium is approached, and the composition of the final reaction mixture is the same from whichever side it is approached. Fig. 12 shows the results of experiments on the action of *Ricinus* lipase on triolein, in one case, and upon a mixture of glycerol and oleic acid in the other. Much of what we know about the reversibility of enzymic reactions was first learned from studies of systems of this kind.

The three fatty acid radicals of a typical triglyceride are not removed simultaneously, but come off one after another under the influence of the digestive lipases, so that di- and monoglycerides are produced as intermediate products and this, as we shall see, is very important in connexion with the absorption of fatty food materials from the small intestine in animals.

Mention must also be made of a curious enzyme found in the venoms of the cobra and the rattlesnake. This acts upon lecithins, in which, it will be recalled, two of the alcoholic groups of glycerol are esterified by fatty acids and the third by phosphocholine. The ordinary digestive lipases are able to remove both of the fatty acid radicals, but the so-called *lecithinase A* of these snake venoms, e.g. crotoxin from the rattlesnake, remove one only, and yield a product in which the remaining fatty acid is of the saturated type. This compound is called lysolecithin, on account of its powerful haemolytic action. The undesirable consequences of being bitten by these reptiles include a large-scale lysis of the red blood cells and consequent disturbances of the respiratory functions of the blood. The venom of the viper, by contrast, causes intravenous clotting of the blood, a process which is catalysed by a proteolytic rather than a lipolytic enzyme. The toxins formed by the gas-gangrene organisms, the *Clostridia*, include lecithinases which, however, differ from the rattlesnake enzyme both in specificity and mode of attack but lead again to haemolysis.

Other esterases of more specific nature include a group of *choline esterases*, enzymes of great importance in animal tissues, in which they catalyse the hydrolysis of acetylcholine, the neuro-hormone of the parasympathetic nervous system.

Phosphatases appear to be almost universally distributed. There appear to be at least three distinct types which may be termed phosphomonoesterases, phosphodiesterases and polyphosphatases, catalysing the hydrolysis of substances of the following general types:

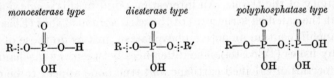

monoesterase type   *diesterase type*   *polyphosphatase type*

(R and R′ represent alcoholic radicals). A very important example of the polyphosphatase type is the *adenosine triphos-*

phatase of muscle. This enzyme is identical with myosin, which, in combination with actin, is the contractile protein which makes up the bulk of the muscle substance. Muscle and other tissues contain other adenosine triphosphatases that are separable from myosin, and similar enzymes have been found in snake venoms, potatoes and elsewhere. Bakers' yeast contains an interesting polyphosphatase which appears to be wholly specific for the hydrolysis of inorganic pyrophosphates, which arise biologically in certain reactions (pp. 358, 359), and is devoid of action upon adenosine triphosphate and other organic pyrophosphates.

Generally speaking, phosphatases of the monoesterase type seem not to be specific with respect to the nature of the alcoholic radical, and act alike on many organic phosphates such, for instance, as phospho-:-glycerol, glucose-6-:-monophosphate and other phosphate esters. The reactions they catalyse may be generally expressed as follows:

$$\text{R—O℗} + \text{H.OH} \rightarrow \text{R—OH} + \text{HO℗}.$$

One such enzyme plays an important part in the ossification of cartilaginous structures such as the bones and teeth. Unossified cartilage, and cartilaginous structures which do not undergo ossification, contain no phosphatase, but the enzyme makes its appearance just at the time that ossification sets in. Acting upon organic phosphates present in the blood, the enzyme is thought to catalyse a localized liberation of phosphate ions, which unite with calcium ions, also provided by the blood, to form the insoluble calcium phosphate, $Ca_3(PO_4)_2$. This is deposited in an ordered, crystalline manner in the cartilaginous matrix. The more rapidly ossification proceeds the higher is the phosphatase activity of the tissue. An interesting point in this connexion is that the calcified structures of the cartilaginous fishes (Elasmobranchii) contain an active phosphatase, just as do those of the bony fishes (Teleostei). The differences between the mechanical properties of calcified cartilage and true bone appear to be due to differences in the manner in which the calcium phosphate is deposited in the two cases.

In addition to being present in cells of nearly every kind, phosphatase is present in milk. If milk is pasteurized in the correct manner the treatment accorded is just sufficient to inactivate the milk phosphatase, so that the absence of phosphatase activity may be taken as an indication that the process has been properly carried out. The method used for routine testing depends upon the hydrolysis of phenyl-:-phosphate with formation of free phenol.

The group of phosphatases includes some of the enzymes concerned in the hydrolysis of nucleic acid. *Nuclease*, recently crystallized, appears to be a kind of polyphosphatase, but its specificity has not yet been very thoroughly examined. This enzyme splits nucleic acids into their component nucleotides. The so-called *nucleotidases* appear to be phosphatases of the monoesterase type, and these split off phosphate to liberate the corresponding nucleosides.

Among the phosphatases are many enzymes that require magnesium ions as activators. Very minute concentrations of Mg^{++} are all that are required in many cases, and the mode of action of these ions is still uncertain; probably they provide a means through which the enzymes can combine with their substrates (cf. p. 41).

In conclusion it may be mentioned that some phosphatases of plant and animal origin can catalyse transfer reactions (p. 123).

OTHER HYDROLYTIC ENZYMES

Arginase, a very important enzyme of which larger or smaller concentrations are present in most animal cells, catalyses the hydrolytic deamidination of arginine to yield urea and ornithine (see p. 10), and plays a central part in the mechanism whereby urea is synthesized in the mammals and other ureotelic vertebrates. It is a manganese-containing protein, and is one of the most specific hydrolases known. Arginase is very powerfully inhibited by ornithine, though not by urea, a circumstance which suggests that it must combine with the ornithine radical. It is also inhibited by the closely related amino-acid, lysine. Its optimum pH lies far in the alkaline range, probably about 10, at which pH it is very unstable.

Urease occurs in large concentrations in certain seeds, notably in jack- and soya-beans, from which it is usually prepared. It has been found in numerous other plant tissues and in the tissues of a few invertebrates, though it appears to be totally lacking from vertebrate organisms. Urease had the distinction of being the first enzyme to be obtained in the crystalline state. It was extracted from jack-bean meal by Sumner, purified and crystallized in 1926, and shown to be a protein. Crystalline urease gives all the usual tests for proteins apart from the Mölisch reaction, so that it may be presumed to contain no carbohydrate groupings. It catalyses the following reaction:

$$CO(NH_2)_2 + H_2O \rightarrow CO_2 + 2NH_3.$$

Urease possesses a number of very unusual properties. Unlike most enzymes, it is inhibited by high concentrations of its substrate, an effect which can be abolished by the addition of glycine, as is shown in Fig. 13. This phenomenon is usually

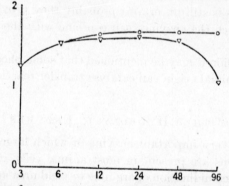

Fig. 13. Influence of urea concentration on activity of urease ($\triangledown$). The inhibitory influence of high concentrations of urea is counteracted by $0·2$ % glycine ($\bigcirc$). Ordinate: initial velocity of hydrolysis. Abscissa: concentration of urea. (After Haldane, from Kato, 1923.)

explained on the supposition that, in addition to combining with urea to form a reactive complex, *ES*, which is then hydrolysed, it tends to combine with a second molecule of urea when the concentration of the latter is high, to form a stable complex, ES_2. Another, and possibly a unique feature is that the optimum pH of urease is not fixed but is proportional to the logarithm of the substrate concentration.

The specificity of urease is very high. Its action has been tested upon a large number of substituted ureas, none of which appears to be attacked, with possible though dubious exceptions in the cases of the *sym.* dimethyl- and diethyl-ureas.

Hydrolytic deaminases and deamidases other than urease are also known. *Adenase*, which catalyses the hydrolytic deamination of adenine to yield hypoxanthine, and *guanase*, which similarly converts guanine into xanthine, are present in the liver tissue of most mammals, and must probably occur elsewhere. Another important enzyme concerned with the metabolism of purine derivatives is the *adenylic deaminase* of muscle. This enzyme, which is not identical with adenase, catalyses the hydrolytic deamination of adenylic acid to yield inosinic acid.

Animal tissues contain a powerful *glutaminase* and plants an homologous *asparaginase*. These enzymes catalyse the irreversible hydrolysis of the amides of the dicarboxylic amino-acids, e.g.

$$
\begin{array}{ccc}
CONH_2 & & COOH \\
| & & | \\
CH_2 & & CH_2 \\
| & & | \\
CH_2 + H_2O \longrightarrow & CH_2 + NH_3 \\
| & & | \\
CH.NH_2 & & CH.NH_2 \\
| & & | \\
COOH & & COOH \\
glutamine & & glutamic\ acid
\end{array}
$$

ADDING ENZYMES

Enzymes adding or removing water

Aconitase plays a part of great importance in oxidative metabolism. It might be classified either as a hydrating enzyme or as an isomerase, since it catalyses the interconversion of citric and *iso*-citric acids through the intermediate stage of *cis*-aconitic acid. A water molecule can be removed from citric acid to yield aconitic acid. If the water molecule is then replaced the other way round, *iso*-citric acid is formed:

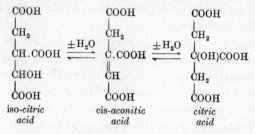

COOH	COOH	COOH
CH₂	CH₂	CH₂
CH.COOH ⇌ ±H₂O	C.COOH ⇌ ±H₂O	C(OH)COOH
CHOH	CH	CH₂
COOH	COOH	COOH
iso-*citric* acid	cis-*aconitic* acid	*citric* acid

Both reactions are reversible, and the enzyme is strongly inhibited by *trans*-aconitate and by fluorocitrate.

Enolase, another enzyme of great importance in oxidative metabolism and of very wide distribution, catalyses the interconversion of 2-phosphoglyceric and phospho-*enol*-pyruvic acids, an energy-rich phosphate bond being generated in the process:

$$
\begin{array}{ll}
CH_2OH & CH_2 \\
CHO\textcircled{P} \rightleftharpoons & C.O\sim\textcircled{P} + H_2O \\
COOH & COOH
\end{array}
$$

This enzyme requires the presence of magnesium in fairly high concentrations. It has been isolated in the form of a catalytically inert mercury compound which becomes active if the mercury is removed and replaced by magnesium, manganese or zinc. The naturally occurring enzyme is believed to be the magnesium complex on account of its extreme sensitivity towards fluoride, which forms a complex magnesium fluorophosphate in the presence of inorganic phosphate, thus preventing access of the substrate to the combining groups of the enzyme.

Fumarase catalyses the interconversion of fumaric and malic acids thus:

$$
\begin{array}{ll}
COOH & COOH \\
CH_2 & CH \\
CHOH \rightleftharpoons & CH + H_2O \\
COOH & COOH
\end{array}
$$

It is very widely distributed and plays a very important part in metabolic oxidations.

Glyoxalase, an enzyme that is very widely distributed among animal tissues, catalyses the conversion of methyl glyoxal to lactic acid:

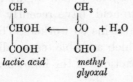

$$\begin{array}{ccc} CH_3 & CH_3 & \\ | & | & \\ CHOH & \longleftarrow & CO & + H_2O \\ | & | & \\ COOH & CHO & \\ \textit{lactic acid} & \textit{methyl} & \\ & \textit{glyoxal} & \end{array}$$

It requires glutathione as an activator, and the relationship appears to be quite specific, for glutathione cannot be replaced by other —SH compounds such as cysteine. Two enzymes are involved in reality, the first of which catalyses the union of methyl glyoxal with the irreplaceable glutathione, while the second ('factor') catalyses the decomposition of the complex to yield lactic acid and regenerate glutathione. The function of glyoxalase is rather obscure. Methyl glyoxal is a somewhat toxic body and there is some evidence that it can arise spontaneously from phosphoglyceraldehyde, a very important intermediary in carbohydrate metabolism. It is possible, therefore, that glyoxalase is a 'detoxicating enzyme' since the product, lactic acid, is virtually innocuous.

'*Serine deaminase*' is an enzyme that is involved in the deamination of serine. It catalyses the dehydration of serine to yield α-amino-acrylic acid which, by intramolecular rearrangement, yields α-iminopropionic acid and this is spontaneously hydrolysed to give ammonia and pyruvic acid:

$$\begin{array}{ccc} CH_2OH & CH_2 & \\ | & \| & \\ CH.NH_2 & \rightleftharpoons & C.NH_2 +H_2O; \\ | & | & \\ COOH & COOH & \end{array}$$

$$\begin{array}{cccc} CH_2 & CH_3 & & CH_3 \\ \| & | & +H_2O & | \\ C.NH_2 & \rightleftharpoons & C=NH & \longrightarrow & CO & +NH_3 \\ | & | & & | \\ COOH & COOH & & COOH \end{array}$$

This appears to be the only mechanism available for the deamination of serine. A similar and perhaps identical enzyme is involved in the deamination of threonine.

Enzymes adding or removing carbon dioxide

Amino-acid decarboxylases, each highly specific with respect to a particular amino-acid, have recently been thoroughly investigated by Gale and his co-workers. These workers studied bacteria, many of which are able, especially in somewhat acid media, to catalyse reactions of the following general type:

$$R.CH(NH_2) \overset{...}{|} COO \overset{...}{|} H \longrightarrow R.CH_2NH_2 + CO_2.$$

The products formed in this way include such highly toxic bodies as tyramine, histamine, putrescine and cadaverine, all of which are strongly basic and tend, therefore, to neutralize the acidity of the medium in which they are produced. The bacterial decarboxylases acting upon lysine, tyrosine, arginine, ornithine and glutamic acid require the co-operation of a 'co-decarboxylase' which has been isolated and identified with pyridoxal phosphate. Another decarboxylase of bacterial origin, active towards histidine, does not appear to require this coenzyme. Pyridoxal, it will be remembered, is a member of the B_2 group of vitamins.

Animal tissues contain few enzymes comparable with the bacterial decarboxylases; the few that have been discovered include enzymes that are specific for the α-decarboxylation of glutamic acid, tyrosine, histidine and cysteic acid; some or all of these require pyridoxal phosphate as a coenzyme. At present there is no evidence that any of these amino-acid decarboxylases act reversibly.

Carbonic anhydrase, an enzyme that plays an important part in the transport of respiratory carbon dioxide in the higher animals, may be regarded either as a hydrating enzyme or, alternatively, as the prototype of the important group of carboxylases and decarboxylases. Carbonic anhydrase itself catalyses the splitting of carbonic acid to yield carbon dioxide and water and, in the reverse direction, the hydration of carbon dioxide to yield carbonic acid:

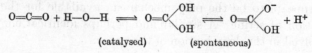

(catalysed)   (spontaneous)

This enzyme has a wide distribution in animal tissues, and is especially abundant in erythrocytes, from which it has been prepared, highly purified, and shown to be a zinc-containing protein. It plays an important part in the secretion of HCl by the gastric mucosa.

Carboxylase, originally discovered in yeast, appears to occur in some other micro-organisms and also in plants. It is, however, entirely absent from animal tissues. This enzyme contains magnesium and in the presence of its coenzyme, co-carboxylase, which is identical with the diphosphate of vitamin B_1 (diphosphothiamine), carboxylase catalyses a simple decarboxylation of α-keto-acids, notably that of pyruvic acid:

$$
\begin{array}{c}
CH_3 \\
| \\
CO \\
\overset{\cdots\cdots}{COOH}
\end{array}
\longrightarrow
\begin{array}{c}
CH_3 \\
| \\
CHO
\end{array} + CO_2
$$

There seems to be no reason to believe that this enzyme can act reversibly.

Malic decarboxylase may be mentioned at this point. This enzyme may be classed as a decarboxylase and as a dehydrogenase, for it catalyses a simultaneous dehydrogenation and decarboxylation of malic acid, using coenzyme II as its hydrogen acceptor:

$$
\begin{array}{c}
COOH \\
| \\
CH_2 \\
| \\
CHOH \\
| \\
COOH
\end{array} + Co\ II \rightleftharpoons
\begin{array}{c}
CH_3 \\
| \\
CO \\
| \\
COOH
\end{array} + CO_2 + Co\ II.2H
$$

In this case the reaction, an atypical oxidative decarboxylation, is reversible (cf. 'pyruvic oxidase', p. 116). This enzyme, which has been obtained from pigeon liver and highly purified, plays an important part in CO_2-fixation in liver tissue and is suspected of having counterparts which are involved in the CO_2-fixation which is of such great and characteristic importance in green plants.

Oxaloacetic decarboxylase is an important and widely distributed enzyme which catalyses the reversible interconversion of pyruvic acid and oxaloacetic acid by addition and removal of carbon dioxide as follows:

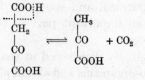

There are indications that biotin, another B_2 vitamin, is in some way implicated in the action of this and perhaps other carboxylating enzymes.

Oxalosuccinic decarboxylase similarly catalyses the interconversion of oxalosuccinic (α-keto-β-carboxyglutaric) and α-ketoglutaric acids:

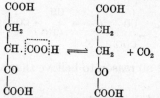

Like the other members of the carboxylase group, this enzyme has the distinction, which is shared by aldolase (see below), of catalysing the formation and rupture of direct carbon-to-carbon linkages. It requires manganese ions for activation.

'*Pyruvic oxidase*' contrasts sharply with carboxylase (p. 115), for it catalyses a process of decarboxylation that is essentially oxidative in nature and is for that reason known as oxidative decarboxylation:

$$
\begin{array}{c}
CH_3 \\
| \\
CO \\
| \\
COOH
\end{array}
\quad \xrightarrow{\ +\frac{1}{2}O_2\ } \quad
\begin{array}{c}
CH_3 \\
| \\
COOH
\end{array}
\ + CO_2
$$

The so-called pyruvic oxidase is, in all probability, not a single enzyme but a somewhat complex catalytic system as we shall see, but it resembles carboxylase in two noteworthy respects, first that it catalyses the decarboxylation of α-keto-acid but has no action upon β-keto-acids, and secondly that its activity requires the participation of co-carboxylase. Like carboxylase it seems that pyruvic oxidase does not act reversibly, at any rate under biological conditions such as obtain in animal tissues. In plants and in some bacteria, however, the reverse reaction does appear to be possible.

Oxidative decarboxylation is known to be attended by the generation of energy-rich phosphate bonds and we shall return later on to this aspect of the process (pp. 421 et seq.).

Other adding enzymes

Aldolase (zymohexase). This important enzyme was originally discovered in yeast but is now known to be very widely distributed indeed. It catalyses the splitting of one molecule of fructofuranose-1:6-diphosphate into two molecules of 'triose phosphate', i.e. one molecule each of L-3-phosphoglyceraldehyde and α-phosphodihydroxyacetone. The process is reversible:

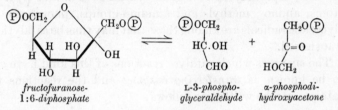

| fructofuranose-
1:6-diphosphate | L-3-phospho-
glyceraldehyde | α-phosphodi-
hydroxyacetone |

Aldolase is abolutely specific with respect to one of the products, namely, phosphodihydroxyacetone, but is group-specific towards phosphoglyceraldehyde. This can be replaced by other aldehydes, which need not necessarily be phosphorylated, so that many new compounds can be synthesized enzymatically by aldolase, including fructofuranose-1-monophosphate for example.

Aspartase is an example of an enzyme that catalyses the addition and removal of ammonia:

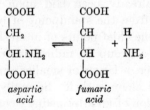

| aspartic
acid | fumaric
acid | |

It occurs in certain bacteria.

CHAPTER V

TRANSFERRING AND ISOMERIZING ENZYMES

General Introduction

One of the most striking advances in biochemistry in recent years has been the discovery that there exist many enzymes capable of catalysing the transference of some group or radical from one molecule to another, and that transfer reactions of this kind are of fundamental importance in the energetics of biological systems, especially in biological synthesis. Pairs of hydrogen atoms, amino-, methyl- and amidino-groups, phosphatic and glycosidic radicals are among those that may thus be catalytically transferred.

The enzymes which catalyse reactions of this kind have come to be known as *transferring enzymes* and the reactions they catalyse can be written as follows:

$$A.\!:\!G + B \rightleftharpoons A + G.\!:\!B,$$

where $A.G$ stands for the donator of the radical G, and B for its acceptor. The dehydrogenases and related enzymes are a special group of transferring enzymes in which G corresponds to a pair of hydrogen atoms or electrons. They constitute a large and important group of functionally related enzymes concerned especially with tissue respiration, and will be considered separately from the rest.

Emphasis has already been laid upon the importance of transfer reactions from the standpoint of biological energetics (Chapter III) but the chief points of interest may be reiterated here. First, when a group or radical is transferred from one molecule to another, a larger or smaller amount of free energy can be transferred along with it. Secondly, it is necessary to assume the formation of an intermediary complex of some kind because it is difficult otherwise to account for the transference of energy along with the radical. At least three factors may be involved in the formation of such a complex, viz. the reactants (A.G and B, or A and B.G), and the transferring enzyme. This essential feature of these reactions can be expressed by writing the equation in the following general form:

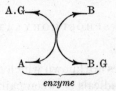

At the present time we have little information about the intimate details that lie behind these reactions. Transference of a group or radical is attended in many and perhaps most cases by a transference of free energy, and the number of ways in which this dual transfer can be achieved is probably limited. We have already considered two possible modes of reaction (pp. 67, 68) which, for the general reaction

$$A.G + B \rightleftharpoons A + B.G$$

may be summarized as follows:

1 (a). $A\overset{\epsilon}{\cdots}G + enzyme \rightleftharpoons A\overset{\epsilon}{\cdots}G—enzyme \rightleftharpoons A—G\overset{\epsilon}{\cdots}enzyme \rightleftharpoons A + G\overset{\epsilon}{\cdots}enzyme,$

  (b). $B + G\overset{\epsilon}{\cdots}enzyme \rightleftharpoons B—G\overset{\epsilon}{\cdots}enzyme \rightleftharpoons B\overset{\epsilon}{\cdots}G—enzyme \rightleftharpoons B\overset{\epsilon}{\cdots}G + enzyme.$

This formulation assumes that the radical G is first transferred to the enzyme and thence to the acceptor B, and there is evidence that this actually takes place in certain cases (see p. 124 for example). The energy ϵ associated with the bond uniting A and G is quantitatively transferred along with G itself, very possibly in the manner indicated in these equations, where a dotted bond represents one that is energy-laden and the usual full line corresponds to a bond that is not.

A second possible formulation assumes that the donator and acceptor are simultaneously accommodated on and activated by the enzyme:

2. $A\overset{\epsilon}{\cdots}G + B \rightleftharpoons A\overset{\epsilon}{\cdots}G—B \rightleftharpoons A—G\overset{\epsilon}{\cdots}B \rightleftharpoons A + G\overset{\epsilon}{\cdots}B.$

In cases where the bond-energy is quantitatively transferred it is evident that each step in the process must be reversible, but in others, e.g. in the hexokinase reaction (p. 72), some one or other of the intermediate steps must be supposed to be irreversible.

TRANSPHOSPHORYLATION

High-energy transfers

A number of enzymes are known which can catalyse the transference of phosphate radicals between pairs of molecules, adenosine di- and triphosphates being employed as the carrier system. Not all of these enzymes have so far been named, however, and they might be collectively called 'transphosphatases' or, following the suggestion of Dixon, 'phosphokinases', after hexokinase, the longest-known representative of the group. Whichever name is used (and we shall use 'phosphokinases' here) it should be restricted to enzymes catalysing reactions that involve the ATP/ADP system.

It will be convenient now to refer once more to the Lohmann reaction, i.e. the transference of a phosphate radical from adenosine triphosphate to creatine, or to adenosine diphosphate from creatine phosphate. If we represent energy-rich bonds by the usual symbol $\sim$, the structure of adenosine triphosphate may be expressed as follows:

$$
\begin{array}{ccc}
\overset{\displaystyle O}{\underset{}{\|}} & \overset{\displaystyle O}{\underset{}{\|}} & \overset{\displaystyle O}{\underset{}{\|}} \\
A-P-O\sim P-O\sim P-OH \\
\underset{\displaystyle OH}{|} & \underset{\displaystyle OH}{|} & \underset{\displaystyle OH}{|}
\end{array}
$$

Further, it is known that creatine phosphate also contains an energy-rich bond, and its structure may accordingly be written thus:

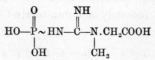

Accordingly, the Lohmann reaction can be conveniently represented in the following terms:

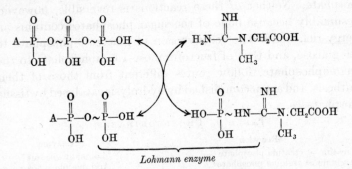

Lohmann enzyme

We do not know how this reaction takes place, whether by 'parking' the terminal phosphate radical of ATP on the enzyme to be 'picked up' later by creatine, or whether both substances react together on the surface of the enzyme to give a tautomeric complex: the most important feature of this reaction is that it accomplishes the transference of a phosphate radical from one molecule to another, *together with the whole free energy of an energy-rich phosphate bond*.

Phosphokinases occur widely and probably universally among living cells and tissues. In all cases of phosphokinase activity known at the present time, adenosine triphosphate and the corresponding diphosphate are obligatory reactants. The second reactant may be any of a considerable number of substances; the identities of some of them and the nature of the corresponding reactions are summarized in Table 9. It is quite certain that substances other than those listed in the table can also enter into transphosphorylation reactions, and there is evidence that the enzymes concerned are highly specific for their substrates as well as for the carrier, which plays the part of a coenzyme. In most cases the reactions are freely reversible, but to this some important exceptions are known.

Glucose, galactose, mannose and fructose can be irreversibly phosphorylated at the expense of adenosine triphosphate under the influence of hexokinase, galactohexokinase, mannohexokinase and fructohexokinase respectively. Phosphohexokinase catalyses a similar phosphorylation of fructofuranose-6-monophosphate. Neither of these reactions is reversible, however, presumably because none of the sugar phosphates contains an energy-rich bond. The reconversion of glucose-6-phosphate to free glucose, and that of fructofuranose-1:6-diphosphate to the 6-monophosphate, follow routes different from those of their synthesis, and are accomplished by hydrolysis catalysed by tissue phosphatases.

TABLE 9. PHOSPHOKINASES

Reaction	Enzyme
Creatine ⇌ creatine phosphate	'Lohmann enzyme'
Arginine ⇌ arginine phosphate	Arginine phosphokinase
Glucose → glucose-6-phosphate	Hexokinase
Fructose → fructose-6-phosphate	Fructohexokinase
Mannose → mannose-6-phosphate	Mannohexokinase
Galactose → galactose-1-phosphate	Galactohexokinase
Fructose-6-phosphate → fructose-1:6-diphosphate	Phosphohexokinase
3-Phosphoglyceric acid ⇌ 1:3-diphosphoglyceric acid	Phosphoglyceric phosphokinase
Pyruvic acid ⇌ phospho-*enol*-pyruvate	Pyruvic phosphokinase
Adenosine monophosphate ⇌ adenosine diphosphate	Myokinase
Adenosine → adenosine monophosphate	Adenosinekinase
Riboflavin → riboflavin phosphate	Flavokinase
Coenzyme I → coenzyme II	(Unnamed)

Myokinase is a somewhat special example of the group of phosphokinases. This enzyme catalyses the transference of a phosphate radical from one molecule of adenosine diphosphate to a second, so that the products are adenosine monophosphate, on the one hand, and the corresponding triphosphate on the other. In this case the reaction can be represented in the following manner:

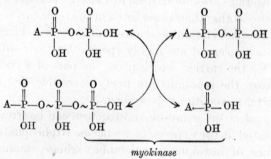

myokinase

We shall have numerous occasions to refer to the other phosphokinases listed in Table 9, for all play important parts in the metabolism of cells and tissues. But still other phosphokinases undoubtedly exist. We know, for instance, that ATP can act as an energy source in the biological synthesis of glutamine, hippuric acid, urea, glutathione and many more compounds of interest and importance. Each of these syntheses must probably involve a priming reaction in which $\sim ℗$ is transferred from ATP to one of the reactants, the transfer being catalysed by an enzyme which must, by definition, be a phosphokinase of some kind.

Low energy transfers

We come next to a group of reactions in which a phosphate radical is again transferred from one reactant to another but this time *without the participation of ATP and ADP*. Characteristically these are 'low-energy' as contrasted with 'high-energy' transfers of the kind catalysed by the phosphokinases and in which ATP and ADP are involved. It seems desirable to find some distinctive title for the enzymes concerned in these 'low-energy' transfers but no suitable name seems to have been proposed. This perhaps is not a very serious matter however for, in all cases so far reported, low-energy phosphate transference is catalysed by phosphatases, i.e. by enzymes which ordinarily catalyse the *hydrolysis* of organic esters of phosphoric acid. Few cases indeed are known of enzymes capable of catalysing more than one kind of chemical change in one and the same substrate molecule. Perhaps we may describe these curious enzymes as *transferring phosphatases*.

The juice of citrous fruits contains phosphatases of the mono- and poly- but not of the di-esterase type. The phosphomonoesterase appears at first glance to be a typical hydrolase since it can catalyse reactions of the usual hydrolytic type, e.g.

$$R.O℗ + H.OH \longrightarrow R.OH + HO.℗,$$

but it can also catalyse reversible transfer reactions of the following kind:

$$R.O℗ + R'.OH \rightleftharpoons R.OH + R'O.℗.$$

Thus Axelrod, the first to discover this phenomenon, found that by starting with nitrophenylphosphate and methyl alcohol, pure monomethyl phosphate could be obtained. The same effect has been obtained with several (e.g. apple) but not with all fruit phosphatases, and with phosphatases from some (e.g. prostate) but not all animal sources. Other reactions catalysed by these 'transferring phosphatases' include such interesting and important processes as the following:

$$\text{glucose-1-phosphate} + \text{glycerol} \rightleftharpoons \text{glucose} + \text{phosphoglycerol}.$$

The free energy for the synthesis of the new ester arises from the phosphate bond of the first, and in later experiments it has been found possible to push reactions of this kind very much further towards the right by using creatine phosphate, with its energy-rich bond, as the source of phosphate plus energy.

Axelrod himself showed that the phosphate radical does not have even a transient free existence as the transfer takes place. Working with a donator containing radioactive phosphorus and in the presence of inorganic phosphate he found that transfer took place without the appearance of any radioactive phosphate in the medium. It is therefore believed that the donator attaches itself to the enzyme and 'parks' its phosphate radical in the manner indicated in reaction (1) on p. 119 to form 'enzyme phosphate'. This might now react in either of two ways, both of which the enzyme is competent to catalyse. These are: (i) reaction with a phosphate acceptor to yield a new ester, and this path is followed if such an acceptor is present, or (ii) reaction with water to undergo hydrolysis. In the first case the bond energy of the phosphate is conserved but in the second it is dissipated. This is a most interesting phenomenon. It is, as was pointed out in our discussion of energetics, a universal observation that free energy always tends to escape when a chemical reaction takes place. It might have been anticipated, therefore, that hydrolysis rather than transfer would always result in the presence of a transferring phosphatase. Apparently, however, the available free energy is not lost all at once and in a single reaction: rather does it seem that free energy tends when possible to escape in stages. Other examples of successive losses of free energy are known and exemplify the so-called 'law of successive reactions'.

The free energy of the bonds involved in reactions of this kind is usually of the order of 3000 cal. per g.mol. and it is evident that this bond energy is transferred along with the phosphate radical itself when the 'enzyme phosphate' is formed, and subsequently passed on, again in company with the phosphate radical, to the acceptor; otherwise, the reaction as a whole would not be reversible. In the hydrolysis of the 'enzyme phosphate' complex, however, the enzyme-phosphate bond is ruptured and its free energy spilled out so that, like phosphatase-catalysed hydrolyses in general, this is an exergonic and biologically irreversible process.

How important these phosphatase-catalysed transfer reactions are in metabolism we do not know at the present time. Phosphate esters of the sugars, of glycerol and other alcoholic compounds are of very general occurrence and great metabolic importance, however, and in these 'low energy' transfer reactions we have mechanisms for the phosphorylation of sugars, glycerol and so on, in which low-energy compounds can serve as starting materials instead of the high-energy source used in the phospho-kinase systems, viz. ATP. Ultimately, however, the bond energy of these compounds probably comes from ATP, most usually perhaps through the hexokinase reaction.

TRANSGLYCOSIDATION

There exist numerous enzymes capable of catalysing the transference of glycosidic radicals from one molecule to another. Glucosidic and fructosidic radicals are among those that may be thus transferred. Often, though by no means always, the starting material is α-glucose-1-phosphate. A number of the enzymes concerned with transglycosidation are known as *phosphorylases*. They were originally so named by analogy with the hydrolases, to which they bear a certain resemblance, though the resemblance now appears to be rather more superficial than it formerly seemed:

$$\begin{array}{lll} \textit{Hydrolysis} & \text{R:R}' + \text{H.OH} & \rightleftharpoons \text{R.OH} + \text{H.R}', \\ \textit{Phosphorolysis} & \text{R:R}' + \text{HO.}\circledP & \rightleftharpoons \text{R.O}\circledP + \text{H.R}'. \end{array}$$

Sucrose phosphorylase. Sucrose cannot be synthesized biologically by simple reversal of its hydrolysis. It has, however, been shown that certain bacteria (e.g. *Pseudomonas saccharophila*) can catalyse a synthetic production of sucrose from α-glucose-1-phosphate and free fructose. The synthetic process, which is freely reversible, is one of 'dephosphorolysis', i.e. elimination of phosphoric acid:

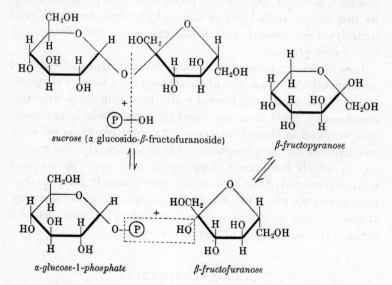

sucrose (α glucosido-β-fructofuranoside)   *β-fructopyranose*

α-glucose-1-phosphate   *β-fructofuranose*

The synthesis of sucrose is, of course, a particularly important process in the metabolism of plants, but it is not at present known whether it is accomplished in plants in the same way as in *P. saccharophila*.

Clearly, the synthetic process can be regarded as a condensation-like reaction in which the elements of water are replaced by those of phosphoric acid. But it can also be regarded as a process of transglucosidation in which a glucosidic radical is transferred from one aglucone, in the form of a phosphate radical, to another, which in this case happens to be glycosidic also. This second aglucone, a fructofuranoside radical, is available in aqueous solutions of fructose, which contain considerable amounts of fructofuranose in equilibrium with the more stable pyranose form.

The free energy required for the formation of the new glucosidic link is already available in that of the starting material, α-glucose-1-phosphate, or phospho-α-glucoside, and is transferred along with the glucoside radical from the first aglucone to the second. Free glucose cannot serve as a starting material for this synthesis because its free-energy level is too low: it can, however, be raised to a high enough level through the hexokinase reaction, in which ATP provides the necessary free energy for the formation of glucose-6-phosphate, from which α-glucose-1-phosphate can then be formed by the action of phosphoglucomutase. In the end, therefore, the free energy for the synthesis of sucrose comes, in all probability, from ATP.

Now while sucrose phosphorylase is absolutely specific with respect to the glucosidic portion of the substrate molecule it is only group-specific towards the aglucone. Thus the fructosidic aglucone can be replaced by phosphate or by any of a number of other substances, including certain sugars, so that new disaccharides can be synthesized by the action of the enzyme. Other aglucone radicals can be furnished by L-sorbose, D-xyloketose and L-arabinose for example. Nor is this all. *Any of these aglucone radicals can be replaced by any other without the intervention of phosphate*; for instance:

$$\alpha\text{-glucose-1-fructoside} + \text{sorbose} \rightleftharpoons \alpha\text{-glucose-1-sorboside} + \text{fructose.}$$
(sucrose)

A number of other similar reactions have been demonstrated, so that the transglucosidic properties of sucrose phosphorylase cannot be held in any sort of doubt.

Synthesis of polysaccharides by transglycosidation. Somewhat similar transglycosidations leading to the synthesis of polysaccharides from sucrose have been observed in a variety of other micro-organisms. In *Leuconostoc dextranicum*, for example, there is an enzyme which acts upon sucrose to yield fructose, which is metabolized by the organism, together with a *dextran* built up from 1:6-α-linked glucopyranoside units. In certain spore-forming aerobes sucrose is again split into glucose and fructose, but in this case the glucose is metabolized and the fructose units are built up into *levans* formed from 2:6-linked fructofuranoside units. In both these cases the sugar units not katabolized for energy production by the organism are transferred one after another to build up these specialized polysaccharides, and in neither case is phosphate in any way involved. The free energy required to form each new glycosidic link is derived from the free energy of the old.

Sucrose is also the starting material for the synthesis of a glycogen-like polysaccharide produced by an enzyme, 'amylosucrase', of another micro-organism, *Neisseria perflava*: here the newly formed glycosidic linkages are mainly of the 1:4-α- type and phosphate again plays no part in the transglycosidation process. Nor is sucrose the only disaccharide that can serve as starting material for polysaccharide synthesis by transglycosidation, especially among micro-organisms. For example, certain strains of *Escherichia coli* yield cell-free extracts containing an enzyme, 'amylomaltase', which converts maltose into glucose together with a starch- or glycogen-like polysaccharide, without intervention by phosphate.

Remarkable examples of transglucosidation have recently been demonstrated with intestinal maltase, a typical hydrolytic enzyme. Acting upon maltose this enzyme can form longer or shorter chains of 1:4-α-linked glucose radicals by transglucosidation. Phosphate is not involved. One glucose radical is set free from maltose in this process while the other is transferred to form the new, higher saccharide, for example:

$$2 \text{ maltose} \rightleftharpoons \text{glucose} + \text{maltotriose},$$
$$\text{maltose} + \text{maltotriose} \rightleftharpoons \text{glucose} + \text{maltotetrose},$$

and so on.

Cyclical dextrans, amylose-, amylopectin- and glycogen-like polysaccharides are produced by many micro-organisms of various kinds, sometimes with, but often without, the participation of phosphorylated intermediates, but space will not allow us to discuss these interesting syntheses in detail. Progress in this field is very rapid at the present time.

Starch and glycogen phosphorylases (amylophosphorylases)

Many animal and plant tissues contain enzymes capable of breaking down starch and glycogen, and it is certain moreover that plant and animal tissues can produce starch and glycogen from glucose. For many years it was supposed that the synthesis must involve enzymes essentially similar to the amylases already known to be concerned in the digestive breakdown of these polysaccharides. A series of investigations carried out by Hanes in England and by Cori & Cori in America showed, however, that the intracellular breakdown and synthesis of starch and glycogen follow pathways that are quite different from those of digestive hydrolysis. The degradation is not, in fact, hydrolytic but phosphorolytic, yielding α-glucose-1-phosphate as the first product of breakdown. The digestive amylases, it will be remembered, yield mainly maltose, a disaccharide, and a little glucose.

Hanes and the Coris succeeded in obtaining preparations containing the phosphorylases of peas, potatoes, liver, muscle and other tissues, and were able to show that they catalyse the decomposition of starch and glycogen in the presence of phosphate, thus:

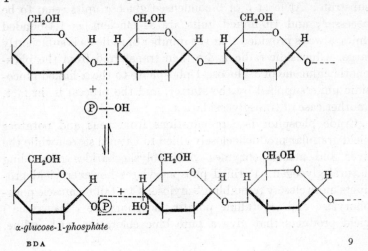

α-glucose-1-phosphate

This reaction is reversible. If α-glucose-1-phosphate is added to a suitable preparation of a phosphorylase, polysaccharides can be synthesized, but these enzymes have no action upon β-glucose-1-phosphate. Recent work with highly purified enzymes has shown that the complete synthesis of starch and glycogen, like their digestive hydrolysis (see pp. 95–99) involves several different enzymes, and the names of these and the nature of the linkages synthesized by their action are summarized in Table 10.

TABLE 10. LINKAGES FORMED BY ENZYMES
SYNTHESIZING STARCH AND GLYCOGEN

Name of enzyme	Nature of linkage synthesized
Phosphorylase (animals) ⎫ P-enzyme (plants) ⎬	$1:4$-α-
Branching factor (animals) ⎫ Q-enzyme (plants) ⎬	$1:6$-α-
Unknown (? Z-) enzyme	$1:3$-β-

An interesting feature of these syntheses is that the phosphorylases cannot act upon α-glucose-1-phosphate except in the presence of a suitable 'starter' such as a little added starch or glycogen: presumably therefore the enzyme needs an 'anchor' to which the new glucosidic units can be transferred from the substrate. At least 5 or 6 condensed glucose units seem to be necessary and 1:6-linked units are as efficient as 1:4-bonded units, always provided that the number of radicals is sufficiently large. Glucosidic radicals are then transferred from the phosphatic aglucone of α-glucose-1-phosphate to the α-linked glucosidic units supplied by the starter, and the process is, in fact, another case of transglycosidation.

Crude phosphorylase preparations from peas and potatoes yield granular products closely allied to natural starch while the liver and muscle enzymes yield polysaccharides resembling natural glycogen. Purified phosphorylases however yield products more closely resembling amylose. Crystalline muscle phosphorylase and crystalline potato phosphorylase ('P-enzyme') yield products that give a pure blue coloration with iodine.

Examination of one such product showed that it could be completely degraded to maltose by the action of crystalline β-amylase and contained about 80 glucose units. Natural amylose, however, is only 70 % degraded by crystalline β-amylase and contains 200 or more glucose units, a few of which are incorporated through 1:3-β-linkages (p. 96). But both the P-enzyme and β-amylase are wholly specific for 1:4-α-links, so that the formation of natural amylose must be presumed to involve an additional enzyme, which may be the *Z-enzyme* (p. 95) acting in reverse.

Impure phosphorylase preparations acting upon α-glucose-1-phosphate yield products which stain reddish brown or purple with iodine; evidently they contain other factors which can catalyse the formation of branching linkages, which are usually (p. 96) of the 1:6-α-type. The presence of such *branching factors* has been demonstrated in muscle, liver and various plant materials, and a highly purified factor of this kind has been isolated from potatoes ('Q-enzyme'). It was at first considered that the 'branching factor' must probably be another kind of phosphorylase ('isophosphorylase'), but work with the purified Q-enzyme shows that it operates without the participation of phosphate although, like the P-enzyme itself, it is a transglucosidase but possesses rather special properties.

If purified Q-enzyme is allowed to act upon purified amylose, which contains mainly 1:4-α-linkages, amylopectin-like substances are formed, containing 1:6-α- as well as 1:4-α-glucosidic links. Careful studies of the products shows that two processes take place simultaneously: 1:4-linkages disappear and 1:6-linkages take their place. Apparently, therefore, the Q-enzyme can detach chains of 1:4-linked glucosidic units from the main chain of amylose and transplant them into 1:6-positions. As in other transglycosidation reactions, the free energy required for the formation of the new glycosidic links is drawn from that of the old, but, whereas in most other cases of transglycosidation single glycosidic radicals are transferred serially, the Q-enzyme can transfer and transplant a chain of about twenty 1:4-α-linked glucose units in one operation, and phosphate plays no part in this process.

The reaction catalysed by the Q-enzyme seems to be irreversible, for phosphorylase plus Q-enzyme cannot accomplish the complete breakdown of natural glycogen or amylopectin. Phosphorylases, like β-amylases, cease to act when a branching linkage is reached and it therefore seems certain that the Q-enzyme cannot catalyse the breakdown of the 1:6-α-links which are formed by its own activity. Muscle however contains a hydrolytic *amylo-1:6-α-glucosidase* (p. 97) which is competent to break these branching linkages, and similar 'debranching factors' (*R-enzymes*) are present in plant materials (beans, potatoes). These enzymes can act together with either phosphorylases or amylases to catalyse a complete degradation of glycogen or amylopectin to α-glucose-1-phosphate or maltose as the case may be. Glucose is also produced as a minor product and arises by hydrolysis of the cross-linkages.

The interconvertibility between starch or glycogen and α-glucose-1-phosphate is due to the higher free energy of the latter as compared with that of free, unphosphorylated glucose. The free energy required for the synthesis of these polysaccharides is introduced into the free glucose molecule by phosphorylation through the action of hexokinase and ATP. This yields glucose-6-phosphate, an ester, in the first instance, and from this the glucoside, α-glucose-1-phosphate, is formed by an intramolecular rearrangement catalysed by phosphoglucomutase (p. 146). In the end, therefore, the energy for the synthesis of these polysaccharides comes once again from ATP.

In the ordinary way, glycogen is stored in the livers of animals and distributed, under very precisely defined conditions, to other tissues by way of the blood, travelling in the form of free glucose. The latter arises by the action of a liver phosphatase upon glucose-6-phosphate formed from α-glucose-1-phosphate, which is itself formed by the action upon glycogen of the enzymes we have been considering here. In the muscles and other tissues, where blood glucose is used as a source of newly-formed glycogen, it seems certain that the glucose, on entering the cells, must first of all be phosphorylated again by hexokinase and ATP to yield glucose-6-phosphate, from which α-glucose-1-phosphate can again be formed and then built up into glycogen once more.

Transribosidation is a form of transglycosidation that appears to be of major importance in the metabolism of nucleosides. The latter are β-N-glycosides of the pentose sugars, D-ribose and D-desoxyribose. They can be phosphorolytically split to yield the corresponding pentose-1-phosphates, together with the parent purine, pyrimidine or other nitrogenous base. Here, therefore, we have another case in which a glycosidic radical is transferred from one aglycone, e.g. a purine or pyrimidine, to a second, in the form of a phosphate radical. We shall refer to this subject again (p. 354).

TRANSPEPTIDATION

Formation of Peptide Links

It has been suspected for some time that the synthesis of polysaccharides and disaccharides by transglycosidation might have some counterpart in the synthesis of peptides and even of proteins. The first positive indications that amino-acid transfer may be a reality appeared very shortly before the preparation of the new edition of this book was begun. Much more information will no doubt be available by the time this appears in print, but the inclusion of a section on peptide-bond formation and transfer here may perhaps pave the way for an understanding of the new results that may be confidently expected.

We know of several reactions in which new peptide bonds are synthesized. The synthesis of *hippuric acid* involves the formation of such a bond. Liver extracts contain an enzyme which will form hippuric acid from benzoic acid and glycine, provided that ATP is available. Recently it has been shown that coenzyme A is probably concerned in this process, which can best be expressed as follows:

$$C_6H_5.COOH + H_2N.CH_2COOH + ATP \longrightarrow$$
$$C_6H_5.CO.HN.CH_2COOH + ADP + HO.\textcircled{P}.$$

The newly formed peptide bond is shown in heavy type. It was for some time believed that ATP and benzoic acid must first react together to form benzoyl phosphate as an intermediate product: being an acyl phosphate such a product would be expected to contain an energy-rich phosphate bond and so might react readily with the amino-group of glycine. In fact, however, benzoyl phosphate does not give rise to hippuric acid if added together with glycine to the enzyme preparation.

Glutamine, the amide of glutamic acid, can readily be hydrolysed by tissue extracts, but its synthesis, which again involves formation of a new peptide bond, can only be accomplished under certain special conditions. Enzyme preparations have been obtained from bacteria and from animal tissues which, if glutamic acid and ammonia are available, catalyse the synthetic formation of glutamine on addition of ATP:

$$
\begin{array}{l}
\text{COOH} \\
| \\
\text{CH}_2 \\
| \\
\text{CH}_2 \\
| \\
\text{CH.NH}_2 \\
| \\
\text{COOH}
\end{array}
\quad + NH_3 + ATP \longrightarrow
\begin{array}{l}
\text{CONH}_2 \\
| \\
\text{CH}_2 \\
| \\
\text{CH}_2 \\
| \\
\text{CH.NH}_2 \\
| \\
\text{COOH}
\end{array}
\quad + ADP + HO.\textcircled{P}
$$

Here again it has been suspected that the γ-acyl phosphate must be formed as an intermediary, but attempts to isolate it have led uniformly to failure. Conceivably coenzyme A may play a part once again.

Another reaction in which peptide bonds are formed is the synthesis of ornithuric acid, a compound formed in bird kidney as a means of detoxicating benzoic acid (p. 294), and here again ATP is required as an energy source. But in none of these cases is a 'typical' peptide bond produced, i.e. a bond formed by the union of the α-carboxyl group of one amino-acid and the α-amino-group of a second. Two such bonds and one atypical bond are formed however in the synthesis of glutathione, which has been much studied recently and in which ATP must once more be provided. The general need for ATP in peptide-bond formation makes it clear that free energy is required for the formation of bonds of this type, just as it is in the formation of glycosidic bonds, but, as we have seen, the free energy required for glycoside formation can be provided by low- as well as by high-energy transfer (p. 123).

Transfer of peptide groups. The suggestion has now appeared that just as certain hydrolytic phosphatases can catalyse low-energy transfer of phosphate radicals, so too hydrolytic peptidases may perhaps catalyse that of peptide-bound amino-acid radicals. Intracellular peptidases are numerous and, moreover, very specific indeed, and might in fact be able to carry out highly specific transferring operations leading to the formation of correspondingly specific peptides. If we assume that transpeptidation is possible—and there is evidence that this is indeed so—there are two ways in which the transfer might be effected. These may be expressed in the following manner:

Transfer of amino-group :

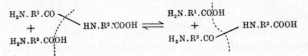

Transfer of carboxyl group :

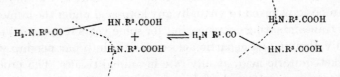

Hanes & Isherwood have used extracts of kidney and pancreas in experiments designed to test the possibility of amino-acid transfer between the tripeptide, glutathione, and its constituent amino-acids, glycine, cysteine and glutamic acid. After incubation with the enzyme the digests were examined chromatographically, and spots were found which indicated the formation of new peptides. New peptides were also produced by interaction between glutathione and other amino-acids, including leucine, valine and phenylalanine. At the time of writing these products have not been identified or isolated, but there cannot be much doubt that amino-acid transfer, or transpeptidation, can indeed occur.

It is too early to speculate far about the significance of this new discovery, but it seems certain that an important new field has been opened up. We may conclude with a quotation from Hanes & Isherwood's preliminary publication: 'The postulated transpeptidation reactions leading to the interconversion of α-peptides by either carboxyl or amine transfer might prove to be closely connected with protein synthesis, since they would provide a mechanism for the rearrangement of amino-acid residues in α-peptide chain structures. Underlying this suggestion, we have had in mind from the beginning the possibility that the different proteolytic enzymes, with their sharply defined specificity characteristics, may catalyse such transpeptidation reactions, in addition to the hydrolytic reactions by which they are normally recognized.'

TRANSAMINATION

Glutamic transaminase is an enzyme that occurs widely among micro-organisms and in plant and animal tissues. It was at one time believed that the amino-group of virtually any amino-acid can be transferred to virtually any keto-acid under the influence of transaminating enzymes, but for some years it appeared that only alanine and aspartic acid can enter into partnership with α-ketoglutaric acid, at any rate in animal tissues. The process of transamination, which is reversible, can be expressed in the following manner:

$$\begin{array}{ccc} \text{R} & \text{R}' & \text{R} & \text{R}' \\ | & | & | & | \\ \text{CH.NH}_2 + \text{CO} & \rightleftharpoons & \text{CO} + \text{CH.NH}_2 \\ | & | & | & | \\ \text{COOH} & \text{COOH} & \text{COOH} & \text{COOH} \end{array}$$

Work with purified specimens of the enzyme shows that one member of the reacting pair must be either L-glutamic acid or α-ketoglutaric acid. L-Aspartic acid or oxaloacetic acid can replace these but react much more slowly, and the enzyme, which is now called L-glutamic transaminase, is thus highly specific towards at least one of the reactants. There is now reason to think that there are at least two such enzymes, one specific towards alanine (or pyruvic acid) and the other towards aspartic (or oxaloacetic) acid. These are known as L-*glutamic alanine transaminase* and L-*glutamic aspartic transaminase* respectively.

The α-ketoglutaric-glutamic acid system itself can act as an amino-group-carrying system. If, for example, we take alanine and add to it a purified sample of glutamic transaminase in the presence of oxaloacetic acid, no direct transference of amino-groups from alanine to oxaloacetic acid takes place. If now a catalytic amount of glutamic or α-ketoglutaric acid is also added, amino-groups are transferred from the alanine to the oxaloacetic acid so that pyruvic and aspartic acids are formed. On account of the free reversibility of the system the reaction does not go to completion but an equilibrium condition is eventually attained:

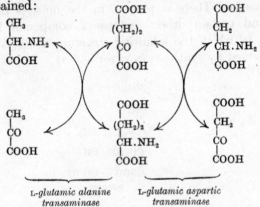

L-*glutamic alanine transaminase*   L-*glutamic aspartic transaminase*

Glutamic transaminase has a prosthetic group which consists of a phosphorylated derivative of pyridoxal, one of the B_2 group of vitamins. Pyridoxal and the corresponding amine, pyridoxamine, have the following structures (the phosphate radical is attached to the alcoholic group):

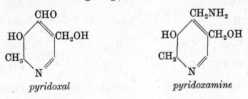

pyridoxal   *pyridoxamine*

We do not know precisely how the prosthetic group functions: probably it acts as a donator and acceptor of the amino-group undergoing transference, thus:

(i) amino-acid$_1$ + pyridoxal—Ⓟ—enzyme ⇌
  pyridoxamine—Ⓟ—enzyme + α-ketoacid$_1$,

(ii) pyridoxamine—Ⓟ—enzyme + α-ketoacid$_2$ ⇌
  pyridoxal—Ⓟ—enzyme + amino-acid$_2$.

In this connexion it is interesting that glutamic acid can react with free pyridoxal to form pyridoxamine and α-ketoglutaric acid.

There is some interesting circumstantial evidence for the formation of tautomeric reaction complexes as intermediates in transamination. There is present in the muscles of *Octopus*, *Pecten* and certain other molluscs a compound known as octopine, to which the following structure has been assigned and confirmed by synthesis *in vitro*:

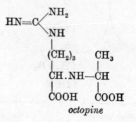

octopine

This is a post-mortem product and arises from arginine. Octopine can be chemically synthesized from arginine and pyruvic acid by simultaneous condensation and catalytic reduction, thus:

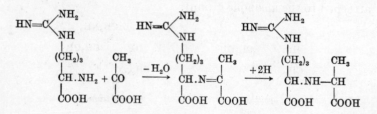

Here there is strong presumptive evidence for the existence *in vitro* of an intermediate complex formed by the condensation of an amino-acid with an α-keto-acid, precisely the type of compound that would be expected as an intermediary in transamination. If we suppose that such a complex is indeed formed under biological conditions, we may write, for the case of glutamic alanine-transaminase, the following reaction sequence:

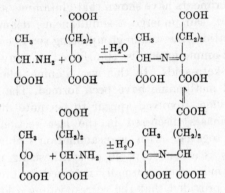

It seems probable, however, that the primary reaction in transamination consists in the transference of amino-group from an amino-acid to the prosthetic group of the enzyme, pyridoxal phosphate, in which case the first stage of the reaction will probably be as follows:

CH₃ ... CH.NH₂ + O=R ⇌ ±H₂O ⇌ CH—N=R ⇌ C=N—HR ⇌ ±H₂O ⇌ CO + H₂N.RH COOH ... enzyme ... enzyme ... enzyme ... enzyme

Here R represents the remainder of the molecule of the phosphate of pyridoxal or pyridoxamine. By further reaction with α-keto-glutaric acid, R.NH₂ could then revert to the aldehyde and yield glutamic acid.

Other transaminases. In very recent times the transaminase system has been re-investigated with special, so-called 'lyophilized', enzyme preparations of heart-muscle, liver and kidney, dialysed and fortified with pyridoxal phosphate. In these newer experiments it has proved possible to demonstrate the transamination of twenty-two amino-acids, over and above alanine, aspartic and glutamic acids. It seems that the glutamic-α-ketoglutaric system plays a central part in these processes and that a different enzyme is probably involved for each amino-acid concerned.

Other experiments have shown that glutamine, as opposed to glutamic acid, can undergo a simultaneous deamidation and transdeamination, the amido-group being set free as ammonia while the α-amino-group is transferred to any of a large variety of α-keto-acids. In this way alanine, phenyl alanine, tyrosine and methionine have been formed. The mechanisms and the enzymes involved appear to be quite different from the transaminases discussed in the last section. This new mechanism, together with transamination—which is reversible—supply reactions capable of synthesizing most, if not all, of the amino-acids normally involved in protein formation, always provided that the corresponding α-keto-acids are available.

Aspartic transaminase. In some plants the place of the glutamic transaminases is taken by similar systems in which aspartic and oxaloacetic acids replace glutamic and α-ketoglutaric acids respectively.

'TRANSIMINATION'

A transfer reaction of an unusual kind takes place at the penultimate stage in the biological synthesis of urea, when citrulline is converted into arginine by what at first appeared to be a transimination reaction. The interchange is catalysed by highly specific enzymes, present in liver and in kidney tissue and perhaps elsewhere, but aspartic acid is an indispensable reactant in the process and the products, arginine and malic acid, have been positively identified. Clearly the amino-group of aspartic acid is exchanged here for an hydroxyl radical, and it is considered that citrulline reacts in its *enol-* and not in its *keto-*form, exchanging its enolic (OH) for the amino-group of aspartate by a process of true transamination:

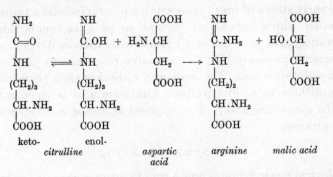

keto-   enol-
     citrulline   aspartic   arginine   malic acid
                                   acid

In this case the amino-group is exchanged, not for a keto-group as it is in ordinary transamination, but for a hydroxyl radical. The mechanism is accordingly different; two special enzymes are required together with magnesium ions, and ATP is also necessary, perhaps to 'prime' citrulline by phosphorylating its enolic hydroxyl group. An intermediate reaction complex is formed and has been isolated in crude form (see p. 323).

TRANSAMIDINATION

Enzymes exist that can catalyse the transference of the amidine group of arginine to other substances, e.g.

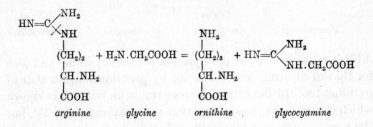

arginine   glycine   ornithine   glycocyamine

Little is known at present about the enzymes involved or about the mechanisms of transfer.

TRANSCARBAMATION

The early stages of urea synthesis (see p. 322) include a transfer reaction which appears at present to be of a unique kind. Glutamic acid is believed to react with carbon dioxide and ammonia, probably by two successive reactions, to yield carbamylglutamic acid. The carbamyl radical is then transferred to ornithine to yield citrulline. Glutamic acid is regenerated at the same time and ATP is required at one or more stages in the process.

TRANSMETHYLATION

Biological methylation is now a well-known process. It has been known for many years that the administration of pyridine to dogs is followed by the excretion of *N*-methyl pyridine in the urine. Similarly, it has been known for some time that glycocyamine undergoes biological conversion into creatine, and this change, too, involves methylation. The methyl groups are furnished by the amino-acid methionine, which is thereby converted into homocysteine. The following example of transmethylation makes this clear.

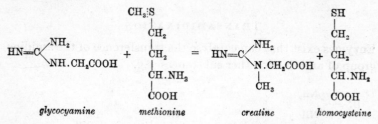

glycocyamine   methionine   creatine   homocysteine

ATP is required for the methylation of glycocyamine and also for that of nicotinic amide and so, by presumption, for that of pyridine too. In the case of glycocyamine an enzyme is known which catalyses its phosphorylation at the expense of ATP, but the position assumed by the phosphate radical does not appear to have been established.

Other important transmethylation reactions reconvert homocysteine to methionine, and these two compounds appear to act as an obligatory transport system in biological methylation. Homocysteine can accept methyl groups from choline, glycine betaine and probably from other donators, and ATP is not required in these cases.

TRANSTHIOLATION

In the foregoing transfer reactions the group being transferred is most usually exchanged for a hydrogen atom. The possibility that groups or radicals other than hydrogen may be exchanged is indicated in 'transimination' and again by the transference of the —SH of homocysteine for the —OH of serine, which takes place under the influence of cystathionase, an enzyme present in rat liver (see p. 285).

TRANSACETYLATION

Acetylation is a not uncommon biological process. It is employed in the detoxication of many foreign substances such, for example, as the sulphonamides. It also plays a part in the formation of mercapturic acids (p. 287) and is important too in the elaboration of acetyl choline from choline. Cell-free extracts of liver contain an enzyme or enzymes which will bring about acetylation in the presence of free acetic acid, coenzyme A (Co A) and ATP. ATP is required to provide free energy, since acetylation is an endergonic process. The acetylating agent is believed to be acetyl-coenzyme A, which can replace free acetate plus ATP plus coenzyme A itself and is probably formed by preliminary reactions between ATP, the coenzyme and free acetate:

$$\text{(i)} \quad \text{CoA} + \text{ATP} \longrightarrow \text{CoA} \sim \textcircled{P} + \text{ADP},$$

$$\text{(ii)} \quad \text{CoA} \sim \textcircled{P} + \text{HOOC.CH}_3 \longrightarrow \text{CoA} \sim \text{OC.CH}_3 + \text{HO.} \textcircled{P}.$$

The acetyl radical can now be transferred to choline, for example, yielding acetyl choline:

$$\overset{+}{(CH_3)_3N}.CH_2CH_2OH + CH_3CO \sim CoA \longrightarrow \overset{+}{(CH_3)_3N}.CH_2CH_2O.OC.CH_3 + CoA.$$

choline   *acetylcholine*

Interestingly enough the 'active' acetyl radical of acetyl-coenzyme A can also react through its methyl group, e.g. with enol-oxaloacetate to form citrate:

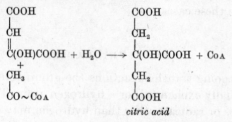

There is reason to think that coenzyme A and the trans-acetylating enzymes with which it co-operates play a part of fundamental importance in the metabolism of fatty acids.

ISOMERIZING ENZYMES

There remains to be considered a group of enzymes which catalyse isomerization in their substrates. There appear to be at least two types, the first, the members of which catalyse simple isomerization, being known as *isomerases*.

Phosphotriose isomerase is the longest known of the group, and was formerly known simply as 'isomerase'. It catalyses the interconversion of 3-phosphoglyceraldehyde and phosphodihydroxyacetone:

$$
\begin{array}{ccc}
CH_2O\textcircled{P} & & CH_2O\textcircled{P} \\
| & & | \\
CHOH & \rightleftharpoons & CO \\
| & & | \\
CHO & & CH_2OH
\end{array}
$$

It is usually found in association with aldolase, from which it has been separated and highly purified. Its mode of action is unknown, but conceivably the interconversion takes place by way of the hypothetical di-enol which is common to both substances:

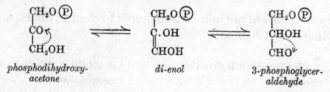

phosphodihydroxy-   di-enol   3-phosphoglycer-
     acetone   aldehyde

Aconitase, which we have already considered (p. 111), acts by converting citric and *iso*-citric acids into a common intermediate, *cis*-aconitic acid, and it is possible that the isomerases in general act by converting the pairs of isomeric substances upon which they act into intermediate compounds which are common to both members of each pair.

Oxoisomerase catalyses the interconversion of glucose- and fructofuranose-6-monophosphates:

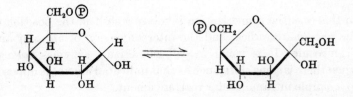

This reaction involves the conversion of an aldose to the corresponding ketose sugar without changing the position of the phosphate radical. A *phosphoriboseisomerase*, more recently discovered, catalyses a similar reaction, viz. the interconversion of ribo-aldose-5-phosphate and riboketose-5-phosphate:

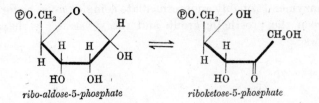

ribo-aldose-5-phosphate riboketose-5-phosphate

A *phosphomannose isomerase* has recently been described. In the presence of oxoisomerase, from which it has not so far been separated, it converts mannose-6-phosphate into an equilibrium mixture of glucose-6- and fructose-6-phosphates, but it is not at present known which of these is formed as first product.

Phosphoglucomutase, which is found in association with oxoisomerase, is a representiative of another type of isomerizing enzymes, for it catalyses the interconversion of α-glucose-1-phosphate and glucose-6-monophosphate:

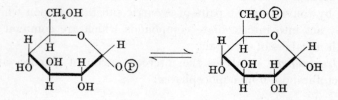

In this case the isomerization involves a shift in the position of the phosphate radical and the interconversion of an ester and a glucoside. It is usual to call isomerizing enzymes *mutases* when there is some shift, such as that indicated above, as opposed to a simple intramolecular rearrangement.

It has been shown that this enzyme possesses a prosthetic group consisting of glucose-1:6-diphosphate. It appears that each molecule of the monophosphorylated substrate can take over a second phosphate radical from the diphosphorylated prosthetic group, which thus becomes the product of the reaction, the former substrate molecule becoming the new prosthetic group. There is thus a continuous stream of traffic across the active groups of the enzyme. Probably an intermediate complex must be formed between the prosthetic group and the substrate, perhaps as follows:

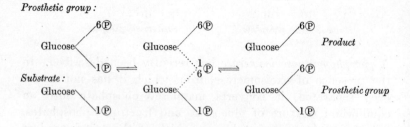

Phosphoribomutase similarly catalyses the interconversion of ribose-1- and ribose-5-phosphates and may well act in an essentially similar manner.

Phosphoglyceromutase is another enzyme of the phosphomutase type. It catalyses the interconversion of 3-phosphoglyceric acid and the corresponding 2-phospho-derivative:

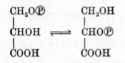

Here again a prosthetic group is present and consists of 2:3-diphosphoglyceric acid. Its mode of action probably resembles that of phosphoglucomutase and can be represented in similar terms.

Other isomerizing enzymes undoubtedly exist. One such is present in yeast and is of rather special interest since it catalyses the interconversion of galactose-1-phosphate and glucose-1-phosphate, a change which involves a Walden inversion at carbon 4. This enzyme requires a coenzyme which is present in yeast and also in mammalian liver. The coenzyme has recently been isolated and shown to contain uridine (uracil nucleoside), glucose and two phosphate radicals but its mode of action is still unknown at the present time.

It is difficult to know how these isomerases and mutases can best be classified. Certainly some of them make use of transfer processes in the course of the reactions they catalyse. It has therefore seemed best to consider them here as a specialized if decidedly aberrant sub-group of transferring enzymes for it is difficult to trace any closer connexion between them and the hydrolysing and adding enzymes which compose the great group of 'splitting enzymes'.

Next in order we shall deal with oxidizing and reducing enzymes. These are typical transferring enzymes which deal in hydrogen atoms or electrons; they are so numerous and so closely related in function that they deserve separate chapters to themselves.

CHAPTER VI

OXIDIZING ENZYMES

THE OXIDATION OF ORGANIC COMPOUNDS

CHEMICAL compounds may be oxidized in a number of different ways. Oxygen may be added to the molecule, as when hydrogen is oxidized to form water, or hydrogen may be removed, as when hydrogen sulphide is oxidized to free, elemental sulphur. Again, oxidation can be effected by the removal of electrons, as when ferrous salts containing Fe^{++} are oxidized to the corresponding ferric compounds, in which Fe^{+++} is present. Among organic compounds, however, oxidation most commonly takes place by the removal of hydrogen, i.e. by the process known as *dehydrogenation*. This conclusion was first reached as the result of an extensive series of studies by Wieland, who drew attention to the fact that if colloidal palladium is added to aqueous solutions of many organic compounds, catalytic oxidation ensues, the palladium becoming charged with hydrogen in the process. In the case of lactic acid, for example, the reaction proceeds in the following manner:

$$CH_3CH(OH)COOH + (Pd) = CH_3COCOOH + (Pd).2H.$$

Aldehydes also can be oxidized in this manner, but in this case a molecule of water is involved:

$$CH_3CHO + H_2O + (Pd) = CH_3COOH + (Pd).2H.$$

The oxidation of aldehydes is a matter of great biochemical importance, as we shall see, and it might have been anticipated that their oxidation would proceed by the addition of oxygen directly to the aldehyde molecule as follows:

$$2R.CHO + O_2 = 2R.COOH.$$

Wieland tested this possibility by treating chloral dissolved in dry benzene with dry silver oxide, and found that no oxidation takes place. If, however, chloral hydrate was substituted for chloral itself, it was oxidized according to the following equation:

$$CCl_3CH(OH)_2 + Ag_2O = CCl_3COOH + 2Ag + H_2O.$$

Evidently, therefore, the water molecule plays an integral part in the process, and it is now generally believed that, in aqueous solution, an aldehydic radical can become associated with a molecule of water, though it is only rarely, as in the cases of chloral and glyoxylic acid, that the aldehydic hydrate is sufficiently stable to be isolated. The following general equations can therefore be written to describe the oxidation of aldehydes:

$$\text{(i)} \quad R.CHO + H_2O = R.CH \begin{smallmatrix} OH \\ \\ OH \end{smallmatrix} \; ;$$

$$\text{(ii)} \quad R.CH \begin{smallmatrix} OH \\ \\ OH \end{smallmatrix} - 2H = R.C \begin{smallmatrix} OH \\ \\ O \end{smallmatrix} \;.$$

It must be remembered that whenever one substance is oxidized at the expense of another, the oxidation of the first is necessarily attended by the reduction of the second. Hence it is usual to speak of an 'oxidation-reduction reaction', sometimes abbreviated 'O/R reaction'. If the process is a biological one it can usually be represented in general terms by the equation:

$$A.H_2 + B \rightleftharpoons A + B.H_2,$$

and we can define a number of terms which are in general use in discussions of reactions of this kind. The reductant, AH_2, is known as the *hydrogen donator*, and the oxidant, B, as the *hydrogen acceptor*. A third factor is involved in biological oxidation-reduction reactions, viz. the *catalyst*. In Wieland's experiments colloidal palladium played the part of a combined catalyst and hydrogen acceptor.

Wieland also found that specimens of palladium that had become 'charged' with hydrogen in the manner just described can pass on their hydrogen to certain reducible substances such as the synthetic dye, methylene blue. In the case of methylene blue itself, reduction yields a colourless substance, leuco-methylene blue, which we may write for the sake of convenience as MB.2H. Thus, in the presence of an oxidizable substance, AH_2, together with methylene blue, palladium black catalyses two processes, first the dehydrogenation of AH_2 (reaction a), and secondly the reduction of methylene blue (reaction b):

(a) $AH_2 + (Pd) = A + (Pd).2H,$

(b) $(Pd).2H + MB = (Pd) + MB.2H.$

Hydrogen taken up from the primary hydrogen donator, AH_2, is passed on to the dye, the catalyst acting as an *intermediary carrier of hydrogen*. This significant fact becomes more apparent if we write the equations in the following unorthodox but very descriptive fashion:

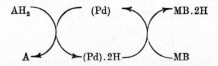

By using this method of expression we can emphasize the essentially *cyclical* manner in which the carrier catalyst acts, a small amount being alternately hydrogenated and dehydrogenated over and over again, and thus participating in a very large amount of chemical change. Alternatively, if we only knew that palladium acts catalytically, but did not know how it does so, we might write the overall process as follows:

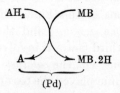

The bracket is used here to indicate that (Pd) acts as the catalyst, and the scheme should be interpreted as meaning that AH_2 and methylene blue react together under the catalytic influence of (Pd) with production of A and leuco-methylene blue.

Now living cells and extracts prepared from them by suitable methods are able to oxidize many organic compounds such, for example, as glucose, lactate and succinate. These compounds are quite stable in aqueous solution, and it follows, therefore, that the cells contain enzymes which catalyse their oxidation. The nature and distribution of these enzymes, to which the name of *dehydrogenases* has been given, were studied extensively by Thunberg, who took advantage of the extreme ease with which

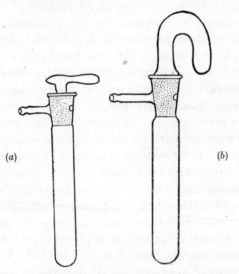

(a)   (b)

Fig. 14. Thunberg vacuum tubes. (a) Original type, (b) newer type, with hollow stopper. (Drawings by H. Mowl.)

methylene blue can be reduced. If methylene blue is added to a suspension of chopped muscle, brain, kidney, etc., or to a suspension of yeast or bacteria, the dye is rapidly reduced, thus revealing the presence in the cells of reducing systems. If such an experiment is tried in the laboratory it is usually found that the dye is decolorized in the bulk of the mixture but not at the surface. This is because leuco-methylene blue is rapidly and spontaneously re-oxidized by atmospheric oxygen. To obviate this difficulty Thunberg introduced the use of vacuum tubes of the type illustrated in Fig. 14, in which is also shown a modern version in which the simple stopper is replaced by a curved, hollow device. Reagents can be put into the hollow stoppers of these tubes and tipped into the rest of the reaction mixture at any desired moment. Suitable tissue preparations are placed in these tubes, together with buffer, methylene blue and other appropriate reagents, the stoppers are greased and inserted, and the tubes are then evacuated at the pump. When exhaustion has been completed the stopper is turned and the tube is thus sealed. Alternatively, the tubes may be filled with an inert gas, such as hydrogen or nitrogen. In the presence of an active reducing system the methylene blue is reduced, and its reduction is, in effect, an indication of the presence of such a system. This method has been used extensively for studies of tissue respiration. It is quick, very convenient, and has the additional advantage of giving quantitative results, since the time taken to decolorize a given quantity of methylene blue under standard conditions of temperature, pH and so on gives an inverse measure of the activity of the systems concerned. Other dyes such as cresyl blue, pyocyanine, and simpler organic substances such as m-dinitrobenzene and o-quinone can replace methylene blue.

With the aid of this simple but ingenious technique, Thunberg carried out many important investigations on living tissues. If a sample of minced muscle tissue is placed together with buffer and methylene blue in a vacuum tube, and the latter evacuated, the dye is reduced very rapidly. If now the experiment is repeated using boiled muscle the dye is no longer reduced, indicating that the catalysts concerned are thermolabile and therefore probably enzymes. If a third experiment is performed in which unboiled and unwashed muscle tissue is replaced by tissue that has been minced and well washed, the time taken for the reduction of the dye is much increased. Some part of the complete reducing system has therefore been removed by washing. If now substances such as succinate, lactate and the like are added to the mixture of washed tissue, buffer and methylene blue, a rapid reduction of the dye can again be demonstrated. Since these compounds do not reduce methylene blue spontaneously it follows that the tissue must contain agents capable of catalysing their oxidation. Working in this manner Thunberg demonstrated, in cells and tissues of many different kinds, the presence of dehydrogenases catalysing the dehydrogenation of a very wide range of organic materials and, as was later shown by Stephenson, even molecular hydrogen can be oxidized by a bacterial enzyme. Succinate, lactate, malate, α-glycerophosphate, glucose, aldehydes and alcohols are among the many substances that can be activated by tissue dehydrogenases from one or another source. Some dehydrogenases are relatively uncommon and can only be found in certain tissues, and in such cases their individuality cannot be doubted. Again, the same tissue, worked up in different ways, can yield preparations which catalyse the oxidation of some compounds but not that of others, and by systematic work along these lines a great deal has been learned about the specificities of the dehydrogenases.

We know now that there is not one single, master dehydrogenase but a considerable number of different individual dehydrogenases. Some, of which the succinic enzyme is an example, act only upon one substrate, in this case succinic acid; others, such as the aldehyde oxidase (Schardinger enzyme) of milk, catalyse the oxidation of any of a wide range of substrates, in this case aldehydes, aliphatic or aromatic. The dehydrogenases thus show the phenomenon of specificity. They are thermolabile, and their activity is profoundly affected by pH. They are susceptible to the action of many enzyme inhibitors, and often to that of narcotic substances such as the higher alcohols and various substituted ureas. In short, they show all the properties characteristic of enzymes. It was realized fairly early in the history of the dehydrogenases that some members of the group require the co-operation of coenzymes because, after exhaustive washing of the tissues, the reduction time for some substrates is very much increased. It can, however, be shortened again by adding boiled extracts of muscle, in which the necessary coenzymes are present. In other cases, however, the addition of boiled muscle-juice does not restore activity, the reason being that some dehydrogenases are themselves soluble in water and are therefore removed by vigorous washing of the tissue.

It must be emphasized that the use of methylene blue is not in any sense a 'natural' procedure. The dye does not occur in nature, and is used simply as a convenient hydrogen acceptor for the visual demonstration of the existence of natural reducing systems. Methylene blue *replaces* the natural hydrogen acceptors of the tissues, and our next inquiries must be into the nature and identity of these substances.

The first likely natural hydrogen acceptor that comes to mind is, of course, molecular oxygen, since it is at the expense of molecular oxygen that tissue oxidations are ultimately carried out. But if we set up experimental systems in which a given dehydrogenase and its substrate are mixed together in the presence of oxygen instead of methylene blue, we find that of all the known dehydrogenase systems only a few actually take up oxygen. Thus, contrary to all expectation, *molecular oxygen is not the natural hydrogen acceptor for most dehydrogenase systems*, and we must look further. In the meantime, however, we can distinguish between two groups of dehydrogenases: those which can utilize molecular oxygen directly as a hydrogen acceptor and are now called *aerobic dehydrogenases*, and the remainder, which operate through other hydrogen acceptors and are known as *anaerobic dehydrogenases* (see Table 11).

TABLE 11. CLASSIFICATION OF DEHYDROGENATING ENZYMES

		H-acceptors reduced	
		MB	O_2
Dehydrogenases	anaerobic	+	−
	aerobic	+	+
Oxidases	aerobic	−	+

Attention must also be drawn to another important group of oxidizing enzymes. Like the dehydrogenases in general they catalyse the dehydrogenation of their substrates, but, unlike Thunberg's classical dehydrogenases, cannot reduce methylene blue and similar hydrogen acceptors. Instead they use molecular oxygen, and are therefore known as *aerobic oxidases*. It may be doubted whether their inability to reduce synthetic dyes like methylene blue constitutes adequate grounds for regarding them as essentially different from the aerobic dehydrogenases, but there are other differences too. As a matter of convenience they will be considered here along with the aerobic dehydrogenases under the general heading of oxidases.

OXIDASES

The oxidases are distinguished from the other dehydrogenating enzymes by their ability to use molecular oxygen directly as a hydrogen acceptor. The aerobic oxidases are specifically confined to oxygen as a natural acceptor and cannot use other naturally occurring substances, but in the case of the aerobic dehydrogenases, molecular oxygen can be replaced for experimental purposes by methylene blue.

The oxidases may be divided into two groups, the first of which catalyses the reduction of molecular oxygen to water; most aerobic oxidases behave in this way. The second group, comprising most of the anaerobic dehydrogenases, leads to the formation of hydrogen peroxide. These reactions may be generally expressed as follows:

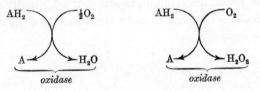

It seems to be characteristic of these enzymes that they are conjugated proteins, although in a few cases no prosthetic group has so far been identified. In general, however, the presence of such a group has been demonstrated and its identity established in a number of cases. Among the known prosthetic materials are copper, iron, and perhaps zinc in aerobic oxidases, and adenineflavin dinucleotide in aerobic dehydrogenases.

Aerobic Oxidases

Phenol Oxidases

The phenol oxidases are a group of enzymes that catalyse the oxidation of phenolic substances. Several representatives of the group have been purified and shown to be copper-containing proteins, thus resembling oxygen-carrying pigments of the haemocyanin type.

Monophenol oxidase, isolated from mushrooms, catalyses the oxidation of mono-phenols to the corresponding *o*-quinones:

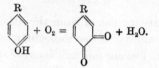

The intimate details of the process are not known. It is perhaps unlikely that an *o*-diphenol is formed as an intermediary product, since this enzyme acts much more strongly upon mono- than upon diphenols. Like other oxidases it uses molecular oxygen as hydrogen acceptor but cannot, however, reduce methylene blue. It is, therefore, an aerobic oxidase rather than an aerobic dehydrogenase.

Polyphenol oxidases have been isolated from mushrooms and potatoes and these too are copper compounds. They have no immediate action upon monophenols, but act rapidly upon *o*-diphenols such as catechol to form the corresponding *o*-quinones in the first instance:

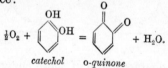

Triphenols such as pyrogallol are also attacked. Another member of this group of phenol oxidases, *laccase*, has been isolated from the latex of the lac tree, and this too is a copper protein but differs somewhat from the others in specificity.

The primary oxidation is followed as a rule by further changes which are spontaneous, but before we consider these further reactions, attention may be drawn to one very important feature of the polyphenol oxidase system. The *o*-quinones formed can be rapidly reduced again by ascorbic acid, and by certain reducing systems such, for example, as hexosemonophosphate dehydrogenase together with its substrate and the appropriate coenzyme (Co II). If we represent the reducing substrate by AH_2 the reactions can be written in the following manner:

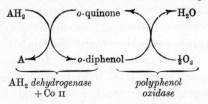

$$\underbrace{\text{AH}_2 \text{ dehydrogenase} + \text{Co II}}_{} \qquad \underbrace{\text{polyphenol oxidase}}_{}$$

In this system a very small amount of the diphenol, e.g. catechol, or the corresponding quinone can be alternately reduced and oxidized many times and thus can act as an intermediate carrier of hydrogen between a theoretically unlimited amount of AH_2 on the one hand and molecular oxygen on the other. Such a system catalyses a continuous uptake of oxygen and a simultaneous oxidation of AH_2 in equivalent amount. The amount of carrier required is very small indeed, and the carrier must, in fact, be regarded as a catalyst in its own right. We have in this system a biological counterpart of the palladium systems studied by Wieland (p. 150), while Thunberg's methylene-blue systems can act in a similar way under aerobic conditions:

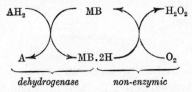

$$\underbrace{\text{dehydrogenase}}_{} \qquad \underbrace{\text{non-enzymic}}_{}$$

Systems of this kind are very interesting because they can be regarded as 'models' of the respiratory systems of living cells. The latter contain reducing substances, represented by AH_2, together with the appropriate dehydrogenases and co-enzymes. These pass on hydrogen to acceptors, the identity of which we have to discuss here, and, at the other end of the chain, molecular oxygen acts as the ultimate hydrogen acceptor and is reduced in the process. Whether systems involving polyphenol oxidase play any important part in the respiration of plant tissues is uncertain, but the possibility has certainly not been excluded. Indeed, the respiration of spinach leaves is greatly increased by dihydroxyphenylalanine. This is a natural diphenolic constituent of the leaves and is susceptible to the action of polyphenol oxidase, which is abundant in these leaves.

Polyphenol oxidase systems are also involved in the 'browning' of potatoes, apples and other plant materials that takes place when a cut surface is exposed to the air. It is usually found that plants containing polyphenol oxidase also contain traces of *o*-diphenols, especially of catechol. Catechol, for example, is oxidized to the corresponding *o*-quinone through the agency of the oxidase (reaction (i)) and the remaining stages take place spontaneously:

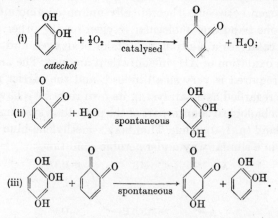

Finally, (iv), the hydroxyquinone undergoes polymerization to yield complex, dark-coloured, melanic products, the constitution of which is still unknown. *o*-Quinone formed in reaction (i) is consumed in reactions (ii) and (iii), so that melanic products can continue to be formed only so long as *o*-quinone is supplied by the action of polyphenol oxidase in reaction (i).

Tyrosinase, another phenol oxidase, occurs widely, in plants and animals alike. It is this enzyme that is responsible for the production of most of the dark brown and black pigmentation of animals. Tyrosine itself is probably the starting material in many cases of melanin formation, but other phenolic compounds too may be used. From certain insects, for example, proto-catechuic (3:4-dihydroxybenzoic) acid has been isolated as a natural substrate; others contained 3:4-dihydroxyphenyl-acetic acid and 3:4-dihydroxyphenyl-lactic acid. In albinism, where there is a characteristic and complete lack of melanins, tyrosinase is absent, while in piebald animals such as rabbits and guinea-pigs the dark portions of the skin contain tyrosinase, but the enzyme is absent from the white parts. In certain insects, on the other hand, melanic pigmentation is determined by localization of the substrate rather than by that of the enzyme. Again, the dark brown or black 'ink' of the squids and octopuses consists of a fine suspension of melanin, which is very insoluble. It is elaborated in a special gland, the ink-sac, the walls of which contain tyrosinase and are at the same time very rich in copper. This was until recently the only indication we had that the tyrosinase of animals is a copper protein, but we now know that mammalian tyrosinase is inhibited by reagents, e.g. cyanide, which form complexes with copper, and is released from this inhibition by Cu^{++} though not by other metallic ions.

The first stage in the formation of melanin from tyrosine probably consists in the oxidation of tyrosine to the quinone of dihydroxyphenylalanine ('dopa quinone'). This is followed by spontaneous ring closure and by the possibly enzymic oxidation of the product to yield a red intermediate compound. Further changes, which are mainly spontaneous and include polymerization, give rise to melanin itself:

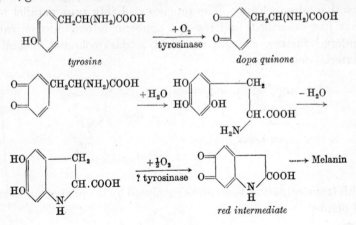

tyrosine   *dopa quinone*

red intermediate

Tyrosinase is involved at perhaps two stages in this reaction sequence, first in the oxidation of tyrosine to dopa quinone, a reaction that can also be catalysed by the monophenol oxidase of plants, and later in the oxidative production of the red compound from the corresponding *o*-diphenol, a process that can be catalysed by plant polyphenol oxidase.

It may be, therefore, that tyrosinase acts both as a mono- and as a polyphenol oxidase. On the other hand, the oxidative formation of the red intermediate from the corresponding diphenol might take place spontaneously at the expense of the reduction of a second molecule of dopa quinone (cf. equation (iii), p. 158), which can be formed from tyrosine by tyrosinase. If so, tyrosinase need only be involved in the capacity of a monophenol oxidase, with the sole function of producing dopa quinone from tyrosine. In this case, however, dopa itself would be formed, and its reoxidation to the quinone would presumably call for polyphenol oxidase activity on the part of tyrosinase. As yet the position has not been satisfactorily cleared up, and we do not know whether tyrosinase is a single enzyme of the monophenol oxidase type, a mixture of a mono- and a polyphenol oxidase, or a single enzyme with the combined activities of phenol oxidases of both types.

Another interesting transformation that can be catalysed by tyrosinase is the conversion of adrenaline into the physiologically inactive adrenochrome. The process probably runs parallel to that just described, and the red pigment, adrenochrome, can undergo further changes to yield a dark-coloured melanic material once more:

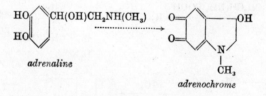

adrenaline → *adrenochrome*

This transformation, too, can be catalysed by the phenol oxidases of plants.

Ascorbic Oxidase. Although ascorbic acid is one of the sub-stances known to be oxidizable through the polyphenol oxidase-catechol system of plants, many plants, notably the *Brassica* family, are rich in an ascorbic oxidase. This enzyme catalyses the oxidation of ascorbic to dehydroascorbic acid:

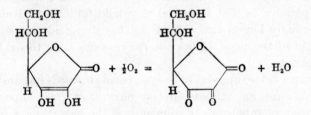

The ascorbic oxidase system can reduce *o*-quinonoid bodies formed by the action of polyphenol oxidase and, so long as any ascorbic acid is present in the plant or other tissue, *o*-quinones do not accumulate and discoloration, due to melanin production from such *o*-quinones (p. 158), is held in check.

The enzyme has been isolated from squash and shown to con-tain copper, and it is interesting to notice that a mixture of egg albumin with traces of copper ions can imitate the action of ascorbic oxidase remarkably closely.

Urico-oxidase (uricase), an enzyme concerned in purine meta-bolism, catalyses the oxidation of uric acid to allantoin. Its action is almost certainly complex, but the overall reaction may be written as follows:

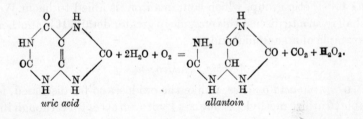

This enzyme occurs in the livers of animals which are not urico-telic, and is present, for instance, in most mammalian livers. To

this, however, there are certain curious exceptions, for man and
the higher apes are devoid of the enzyme and excrete uric acid
unchanged. Uric acid is also largely excreted in the unoxidized
form by the Dalmatian dog, though not by dogs of other breeds.
It is a strange fact that the liver of the Dalmatian dog is nevertheless fairly rich in urico-oxidase; one possible explanation of
this paradox is that the renal threshold for uric acid may be
abnormally low in this animal, so that uric acid escapes very
rapidly in the urine before the enzyme has time to oxidize it
completely.

Urico-oxidase appears to be less specific towards its substrates
than is xanthine oxidase, another enzyme of great importance
in purine metabolism. It will catalyse the oxidation of several
purines other than uric acid, and is competitively inhibited by
certain other purines, notably by methylated derivatives of uric
acid. It may be that the overall reaction includes spontaneous
as well as catalysed processes, as in the case of melanin formation
by tyrosinase. This is an example of an aerobic oxidase that
produces not water but hydrogen peroxide as the product of
reduction of the oxygen used as hydrogen acceptor.

The purest preparations so far obtained contain both iron
and zinc. Enzymes containing one or other of these metals are
known, but no enzyme so far obtained in the pure state has been
found to contain more than one metal, apart, of course, from
urico-oxidase itself.

Cytochrome oxidase, a very important and almost universally
distributed enzyme, is another example of a metalloprotein, and
its prosthetic group, which contains iron, is allied to haem. We
shall return to discuss this enzyme in greater detail. It is another
example of an aerobic oxidase.

Aerobic Dehydrogenases

D-*Amino-acid oxidase*, unlike the oxidases so far discussed, is
able to utilize methylene blue as a hydrogen acceptor although its
natural acceptor is molecular oxygen, which it reduces to
hydrogen peroxide. This enzyme occurs in the liver and kidney
tissue of mammals, and is probably present in many other

animal materials. It is a curious fact that this enzyme acts only upon members of the non-natural D-series of amino-acids and is without action upon the natural L-acids. As far as the D-acids are concerned it is group-specific and attacks them all with a few exceptions, e.g. D-glutamic acid.

D-Amino-acid oxidase catalyses the oxidative deamination of its substrates to the corresponding α-keto-acids. This takes place in two stages, of which the first, consisting in the dehydrogenation of the substrate, is catalysed, while the second, in which the resulting imino-acid is hydrolysed, is probably spontaneous:

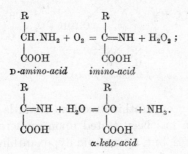

$$
\begin{array}{cc}
\text{R} & \text{R} \\
| & | \\
\text{CH.NH}_2 + \text{O}_2 = & \text{C=NH} + \text{H}_2\text{O}_2 ; \\
| & | \\
\text{COOH} & \text{COOH} \\
\text{D-amino-acid} & \text{imino-acid}
\end{array}
$$

$$
\begin{array}{cc}
\text{R} & \text{R} \\
| & | \\
\text{C=NH} + \text{H}_2\text{O} = & \text{CO} \quad + \text{NH}_3. \\
| & | \\
\text{COOH} & \text{COOH} \\
& \text{α-keto-acid}
\end{array}
$$

As far as is known, D-amino-acids are relatively uncommon in nature, and it may therefore be doubted whether this enzyme has any important biological function. That it exists, however, is certain, and it has in fact been isolated. It is a conjugated protein, the prosthetic group of which is adenineflavin dinucleotide, the mode of action of which is known and will be discussed presently.

Other deaminating oxidases include a specific glycine oxidase and a group-specific L-amino-acid oxidase, both of which appear to be flavoproteins. The powerful L-amino-acid oxidase of viper venom (*Vipera aspis*) also deserves a passing reference.

Xanthine oxidase is present in milk, which offers a relatively rich source from which highly concentrated preparations can fairly easily be obtained. The enzyme is widely though somewhat erratically distributed among animal tissues. It catalyses the oxidation of hypoxanthine to xanthine, and that of xanthine to uric acid: here, as in the oxidation of aldehydes by dehydrogenation, it is probable that intermediate hydrates are formed:

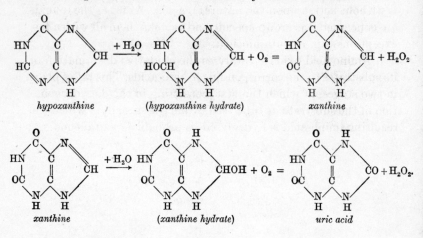

In addition to its action upon the purines, xanthine oxidase has a second sphere of action. It appears to be identical with the Schardinger enzyme of milk, a catalyst which acts upon many aldehydes, oxidizing them to the corresponding acids:

The specificity of xanthine oxidase towards purines is very high. Its action has been tested upon numerous purines and related substances, but, apart from hypoxanthine and xanthine, no naturally occurring purines are attacked at all rapidly. The enzyme does, however, act upon certain synthetic substances such as 6:8-dioxypurine and upon purine itself, while it is strongly and competitively inhibited by adenine.

In addition to its action upon the purines, xanthine oxidase has a second sphere of action. It appears to be identical with the Schardinger enzyme of milk, a catalyst which acts upon many aldehydes, oxidizing them to the corresponding acids:

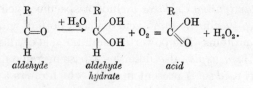

Xanthine oxidase has been highly concentrated and, like those of D-amino-acid oxidase, the purified preparations contain adenineflavin dinucleotide. It is possible, however, that some other prosthetic material is also present, and it is even possible that the supposedly pure preparations are in reality mixtures, since their catalytic action differs somewhat according to the method of preparation.

In addition to catalysing the various oxidations already described, xanthine oxidase can catalyse a process of *dismutation*, i.e. the oxidation of one molecule of the substrate at the expense of the reduction of another, e.g.

$$2 \text{ xanthine} = \text{uric acid} + \text{hypoxanthine.}$$

Dismutation only occurs under anaerobic conditions: in the absence of molecular oxygen, the same enzyme can utilize a second molecule of its substrate as hydrogen acceptor, and a pair of hydrogen atoms is transferred to this molecule from the first. Reactions of this kind play an important part in cellular metabolism under anaerobic conditions and they resemble the well-known Cannizzaro reaction of organic chemistry in certain respects.

Aldehyde oxidase of liver. Mammalian liver contains another aldehyde oxidase and a similar enzyme is present in the potato. These enzymes, like xanthine oxidase, are group-specific towards aldehydic substrates, which they oxidize to the corresponding acids, but, unlike xanthine oxidase, they have no activity towards purines. The prosthetic group appears to be adenineflavin dinucleotide once more.

Notatin, the powerful glucose oxidase of the mould *Penicillium notatum*, has been thoroughly purified in recent years and proves to have adenineflavin dinucleotide as its prosthetic group. The extremely high specificity of this enzyme makes it a valuable analytical tool, for it can be used for the quantitative estimation of D-glucose, even in mixtures containing several sugars. The product of oxidation is D-gluconic acid, which is formed by way of the δ-gluconolactone (p. 195).

Amine oxidase is a group-specific enzyme that occurs at small concentrations in many animal tissues. It acts particularly rapidly upon compounds such as tyramine and adrenaline, and appears to be identical with the tyramine and adrenaline oxidases described some years ago. Its action upon primary amines may be described as follows:

$$\text{(i) } R.CH_2NH_2 + O_2 = R.CH{:}NH + H_2O_2,$$

$$\text{(ii) } R.CH{:}NH + H_2O = R.CHO + NH_3.$$

The mode of oxidation thus resembles that of the amino-acid oxidases somewhat, and it is probable that the second reaction is not catalysed but spontaneous. The enzyme also acts upon secondary and tertiary amines to form either a lower amine or else an aldehyde, together with ammonia.

An interesting point to notice here is that, while this enzyme acts upon many amines, it is inhibited by those which contain a methyl group in the α-position, for instance by ephedrine and benzedrine. Adrenaline is normally destroyed in the tissues by amine oxidase, in part at least, and its disappearance is much retarded by these drugs. Probably, therefore, these compounds owe their adrenaline-like action upon the organism to an indirect action which inhibits the oxidation of adrenaline itself, rather than to a direct action upon the tissues. The structural relationships between these substances are as follows:

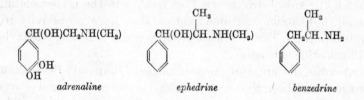

adrenaline   *ephedrine*   *benzedrine*

Diamine oxidase also occurs in animal tissues. It catalyses the oxidation of histamine, putrescine, cadaverine and agmatine, for example, substances which can arise in the gut of animals by bacterial decarboxylation of the corresponding amino-acids. It is probable that both the amine oxidases are important in the oxidative detoxication of the poisonous amines which arise in this manner.

A trimethylamine oxidase has recently been found in fish muscle and probable plays an important part in the formation of trimethylamine oxide. The product is an important substance in the metabolism of certain fishes and occurs in many marine organisms.

The fate of Hydrogen Peroxide

The formation of hydrogen peroxide in the course of the *in vitro* action of certain oxidases may be demonstrated by taking advantage of the fact that cerous hydroxide, a colourless substance only slightly soluble in water, reacts readily with hydrogen peroxide to form an insoluble, yellowish brown ceric peroxide. While there can be no doubt that hydrogen peroxide is indeed formed in isolated enzyme systems, there is little evidence that it is formed, or at any rate that it ever accumulates to any extent, in cells and tissues generally. We must therefore conclude that living cells contain catalysts capable of destroying hydrogen peroxide which, as is well known, is a powerful inhibitor of many enzymes. At least three enzymes are known to participate in its destruction, namely, cytochrome c-peroxidase, peroxidase and catalase.

Cytochrome c-peroxidase has been isolated from yeast and shown to have haematin as a prosthetic group. It is probably responsible for the removal of most of the hydrogen peroxide formed in the cells, but unlike other peroxidases it is strongly specific towards the substrate of oxidation, in this case the reduced form of cytochrome c. This is oxidized to the ferric form, the peroxide being at the same time reduced to water.

Peroxidase occurs in many plants, often in relatively high concentrations. Animal tissues in general appear not to contain enzymes of this kind, though a crystalline peroxidase has been isolated from milk. Horse-radish peroxidase has been shown to be a haematin compound.

Peroxidase forms a spectroscopically recognizable complex with hydrogen peroxide (p. 26), as a result of which the substrate becomes activated and capable of acting as a hydrogen acceptor for the oxidation of other substances. The classical test for peroxidase consists in adding to the suspected enzyme small amounts of hydrogen peroxide, together with guaiacum or benzidine. If peroxidase is present characteristic deep colorations develop owing to the oxidation of the guaiacum or benzidine to yield coloured derivatives. Pyrogallol is similarly oxidized through a series of intermediates to form the orange-coloured purpurogallin, which can be extracted with ether and estimated colorimetrically, a process which has been made the basis of a method for the quantitative estimation of peroxidase activity. The behaviour of the peroxidase-peroxide system can be generally expressed as follows:

$$A\!\!\begin{array}{l} H \\ H \end{array} + \begin{array}{l} O\!-\!H \\ | \\ O\!-\!H \end{array} = A + 2H_2O.$$

It is interesting to notice in passing that most haem and haematin derivatives, including even free haematin, possess weak peroxidase activity.

Catalase occurs both in animals and plants. It has been isolated from mammalian liver and found to be a conjugated protein, the prosthetic group of which can exist in an oxidized or a reduced form, the latter being identical with the haem of haemoglobin. Catalase catalyses the splitting of hydrogen peroxide into water and molecular oxygen and, according to Keilin and Hartree, who have studied this enzyme with great thoroughness, the iron atom of the prosthetic group undergoes alternate oxidation and reduction in the process. Catalase forms spectroscopically recognizable compounds with a number of substances other than hydrogen peroxide, including cyanide, hydrogen sulphide, azide and fluoride, all of which inhibit it. Cyanide and sulphide react with the ferric form of the enzyme while azide prevents reoxidation of the ferrous form.

Catalase appears to be very specific, for it does not act upon organic peroxides such as ethyl peroxide except in very concentrated solutions. Its action upon hydrogen peroxide is very rapid however, and it has been shown that 1 mg. of pure catalase-iron can produce 2740 l. of oxygen per hour from hydrogen peroxide, at 0° C. Expressed in molecular units this corresponds to the decomposition of $4 \cdot 2 \times 10^4$ mol. of hydrogen peroxide per sec. at 0° C. by 1 mol. of catalase. This is the most rapid enzyme-catalysed process at present known.

Although catalase has such a powerful peroxidase-splitting activity its affinity for its substrate is much lower than that of peroxidase ($K_m = 2\cdot5 \times 10^{-2}$ M for catalase; 6×10^{-6} M for peroxidase) so that hydrogen peroxide is unlikely to be split in tissues containing an active peroxidase. Catalase, moreover, has a considerable peroxidase activity of its own and current opinion favours the view that this is probably more important than its catalase action. Splitting of hydrogen peroxide by catalase is only likely to take place if the peroxide is formed more rapidly than it can be consumed by acting as a hydrogen acceptor under the influence of enzymes with peroxidase activity.

Mode of Action of the Oxidases

We saw in an earlier section that in the oxidation of biological substances three factors are involved, viz. the hydrogen donator, the hydrogen acceptor and the catalyst. In a typical oxidase system these are represented by the substrate, molecular oxygen and the oxidase respectively. The system can be analysed a little further, however, for in several cases it has been shown that the prosthetic group participates in the reaction and undergoes alternate oxidation and reduction. As a specific case we may consider the oxidation of a D-amino-acid by D-amino-acid oxidase. In this case the prosthetic group consists of adenineflavin dinucleotide, a substance which shows well-defined absorption in the blue region of the visible spectrum. If a D-amino-acid is added to the oxidase under strictly anaerobic conditions, the spectrum changes in a manner which indicates that the prosthetic group has undergone reduction. If oxygen is then readmitted to the system, the prosthetic group is reoxidized.

Now it is known that adenineflavin dinucleotide can be reduced by fairly powerful reducing agents, even when it is in the free condition and apart from its specific protein partner. It is not, however, reduced by amino-acids unless and until they have been activated by the oxidase. It is therefore reasonable to suppose that the oxidase protein acts as a catalyst which facilitates the transference of hydrogen from the (activated) amino-acid to the dinucleotide. Possibly, however, the protein plays no part in the second stage of the process, in which the reduced dinucleotide is reoxidized by molecular oxygen, for uncombined adenineflavin dinucleotide is spontaneously oxidized by oxygen. Tentatively, then, we may picture the action of this oxidase as a two-stage process, the protein component acting as a catalyst for the first stage, while the prosthetic group (AFDN) functions as a built-in hydrogen acceptor, thus:

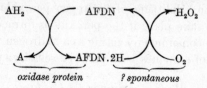

The first stage is a typical transfer reaction of the kind in which the group donator and the group acceptor are simultaneously accommodated on the enzyme protein (cf. p. 119).

Similar considerations probably apply to other aerobic dehydrogenases in which AFDN is present, while in the case of the phenol oxidases of plants there is evidence that the copper of the prosthetic group undergoes alternate oxidation and reduction as the enzyme discharges its catalytic function. How far this analysis can be extended to oxidases in general remains to be seen, but it seems reasonable at the present time to suspect that it will prove to be of fairly general applicability.

In conclusion, attention may be drawn to the evident resemblances between these oxidase systems and the other carrier systems we have encountered, especially the polyphenol oxidase-catechol system (p. 157), the artificial methylene-blue systems studied by Thunberg (p. 157) and the palladium systems of Wieland (p. 150).

WARBURG'S RESPIRATORY ENZYME AND THE CYTOCHROME SYSTEM

Wieland's theory of dehydrogenation and the discovery by Thunberg of the dehydrogenases laid great stress on the importance of the activation of the substrates which undergo oxidation in cells and tissues. Relatively few dehydrogenating enzymes are able to use molecular oxygen, however, and consideration must be given to the possibility that oxygen too may be activated and thus rendered capable of acting as a hydrogen acceptor in systems that are unable to utilize molecular oxygen directly.

In a series of brilliant studies beginning in 1918, Warburg found evidence for the presence, in aerobic cells of every kind, of a catalyst, the function of which was, he believed, the activation of oxygen. His attention was drawn by the fact that iron compounds are capable of catalysing the oxidation of many different organic substances. Blood charcoal, i.e. charcoal prepared by heating blood, catalyses the oxidation of organic substances such as the amino-acids with a simultaneous uptake of oxygen. Pure charcoal made by heating sucrose does not possess this property, and Warburg attributed the catalytic action of blood charcoal to the iron it contains. Even in inorganic form, iron possesses considerable catalytic powers, but Warburg came early to the conclusion that in organic combination with nitrogenous substances its catalytic powers can be very great indeed.

The behaviour of blood-charcoal systems resembles that of living cells to a surprising degree. The oxygen uptake of these charcoal 'models' is powerfully inhibited by a number of substances known to combine with heavy metals and to inhibit cellular respiration. Thus cyanide at concentrations of the order of M/1000 suffices to stop 80–90 % of the total respiration of many cells, and cyanide at similar concentrations also inhibits charcoal systems very powerfully indeed. Hydrogen sulphide acts similarly. Narcotic drugs, such as urethane and the higher alcohols, also inhibit cellular respiration, but do so only at comparatively high concentrations, and they act in the same general manner upon charcoal systems as well. Warburg was led therefore to postulate the existence of a universal, iron-containing and oxygen-activating catalyst concerned in cellular respiration, to which he gave the name of *Atmungsferment*, or respiratory enzyme. It is not necessary here to go into Warburg's work in great detail, but some at least of his evidence is of fundamental importance.

Careful attention was given to certain processes of autoxidation, notably in the case of cysteine. Cysteine undergoes slow autoxidation to cystine on exposure to the air, and the process is known to be catalysed by traces of iron-containing impurities. Cyanide stops this autoxidation, presumably by forming a non-catalytic complex with the iron. The fact that molecular oxygen no longer oxidizes cysteine in the absence of iron lent valuable support to Warburg's contention that it is an essential function of iron compounds to catalyse oxidative processes by activating molecular oxygen.

Most striking of all were the results of certain experiments on the inhibitory effects of carbon monoxide. Warburg found that the respiration of living cells is inhibited by carbon monoxide in the dark, but that the inhibition disappears in the light. Carbon monoxide is known to form complexes with heavy metals, including iron and copper for example, and it is characteristic of the iron complexes that they are photolabile, i.e. are dissociated by light. The copper complexes, by contrast, are not influenced by light. Here, therefore, was further evidence that the respiratory enzyme must contain iron.

Now the effectiveness of light in reversing the inhibition produced by carbon monoxide depends upon the wave-length of the light. In order to be effective, light must be absorbed. Consequently, by plotting the effectiveness of light against its wave-length, it is possible to determine the absorption spectrum of the respiratory enzyme. The resulting curve is reproduced in Fig. 15. It shows a sharp band at 4360 A., and its general pattern resembles that of the haemochromogens (cf. Fig. 16). Further work enabled Warburg to determine the absolute absorption coefficient of the respiratory enzyme, and this again was in general agreement with values obtained for haemochromogens. Thus, without having ever seen his enzyme, Warburg was able to deduce not merely that it contains iron, but that it must be a haemochromogen-like material. A great mass of other work gave general support to his conclusions and indicated that the haematin of the *Atmungsferment* is particularly closely allied to that present in chlorocruorin (a green respiratory pigment found in the blood of a small group of annelid worms) rather than to the haematin derived from the much more widely distributed haemoglobin.

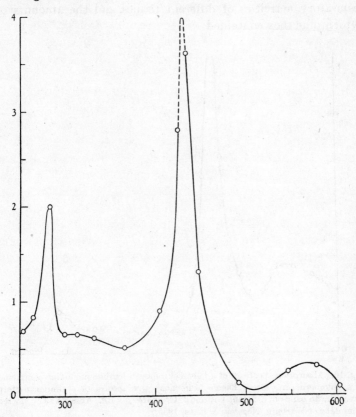

Fig. 15. Absorption spectrum of the carbon monoxide compound of the *Atmungsferment*. Ordinate: $\beta \times 10^8$. Abscissa: λ. (Plotted from data of Warburg & Negelein, 1929.)

In the meantime Keilin rediscovered the presence, in aerobic cells of many different kinds, of a pigment which had been described by MacMunn towards the end of the last century. MacMunn had called his pigment histohaematin or myohaematin, but it was soon forgotten. Keilin rechristened it *cytochrome*. Cytochrome, he found, was present in every kind of aerobic cell he examined, even in facultative anaerobic bacteria: indeed, the only cells in which none could be detected were strictly anaerobic bacteria. There was, moreover, a general parallel between the respiratory activities of different tissues and the amounts of cytochrome they contained.

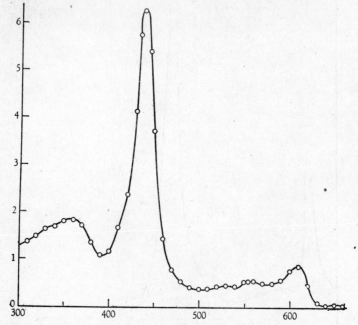

Fig. 16. Absorption spectrum of a haemochromogen (carbon monoxide compound of a chlorocruorin). Other haemochromogens give spectra of a similar pattern but with the bands in different positions. Ordinate: $\beta \times 10^8$. Abscissa: λ. (Plotted from data of Warburg, Negelein & Haas, 1930.)

Cytochrome is clearly recognizable by the well-defined absorption spectrum which it exhibits when in the reduced form. In the oxidized form the spectrum disappears. Slight differences were noticed in the positions of the absorption bands in different tissues, but, on the whole, these differences are not greater than would be expected if the cytochromes, like the haemoglobins, are species-specific. Fig. 17 shows the absorption spectrum of reduced cytochrome as seen in the thoracic muscles of a bee, while Fig. 18 shows the positions of the four absorption bands of the reduced cytochromes of a number of different materials. That one or other of these bands is occasionally found to be absent, and that they vary somewhat in relative intensity

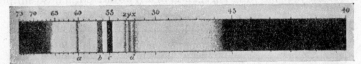

Fig. 17. Absorption spectrum of reduced cytochrome in the thoracic muscles of a bee. (After Keilin, 1925.)

and in the rates at which they fade when oxygen is admitted to the system, shows that cytochrome is not a single substance but a mixture of at least three components, each being a haemochromogen-like compound with a typical two-banded spectrum. Fig. 19 shows how the spectrum of a typical cytochrome could be built up by the superimposition of the spectra of three compounds of this type.

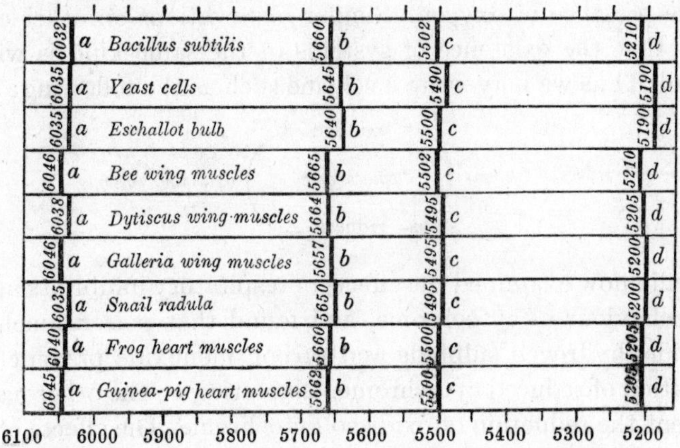

	a	Tissue		b		c		d
6032	a	Bacillus subtilis	5660	b	5502	c	5210	d
6035 6035	a	Yeast cells	5645	b	5490	c	5190 5190	d
6035	a	Eschallot bulb	5640	b	5500	c	5190	d
6046	a	Bee wing muscles	5665	b	5502	c	5210	d
6038	a	Dytiscus wing-muscles	5664	b	5495	c	5205	d
6046	a	Galleria wing muscles	5657	b	5495	c	5200	d
6035	a	Snail radula	5650	b	5495	c	5200	d
6040 6045	a	Frog heart muscles	5660	b	5500	c	5205 5205	d
6045	a	Guinea-pig heart muscles	5662	b	5500	c	5205	d

6100 6000 5900 5800 5700 5600 5500 5400 5300 5200

Fig. 18. Absorption bands of cytochromes of various tissues. (After Keilin, 1933.)

A particularly attractive feature of much of Keilin's work is that it was possible to observe the behaviour of cytochrome within living cells when the latter were subjected to a variety of experimental conditions. Certain of these experiments were of fundamental importance. For example, a suspension of bakers' yeast shows no spectrum of cytochrome so long as oxygen is bubbled through it. If the stream of oxygen is replaced by nitrogen the spectrum of reduced cytochrome makes its appearance, and persists until oxygen is again admitted. These simple

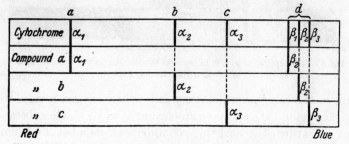

	a	b	c	d		
Cytochrome	α_1	α_2	α_3	β_1	β_2	β_3
Compound a	α_1			β_2		
” b		α_2		β_2		
” c			α_3			β_3

Red   Blue

Fig. 19. Absorption bands of the components of a typical cytochrome.
(After Keilin, 1933.)

observations alone show that the cells contain systems which can reduce oxidized cytochrome and others which can reoxidize it in the presence of oxygen. Similar observations on other cells show that the existence of systems of the same kind is widespread. Thus we may write a scheme such as the following:

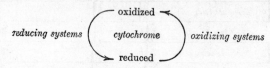

Keilin now examined the effects of respiratory inhibitors upon the behaviour of cytochrome, and found that poisons such as cyanide, hydrogen sulphide and carbon monoxide prevent the oxidation of reduced cytochrome. Narcotics, on the other hand, prevent the reduction of oxidized cytochrome. The effects of all these inhibitors can readily be studied in suspensions of yeast with apparatus no more complicated than a test-tube, a powerful lamp and a suitable spectroscope. The results just outlined indicate the presence in the cells of systems which oxidize reduced cytochrome and are inhibited by cyanide, carbon monoxide, etc., and of reducing systems that are inhibited by narcotics.

A few years later Keilin succeeded in isolating the *c* component of cytochrome from bakers' yeast. The pigment is readily reduced by mild reducing agents, but, once reduced, cannot be reoxidized merely by shaking with oxygen. Yet it is reoxidized readily enough when oxygen is admitted to a cell suspension. This argues for the presence in the cells of an enzyme which may be called *cytochrome oxidase*. The cytochrome oxidase of living cells is insoluble and cannot be separated from the cell debris except with difficulty and by special techniques, but can be studied in the form of thoroughly washed tissue suspensions. It proves to be powerfully inhibited by cyanide, by hydrogen sulphide and by carbon monoxide. Further, as Keilin himself showed, oxidized cytochrome can be reduced by the dehydrogenase systems of Thunberg, e.g. by succinic dehydrogenase together with succinic acid. These dehydrogenase systems are known to be inhibited in many cases by narcotics, and are evidently responsible for the intracellular reduction of cytochrome, the systems for which, as Keilin had shown, are sensitive to the same narcotics. We may therefore summarize the position in the following manner, using heavy arrows to indicate the reactions with which the various inhibitory substances interfere:

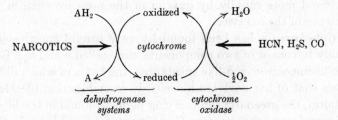

It would thus seem that we have in cytochrome the natural hydrogen acceptor of the dehydrogenase systems. Clearly, therefore, it is necessary to know something about its various components. Most is known about cytochrome *c*, which is the only soluble member of the group, the others remaining closely attached to the tissue debris, especially to the mitochondria. Methods have recently been devised for detaching the insoluble components, but we do not yet possess a great deal of information about them. The only method hitherto available for their study consisted of the spectroscopic observation of their behaviour in very finely divided and exhaustively washed tissue suspensions. Heart muscle provides a relatively rich source of these materials.

Cytochrome c has been found to consist of a protein carrying an iron-containing prosthetic group. The latter is closely allied to, but not identical with, the haem of haemoglobin, and is attached more firmly and in a different manner to its protein partner. This component is readily reduced by fairly mild reducing agents, including biological materials such as cysteine, and by relatively crude dehydrogenase preparations in the presence of their substrates. For its oxidation cytochrome oxidase is required, and the process is inhibited by respiratory inhibitors of the cyanide group but not by narcotics.

Cytochrome b, like *c*, is a conjugated protein of which the prosthetic group, so far as we know, is identical with that of haemoglobin. It, too, is reducible by dehydrogenase systems, but differs from *c* in that it is slowly autoxidizable, i.e. it can be oxidized by molecular oxygen without the intervention of the oxidase. Its oxidation is therefore not totally abolished by cyanide, but there is a marked inhibition nevertheless, since *b* is oxidized more rapidly by oxygen in the presence than in the absence of the oxidase.

Cytochrome a has been found by very careful spectroscopic study to consist of two components, now called *a* and a_3. Both are haemochromogen-like substances, the haem of which differs from that of haemoglobin but closely resembles that of chlorocruorin, the green oxygen-carrying pigment found in the bloods of certain annelid worms. Component *a* resembles *c* in that it is not autoxidizable and can only be oxidized through the agency of cytochrome oxidase, while a_3, which is autoxidizable, differs from all the rest in forming a compound with carbon monoxide, as does haemoglobin. It is considered by many workers to be identical with cytochrome oxidase.

Occasionally *other cytochrome components* are found. In many bacteria, for example, we find new components which differ from those of animal tissues and have been called a_1 and a_2. They are uniquely confined to bacteria. Special cytochromes characteristic of plants have also been described and, in all, more than a dozen different components have now been recognized. Of particular interest is the recent discovery by Bach and Dixon that yeast contains a cytochrome, the spectrum of which resembles that of b but is not identical with it. In the intact cell the spectrum of this substance, to which the title of b_2 has been given, is not observable because it is too dilute, but the pigment has been separated, highly concentrated, and shown to form a part of the lactic dehydrogenase system of yeast. It is improbable that all the naturally occurring components of the cytochrome complex have yet been discovered, especially because some, such as b_2, are known to occur at concentrations too small to allow of their direct spectroscopic observation.

The mechanism of the oxidation and reduction of the cytochromes is not certainly known. Reduction presumably involves the gain of one electron or the loss of one proton because the only observable difference between the oxidized and reduced forms of c lies in the valency of the iron atom, which passes with reduction from the ferric to the ferrous condition, a change which is analogous to that which takes place when methaemoglobin is reduced to haemoglobin:

$$-Fe^{+++} + e \rightarrow -Fe^{++}$$

or $\qquad -Fe^{+++} + H \rightarrow -Fe^{++} + H^+.$

Identity of Cytochrome Oxidase

Oxidized cytochrome is readily reduced by many mild reducing agents such as cysteine, p-phenylene diamine, hydroquinone and the like. Keilin studied the behaviour of cytochrome oxidase in reconstructed systems in which the natural reducing systems of the cell were replaced by cysteine, while cytochrome was represented by its c component. The oxidase preparation employed consisted of a finely divided and exhaustively washed suspension of heart muscle.

It had already been known for many years that most living cells and tissues contain an enzyme which catalyses the oxidative coupling of a mixture of α-naphthol with dimethyl-p-phenylene diamine, the so-called 'Nadi' reagent, to yield indophenol blue. This enzyme, the natural substrate of which was then unknown, was called *indophenol oxidase*. Keilin found that preparations of indophenol oxidase will catalyse the oxidation of reduced cytochrome *c*, and that preparations of cytochrome oxidase will catalyse the oxidation of 'Nadi'. Furthermore, both enzymes are similarly distributed in living organisms, both are closely bound to the tissue substance, and both are insoluble. Both are powerfully inhibited by cyanide and by hydrogen sulphide, while both are also inhibited by carbon monoxide in the dark but not in the light. Keilin therefore concluded that indophenol oxidase and cytochrome oxidase are one and the same enzyme.

The reader will have noticed that the properties of cytochrome oxidase are also identical with those of Warburg's respiratory enzyme, even in the effect of light upon the inhibition produced by carbon monoxide. The resemblances go even further, for both are apparently universally distributed in living cells, and both, while exceedingly sensitive to cyanide and the like, are relatively insensitive to narcotics. Keilin therefore suggested that Warburg's respiratory enzyme and cytochrome oxidase must be identical.

A more recent contribution comes from Melnick, who determined the photochemical absorption spectrum of the carbon monoxide compound of cytochrome oxidase and obtained the results shown in Fig. 20. The general form of the curve closely resembles that obtained by Warburg in his classical work on the respiratory enzyme (Fig. 15), and the main peak occurs at a similar point in both cases. Warburg's experiments were performed on yeast and on acetic acid bacteria, while Melnick used heart muscle. The fact that there are distinct differences between the two may reasonably be attributed to species-specific differences between the different materials (cf. Fig. 18), and it seems difficult to escape the conclusion that cytochrome oxidase and the respiratory enzyme are truly one and the same catalyst. Even if, as some believe, the systems studied by Warburg on the one hand, and by Keilin and later by Melnick on the other, are not absolutely identical, it is still true that Melnick's results demonstrate that the cytochrome oxidase activity of heart

muscle is associated with a haemochromogen-like, and therefore
iron-containing catalyst, just as did Warburg's work in the case
of the respiratory enzyme of yeast and of acetic acid bacteria.
Both, moreover, are spectroscopically related to the haematin
derivable from chlorocruorin. Probably, therefore, we are justified in concluding, with Keilin, that the respiratory enzyme
is none other than cytochrome oxidase, provided that we allow
for the possibility of species-specific differences between the
protein components in different organisms.

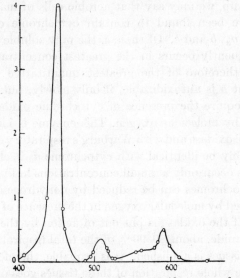

Fig. 20. Absorption spectrum of the carbon monoxide compound of cytochrome
oxidase (heart). Ordinate: $\beta_\lambda/\beta_{436}$. Abscissa: λ. (Plotted from data of Melnick, 1942.)

That cytochrome oxidase appears to be a haemochromogen-
like compound suggests that it might actually correspond to one
of the numerous known components of cytochrome itself, and
this does in fact seem possible. Keilin and Hartree have shown
that there is a close correspondence between the properties of
cytochrome a_3 and cytochrome oxidase. Each forms a compound
with carbon monoxide, and the absorption curve of the CO-cyto-
chrome a_3 complex shows maxima at 5900 and 4300 A. The
carbon monoxide compound of the respiratory enzyme of yeast

shows almost identical maxima. Nevertheless, the identity of cytochrome oxidase with the a_3 component of cytochrome cannot yet be accepted as proven, if only because the carbon monoxide complex of a_3 seems to be stable in the presence of light, and because some cells appear to contain neither a nor a_3, though this may merely be due to their actual presence in concentrations too small to allow direct spectroscopic detection. There is also the serious objection that, if reduced cytochrome c is added to tissue preparations containing oxidized a_3, the two fail to react together.

To sum up, we may say that aerobic cells of many different kinds have been found to contain cytochrome components, usually a, a_3, b and c. Of these c, the only soluble component, not infrequently occurs in the greatest concentration, and is probably therefore of the greatest quantitative importance. Component b is autoxidizable, if only slowly, but a and c by contrast require the presence of cytochrome oxidase for their oxidation by molecular oxygen. This enzyme is identical with indophenol oxidase and with Warburg's respiratory enzyme, and may possibly be identical with cytochrome a_3 itself. All these substances occur only at small concentrations in living cells.

The cytochromes can be reduced by dehydrogenase systems and oxidized by molecular oxygen in the presence of cytochrome oxidase. If the oxidase is put out of action by the addition of $M/1000$ cyanide, about 80–90 % of the total respiration of many cells and tissues is abolished. It is probable, therefore, that the bulk of the whole respiration of these tissues goes on by way of cytochromes a and c. The oxidation of component b is slowed but not stopped by cyanide, and this component may therefore be responsible for a part at least of that fraction of the total respiration that is not abolished by cyanide.

It seems, then, that in the cytochromes we have a group of hydrogen carriers of enormous importance in cellular respiration. On the one hand they are reduced from the ferric to the ferrous condition by reacting with hydrogen (or electrons) drawn from the activated substrates of the dehydrogenases, and on the other they are oxidized by molecular oxygen. Some authorities believe that electrons pass from b, through c to a, and finally to a_3, the presumptive oxidase. By repeated alternate oxidation and reduction, small amounts of these cytochromes are able to participate in the oxidation of relatively enormous amounts of material in living cells: their action is, in fact, that of carriers. The action of the cytochromes may be collectively expressed in the following manner, with the reservation that, in the case of cytochrome b, no oxidase is required to catalyse the reoxidation of the reduced material, though its reoxidation is much faster when the oxidase is active than when it is inhibited:

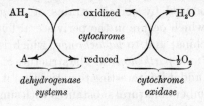

ACCESSORY CARRIER SYSTEMS

We have reason to believe that the bulk of the respiration of many cells is carried out by way of the cytochrome system, if only because cyanide, which inhibits cytochrome oxidase almost completely at concentrations of the order of $M/1000$, stops 80 % or more of their respiration. We have seen already that some part of the normal respiration must be attributed to the action of *oxidases*, some of which, in the presence of the appropriate substrates (e.g. the polyphenol oxidase system; p. 157), are able to act as carrier systems in their own right. But most oxidases are strongly inhibited by cyanide, and it is improbable therefore that they can account for much of the cyanide-stable fraction of the total respiration.

It is known that certain cells and tissues contain carrier substances which, while reducible by the dehydrogenase systems on the one hand, are autoxidizable on the other. One such substance is *cytochrome* b, and it may be that a part of the cyanide-stable respiration is accomplished through this substance, though it is only slowly oxidized by molecular oxygen.

The occurrence of oxidases and of cytochrome b is very wide, and these substances may therefore be of general importance.

But in a few special cases we know of the existence of reversibly oxidizable and reducible compounds, most of which are coloured and capable of acting in much the same way as methylene blue. If methylene blue is added to cells previously poisoned with cyanide, their respiration is largely restored, for the dye can be reduced by the dehydrogenase systems of the cells and reoxidized by molecular oxygen. As the dye is autoxidizable, its reoxidation is not inhibited by cyanide. Of the naturally occurring substances capable of acting in the same manner we may refer to *pyocyanine*, a pigment produced by certain strains of *B. pyocyaneus*; to *echinochrome*, which occurs in the perivisceral fluids and in the eggs of sea-urchins; and to *hallachrome*, which is found in the annelid worm *Halla parthenopaea*. The structure of echinochrome is given below, and it is interesting to notice that it is a quinonoid product. A number of natural substances with similar properties have been described, but it must be realized that while these compounds may possibly play an important part in the cells and tissues in which they occur, they cannot contribute to the cyanide-stable, nor indeed to the normal, respiration of cells in general, and do not therefore detract from the great and general importance of the cytochrome system.

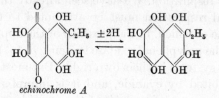

echinochrome A

In conclusion it must be pointed out that the respiration of certain cells is affected little or not at all by cyanide, and this is true of many unicellular organisms, such, for example, as *Chlorella*; the same is true of mammalian retina. In such cases it is probable either that the cytochrome system is not normally concerned in the respiration, or else that carrier substances of some other kind are present. It is in fact probable that cytochrome is altogether absent from some cells.

CHAPTER VII

DEHYDROGENASE SYSTEMS

Dehydrogenases and Co-dehydrogenases

We have already discussed some of the early work on the dehydrogenases, much of which was carried out by the method devised by Thunberg. An essential part of this procedure consists in washing the tissue thoroughly. It happens that some dehydrogenases are water-soluble, and any such would of course be removed by exhaustive washing. Quite apart from these, however, many of the insoluble dehydrogenases lose their power to catalyse the reduction of methylene blue as a result of thorough washing or prolonged dialysis. In such cases the activity is regained if a little boiled tissue juice is added, and it follows, therefore, that activators or coenzymes of some kind are required and that the appropriate co-substances are present in the tissues.

The first attempt to isolate such a coenzyme was made by Szent-Györgyi, who obtained a compound which contained adenylic acid and functioned as a coenzyme with respect to the lactic dehydrogenase of heart muscle. Unfortunately, he was unable to characterize his product more fully. A little later Warburg and Christian showed that the hexosemonophosphate dehydrogenase of red blood corpuscles also requires a coenzyme, and set themselves the task of isolating it. Starting with some 250 l. of horse blood they obtained about 20 mg. of a highly purified product. In the meantime, much interest had attached to the coenzymes of yeast juice, one of which was isolated by Euler. On analysis it appeared that these two coenzymes are closely similar in composition, since the following substances were obtained by hydrolysis:

	Euler's yeast coenzyme = Co I	Warburg and Christian's coenzyme = Co II
Molecules of		
Phosphoric acid	2	3
D-Ribose	2	2
Adenine	1	1
Nicotinic amide	1	1

The constitution of Co I is believed to be that of an adenine-nicotinic amide dinucleotide (for structural formulae of the component nucleotides see pp. 356, 357):

phosphate—D-ribofuranose—adenine
|
phosphate—D-ribofuranose—nicotinic amide

It can be formed biologically by a reaction between nicotinic amide mononucleotide and ATP, which is the pyrophosphate of adenine mononucleotide, thus:

Nicotinic amide mononucleotide + ATP → Co I + inorganic pyrophosphate.

The position taken up by the third phosphate radical in Co II has not been certainly established but there is now good evidence that this third radical is attached at position 2 in the ribose radical of Co I. Co II can be enzymatically formed by phosphate transfer to Co I from ATP:

Co I + ATP → Co II + ADP.

The behaviour of these two coenzymes has been studied by taking advantage of the fact that they show strong absorption bands in the ultra-violet (Fig. 21, p.188). In the oxidized form they show a strong, single band at about 2600 A., while in the reduced form the height of this band is somewhat reduced, and a second band, this time a rather broad one at about 3400 A., makes its appearance. The sharp band at 2600 A. can be accounted for by the known absorption spectra of adenine and nicotinic amide, but the new band at 3400 A., which appears only in the reduced forms of the coenzymes, can be accounted for by neither. It is due, as Warburg was able to show, to reduction of the pyridine ring.

Working with the methiodide of nicotinic amide, he found that reduction leads to the appearance of a new band at 3600 A., so that the 3400 A. band of the reduced coenzymes must probably be due to the presence of a reduced pyridine ring: in other words, the oxidation and reduction of the coenzymes I and II must probably take place at the pyridine ring. The reduction of nicotinic amide methiodide takes place as follows:

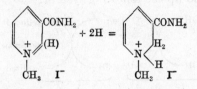

It is believed that the nicotinic amide radical of the coenzymes is linked to the sugar radical through its ring-bound nitrogen, and the reduction of the oxidized to the reduced form of either coenzyme is therefore believed to take place as follows, where R^- represents the remainder of the molecule, which is negatively charged through the ionization of one of its phosphoric acid radicals:

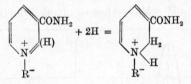

The functional behaviour of Co I can be studied by adding lactic acid and lactic dehydrogenase, for example, to a solution of the oxidized form of the coenzyme in the presence of cyanide, when the following reaction takes place:

$$CH_3CH(OH)COOH + Co\ I \longrightarrow CH_3COCOOH + Co\ I.2H.$$

This particular system tends towards an equilibrium that is very much in favour of lactic acid, and cyanide is added because it forms a cyanhydrin with the pyruvic acid, so that the reaction is pushed over towards the right. The reduction of the coenzyme can be followed by observing the development of the characteristic absorption band at 3400 A.

Clearly, therefore, the coenzyme works by acting as a hydrogen acceptor for the lactic acid-lactic dehydrogenase system. If to this system we add Co I and cytochrome c, the latter is reduced,

provided the dehydrogenase has not been too exhaustively purified, and by the further addition of cytochrome oxidase it is
possible to build up the following system:

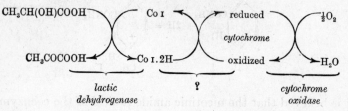

The intermediate stage marked ? also requires a catalyst, the
nature of which will be discussed later, but this is present in
the tissues and in any fairly impure dehydrogenase preparations
extracted from them.

This system, taken as a whole, behaves in a manner parallel
to that of an intact cell except, of course, that it will only
oxidize lactic acid. Nevertheless, it is affected in the same

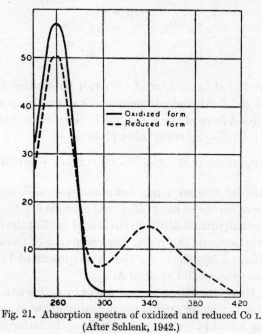

Fig. 21. Absorption spectra of oxidized and reduced Co I.
(After Schlenk, 1942.)

manner and to the same extent as an intact cell by respiratory inhibitors such as narcotics on the one hand and by cyanide, carbon monoxide, etc., on the other. Lactic acid undergoes continuous oxidation in this system, and its oxidation is attended by the uptake of an exactly equivalent amount of oxygen.

With the isolation of the two coenzymes it has become possible to classify dehydrogenases under three headings. Some can reduce methylene blue and cytochrome without the addition of any coenzyme and, according to recent evidence, these reduce cytochrome *b* in the first instance and cytochrome *c* only at second hand. A second group can only reduce cytochrome *c* in the presence of Co I, while a third group requires the presence of Co II: cytochrome *b* is not involved in either of these cases.

We have already seen that dehydrogenases are as specific towards their substrates as are other enzymes, such, for instance, as the glycosidases. We now know that they are specific also with respect to their hydrogen acceptors. Lactic dehydrogenase obtained from muscle, for instance, normally requires Co I and reacts more than 100 times as fast with this as with the closely related Co II. In many cases the specificity appears to be more complete even than this; for example, hexosemonophosphate dehydrogenase requires Co II and cannot collaborate with Co I. In only a few cases are the two coenzymes freely interchangeable. But the relationships between the dehydrogenases and their substrates are more specific than those between the dehydrogenases and their coenzymes, for whereas the same coenzyme can collaborate with more than one dehydrogenase, a given substrate is activated only by an appropriate dehydrogenase and not by any other. A further point to be noticed is that the coenzyme itself is not a very reactive compound, for it can only be reduced by comparatively powerful reducing agents such as dithionite (hydrosulphite). Furthermore, lactic acid is not easily oxidized, and becomes easily oxidized only as a result of its union with the lactic enzyme and consequent activation. Similarly, Co I undergoes a great increase in chemical reactivity in the presence of lactic dehydrogenase, with which it is able to combine. The functional behaviour of the coenzyme is therefore very similar indeed to that of the substrate, and the coenzyme might even be regarded as a second substrate. Both combine with the dehydrogenase protein, and the affinity constants have been determined for both cases. There is now evidence that in the natural state the coenzymes are firmly bound to the dehydrogenase proteins, especially in the mitochondria, and that they become freely dissociable only after the dehydrogenases have been extracted from the tissue substance.

TABLE 12. COENZYME REQUIREMENTS OF DEHYDROGENASES

Co-dehydrogenase required		
None	Co I	Co II
α-Glycerophosphate[1]	α-Glycerophosphate[2]	Glucose
Succinic	Lactic (muscle)	L-Glutamic
Lactic (yeast)	Malic	Hexosemonophosphate
Choline	Triosephosphate	iso-Citric
	Alcohol	Malic decarboxylase
	β-Hydroxybutyric	
	Glucose	
	L-Glutamic	

[1] Insoluble.   [2] Soluble.

For convenience of reference a list of the most important dehydrogenases is given in Table 12 so as to show which coenzyme, if any, is required by which dehydrogenase. In what follows we shall refer to these groups as *cytochrome-specific*, Co I-*specific* and Co II-*specific dehydrogenases* respectively. In the presence of their substrates, the appropriate coenzymes and other factors where necessary, all these dehydrogenases are capable of catalysing the reduction of methylene blue and of cytochrome, providing always that they have not been rigorously purified beforehand. We shall now consider the dehydrogenases individually and in more detail.

Dehydrogenases requiring no coenzyme

α-Glycerophosphate dehydrogenase (insoluble) occurs in animals, plants and micro-organisms alike. It catalyses the oxidation of L-(+)-α-glycerophosphate to 3-phosphoglyceraldehyde at the expense of a suitable hydrogen acceptor, e.g. methylene blue or cytochrome b:

$$\begin{array}{l} CH_2O\textcircled{P} \\ | \\ CHOH \\ | \\ CH_2OH \end{array} + MB \rightleftharpoons \begin{array}{l} CH_2O\textcircled{P} \\ | \\ CHOH \\ | \\ CHO \end{array} + MB.2H.$$

This enzyme is specific for the L-(+)-isomer of α-glycerophosphate: the D-(−)-form is not attacked, nor is β-glycerophosphate.

Succinic dehydrogenase appears to be almost universally distributed and catalyses the oxidation of succinic to fumaric acid:

$$\begin{array}{l} COOH \\ | \\ CH_2 \\ | \\ CH_2 \\ | \\ COOH \end{array} + MB \rightleftharpoons \begin{array}{l} COOH \\ | \\ CH \\ || \\ CH \\ | \\ COOH \end{array} + MB.2H.$$

The enzyme is insoluble and very specific. Apart from succinic acid it is only known to attack dimethylsuccinic acid, and is strongly and competitively inhibited by a number of other dibasic acids, notably by malonic, malic and oxaloacetic acids. As their formulae show, these resemble succinic acid rather closely and so are able to combine with the active groups of the enzyme, but yield inert products:

$$\begin{array}{llll} COOH & COOH & COOH & \\ | & | & | & COOH \\ CH_2 & CH_2 & CH_2 & | \\ | & | & | & CH_2 \\ CH_2 & CHOH & CO & | \\ | & | & | & COOH \\ COOH & COOH & COOH & \end{array}$$
succinic acid   *malic acid*   *oxaloacetic acid*   *malonic acid*

The activity of this enzyme depends upon the presence of its —SH groups, and it is inhibited, this time non-competitively, by agents which oxidize adjacent pairs of —SH groups to form —S—S— linkages. It is also inhibited by fairly high concentrations of monoiodoacetate, which reacts with and blocks the —SH groups irreversibly:

$$-SH + I.CH_2COOH = -S.CH_2COOH + HI.$$

Several other dehydrogenases are similarly affected by iodo-acetate, but the succinic enzyme requires unusually high concentrations for its effective inhibition.

In common with many other '—SH enzymes', succinic dehydrogenase is powerfully inhibited by many war gases, such as the arsenical smokes and vesicants, which act specifically upon —SH groups. Indeed, it has even been suggested that poisoning by oxygen may be due to oxidation of the —SH groups of sulphydryl-dependent enzymes.

Lactic dehydrogenase of yeast is the only soluble member of the cytochrome-specific group. This enzyme is of special interest for two reasons, first because, unlike the lactic enzyme of muscle, it requires no coenzyme. In addition, it has been highly purified and shown to involve a conjugated protein containing haematin, and is thus allied to the cytochromes (cf. p. 179). It catalyses the oxidation of L-(+)-lactic acid to pyruvic acid:

$$
\begin{array}{ccc}
CH_3 & & CH_3 \\
| & & | \\
CHOH + MB & \rightleftharpoons & CO \quad + MB.2H \\
| & & | \\
COOH & & COOH
\end{array}
$$

D-(−)-Lactic acid is not attacked by this enzyme, nor are any of the β-hydroxy-acids tested. Like most dehydrogenases, the lactic enzyme of yeast can act in reverse, producing from the optically inactive pyruvic acid the L- but never the D-form of lactic acid.

Many micro-organisms other than yeast contain similar enzymes, but in some cases at least the D-isomer of lactic acid can be formed and attacked.

Choline dehydrogenase, another insoluble enzyme, occurs in some but not in all animal tissues. It catalyses the oxidation of choline to betaine aldehyde:

$$
(CH_3)_3\overset{+}{N}.CH_2CH_2OH + MB \rightleftharpoons (CH_3)_3\overset{+}{N}.CH_2CHO + MB.2H.
$$

Dehydrogenases requiring Co I

α-Glycerophosphate dehydrogenase (soluble). Animal tissues contain two α-glycerophosphate dehydrogenases, one of which has already been described (p. 190). The soluble enzyme, unlike the insoluble, requires Co I and is specific for the D-(−) instead of the L-(+)- form of α-glycerophosphate. Methylene blue cannot be used directly as hydrogen acceptor in this case, while the reaction product is phosphodihydroxyacetone, not phosphoglyceraldehyde:

$$\begin{matrix} CH_2O\textcircled{P} & & CH_2O\textcircled{P} & \\ | & & | & \\ CHOH & + Co\ I \rightleftharpoons & CO & + Co\ I.2H \\ | & & | & \\ CH_2OH & & CH_2OH & \end{matrix}$$

Lactic dehydrogenase of muscle has been crystallized. Like the lactic enzyme of yeast, this dehydrogenase catalyses the oxidation of L-lactate to pyruvate, again reversibly, but whereas the yeast enzyme can catalyse a direct transfer of 2H to methylene blue, that of muscle requires Co I as its immediate hydrogen acceptor:

$$\begin{matrix} CH_3 & & CH_3 & \\ | & & | & \\ CHOH & + Co\ I \rightleftharpoons & CO & + Co\ I.2H \\ | & & | & \\ COOH & & COOH & \end{matrix}$$

Co II can replace Co I here but the latter reacts more than 100 times faster than the former. This system plays an important part in the metabolism of muscle and other tissues, and has been studied extensively. The equilibrium is very much in favour of the left-hand side, i.e. in favour of the hydroxy-acid, but the reaction can be forced over towards the right by adding an excess of the hydroxy-acid or, alternatively, by adding some trapping reagent, e.g. cyanide, which reacts with pyruvate to form a cyanhydrin.

Malic dehydrogenase is always found in close association with the lactic enzyme, suggesting that there may be some functional association between the two. They are not identical however.

The malic enzyme catalyses the conversion of L-malic acid into oxaloacetic acid:

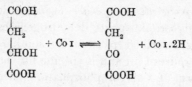

Once again the equilibrium conditions are in favour of the hydroxy-acid. Like the lactic enzyme, malic dehydrogenase can use Co II as well as Co I, but the latter is about fifteen times as active as the former.

β-Hydroxybutyric dehydrogenase occurs in many animal tissues, especially in heart, kidney and liver. It catalyses the inter-conversion of L-β-hydroxybutyric and acetoacetic acids:

$$CH_3CH(OH)CH_2COOH + Co\ I \rightleftharpoons CH_3COCH_2COOH + Co\ I.2H.$$

It has no action upon α-hydroxy- or α-keto-acids. The enzyme does not act upon β-hydroxypropionic acid, the next lower homologue; whether higher homologues are attacked is not known.

Alcohol dehydrogenase of yeast has been obtained in crystalline form. Like the succinic enzyme it requires the presence of its —SH groups for activity. This enzyme is very sensitive indeed to iodoacetate. A somewhat similar enzyme is present in mammalian liver but not, apparently, in other mammalian tissues. The yeast enzyme acts upon primary and secondary alcohols to yield the corresponding aldehydes and ketones:

Primary: $R.CH_2OH + Co\ I \rightleftharpoons R.CHO + Co\ I.2H;$

Secondary: $\begin{matrix} R \\ R' \end{matrix}\!\!>\!CHOH + Co\ I \rightleftharpoons \begin{matrix} R \\ R' \end{matrix}\!\!>\!CO + Co\ I.2H.$

The equilibrium is in favour of the alcohol so that, in order to study the forward reactions, it is necessary to work in the presence of an aldehyde or ketone fixative such as sodium bisulphite.

Glucose dehydrogenase of liver catalyses the oxidation of D-glucose to the corresponding gluconic acid. In this case it is probable that the δ-lactone is formed first of all and then reacts, possibly spontaneously, with water:

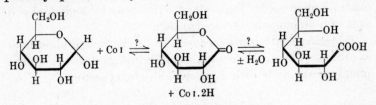

+ Co I.2H

It is not known for certain whether the process is reversible. No sugar other than D-glucose is attacked by this dehydrogenase, which has the distinction of being able to use either Co I or Co II as its hydrogen acceptor. It may be compared with notatin, the very specific glucose oxidase of *Penicillium* (p. 165).

L-*Glutamic dehydrogenase* catalyses the conversion of L-glutamic acid to the corresponding imino-acid, a reaction that is followed by spontaneous hydrolysis of the imino-acid to yield the corresponding α-keto-acid together with ammonia:

$$\begin{array}{ccc}
COOH & & COOH \\
| & & | \\
CH_2 & & CH_2 \\
| & & | \\
CH_2 & + \text{Co I} \rightleftharpoons & CH_2 \quad + \text{Co I.2H} \\
| & & | \\
CH.NH_2 & & C{:}NH \\
| & & | \\
COOH & & COOH
\end{array}$$

$$\begin{array}{ccc}
COOH & & COOH \\
| & & | \\
CH_2 & & CH_2 \\
| & & | \\
CH_2 & + H_2O \rightleftharpoons & CH_2 \quad + NH_3 \\
| & & | \\
C{:}NH & & CO \\
| & & | \\
COOH & & COOH
\end{array}$$

Co I and Co II are interchangeable in this system. Both stages are reversible, and α-ketoglutaric acid can be reductively aminated by ammonia in the presence of the dehydrogenase to yield L-glutamic acid. Similar enzymes are present in yeast and in plants, the yeast enzyme requiring Co II while that of plant tissues requires Co I.

This dehydrogenase appears to be absolutely specific for L-glutamic acid and has no action upon the D-isomer nor upon other L-amino-acids. Its mode of action may be compared with that of D-amino-acid oxidase (p. 162).

Triosephosphate dehydrogenase. The term 'triose phosphate' as ordinarily applied refers to an equilibrium mixture of L-3-phosphoglyceraldehyde with α-phosphodihydroxyacetone:

$$
\begin{array}{ccc}
\text{CH}_2\text{O}\circledP & & \text{CH}_2\text{O}\circledP \\
| & & | \\
\text{CHOH} & \rightleftharpoons & \text{CO} \\
| & & | \\
\text{CHO} & & \text{CH}_2\text{OH}
\end{array}
$$

The so-called triosephosphate dehydrogenase is concerned with only one of these components, namely, with L-3-phosphoglyceraldehyde, and acts upon this only under certain definite conditions. Co I is required and inorganic phosphate also must be present. The oxidation product that accumulates corresponds not to 3-phosphoglyceraldehyde but to 1:3-diphosphoglyceraldehyde, which must accordingly be supposed to be formed as an intermediary product:

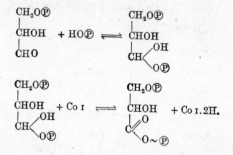

Whether the reaction of the inorganic phosphate with the starting material is catalysed by the dehydrogenase, whether it is spontaneous, or whether it is catalysed by another enzyme, is not clear. Warburg used a crystalline specimen of triosephosphate dehydrogenase in his experiments, but this does not preclude the possibility that another enzyme may have been present, on account of the tendency of proteins in general to form mixed crystals, even when still far from being chemically pure. It seems probable, however, that phosphoric acid can be added on directly, just as water can be directly added on to an aldehydic grouping.

Enzymes similar to the triosephosphate dehydrogenase of muscle are present in yeast and in plant tissues, and are probably very widely distributed indeed. The muscle enzyme is extremely sensitive to iodoacetate, from which it may be deduced that its —SH groups are required for activity. Both stages in the process which it catalyses are reversible, and the equilibrium conditions favour the formation of the acid rather than the aldehyde.

A noteworthy point here is that Co I protects this dehydrogenase against inhibition by oxidized glutathione and alloxan, both of which tend to oxidize the —SH groups of the enzyme. There is a suggestion here that the coenzyme may unite with the dehydrogenase through the latter's —SH groups.

Dehydrogenases requiring Co II

Glucose and L-glutamic dehydrogenases have already been described (p. 195).

Hexosemonophosphate dehydrogenase occurs in red blood corpuscles and in yeast. It requires Co II and catalyses the oxidation of glucose-6-monophosphate to 6-phosphogluconic acid, probably by way of the δ-lactone (cf. glucose dehydrogenase):

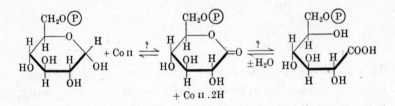

We do not know whether the process is reversible or not. This is a very specific dehydrogenase, for it has no action upon other sugar phosphates, e.g. upon fructofuranose-6-monophosphate or upon fructofuranose-1:6-diphosphate, nor does it act upon glucose itself (cf. glucose dehydrogenase). The oxidation of glucose-6-phosphate to 6-phosphogluconic acid is probably the first step in the formation of the important pentose sugar, D-ribose (p. 353).

iso-*Citric dehydrogenase* is widely distributed in animal and plant tissues and is present also in many micro-organisms. It acts upon L-*iso*-citrate to produce oxalosuccinic (α-keto-β-carboxy-glutaric) acid, and the process is reversible:

$$
\begin{array}{ll}
\text{COOH} & \text{COOH} \\
| & | \\
\text{CH}_2 & \text{CH}_2 \\
| & | \\
\text{CH.COOH} + \text{Co\,II} \rightleftharpoons & \text{CH.COOH} + \text{Co\,II.2H} \\
| & | \\
\text{CHOH} & \text{CO} \\
| & | \\
\text{COOH} & \text{COOH}
\end{array}
$$

This is usually followed by the action of another enzyme which catalyses the β-decarboxylation of the product and gives rise to α-ketoglutaric acid but this second enzyme, unlike the dehydro-genase, requires the presence of manganese ions. In their absence the action of the dehydrogenase can be studied independently.

Malic decarboxylase must be mentioned here. It differs sharply from malic dehydrogenase (p. 193) for it catalyses an oxidative decarboxylation of L-malate, using Co II as hydrogen acceptor and yielding pyruvate and carbon dioxide as products:

$$
\begin{array}{ll}
\text{COO}\colon\text{H} & \text{CO}_2 \\
| & + \\
\text{CH}_2 & \text{CH}_3 \\
| \quad + \text{Co\,II} \rightleftharpoons & | \quad + \text{Co\,II.2H.} \\
\text{CHOH} & \text{CO} \\
| & | \\
\text{COOH} & \text{COOH}
\end{array}
$$

This enzyme thus combines the functions of a decarboxylase and a dehydrogenase but appears nevertheless to be a single entity, every effort to resolve it into simpler components having so far failed.

Work on Reconstructed Dehydrogenase Systems

Much of the recent work on dehydrogenases has been carried out with the aid of what are known as reconstructed systems. It is possible, for example, to build up a system containing succinate, succinic dehydrogenase, cytochrome c, cytochrome oxidase and oxygen, and such a system can 'respire', i.e. can take up oxygen and oxidize an equivalent amount of succinate to fumarate. The lactic system described on p. 188 is another example of such a system. All the reactants employed are substances which occur in nature and all can be obtained from living materials. It seems probable, therefore, that they represent systems which actually participate in the respiration of living cells. But there are certain important criticisms that must be noted.

The fact that a given series of operations can be demonstrated in a reconstructed system is not positive proof that it takes place under biological conditions. As Green has written: 'A sufficiently ingenious mechanic could separate the parts of a baby Austin and use them to make a perambulator or a pressure pump or a hair-dryer of sorts. If the mechanic was not particularly bright and was uninformed as to the source of these parts, he might be tempted into believing that they were in fact designed for the particular end he happened to have in view. The biochemist is presented with a similar problem in the course of his reconstructions. The materials of the cell offer unlimited possibilities of combinations and interaction, but only a few of these possibilities are realized in the cell under normal conditions. There is thus a grave element of risk in trying to reason too closely from reconstructed systems to the intact cell. The reconstruction can have no biological significance until some definite counterpart of these events is observed *in vivo*.'

It will be remembered that the oxidation and reduction of the cytochromes can, in fact, be observed within living cells, while the presence of dehydrogenases in intact cells can be demonstrated by the Thunberg method, using a dye such as methylene blue. The discovery that the specificity of dehydrogenases is such that each can only reduce its own particular natural hydrogen acceptor shows that these substances, which do in fact occur in living cells of all kinds, must necessarily act as intermediates in processes of cellular oxidation. Thus the fact that the substances and the catalysts used in reconstructed systems *do* occur in intact cells, the fact that certain components *can* be observed at work within the cells themselves, and the incontestable facts of enzyme specificity—all these taken together make it seem improbable that we shall be led into gross error by the study of reconstructed systems, provided that the results are cautiously interpreted.

Intact cells, in which substances such as the cytochromes and coenzymes are present only in small concentrations, respire relatively much faster than reconstructed systems containing the same reactants at the same order of concentration. This seems at first to suggest that the two may be fundamentally different. But there are good reasons for believing that whereas events in a reconstructed system take place in a more or less haphazard manner, the enzymes, coenzymes and other reactants of the intact cell are organized in such a way that each is present in the right place at the right time. We shall have other instances of this notion of intracellular organization.

The outstanding properties of the anaerobic dehydrogenases are: their *specificity towards their substrates*, their *specificity towards their hydrogen acceptors*, and the fact that, so far as our information goes, they are all *capable of acting reversibly*. In addition, they possess the usual properties of enzymes, viz. thermolability, dependence upon pH and so on. As we have seen, *three main types can be distinguished*, the cytochrome-, Co I- and the Co II-specific types.

If now we take a dehydrogenase together with its substrate and the appropriate coenzyme, we have a system which can reduce methylene blue or cytochrome, always provided that the enzyme preparation has not been too exhaustively purified. But as purification is carried progressively further and further we find that the system eventually fails to reduce cytochrome and methylene blue. This might be due in part to some kind of damage done to the enzymes by the methods used in their purification, but it might also mean that there must be one or more steps in the whole reaction sequence requiring catalysis by some enzyme or enzymes that are present in crude extracts but eliminated by purification. It is known, in fact, that the cytochrome-specific dehydrogenases cannot reduce cytochrome *c* directly but reduce cytochrome *b* first of all, and that an additional catalyst is required to establish communication between the *b* and *c* components. Again, in the case of dehydrogenases that operate through Co I and Co II, there is definite evidence that additional catalysts are required to accomplish the transfer of hydrogen from the reduced coenzyme to cytochrome *c* or to methylene blue as the case may be. The nature of these additional catalysts we shall consider in the next section.

'REDUCED-COENZYME DEHYDROGENASES': FLAVOPROTEINS

The flavoproteins are a group of conjugated proteins which are characterized by the presence in the prosthetic group of riboflavin. This is a yellow substance which exhibits a strong green fluorescence even in very dilute solutions. It is identical with the flavin of milk (lactoflavin) and with that of egg-white (ooflavin), and occurs very widely indeed among cells and tissues, its importance in which may be gauged from the fact that it is a member of the B_2 group of vitamins. It is derived from the nitrogenous base 6:7-dimethyl-*iso*-alloxazine and the pentahydric sugar alcohol D-ribitol, linked together in the following manner:

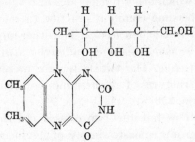

Certain points call for special comment. The substance can exist in the oxidized form shown above, but can be reduced by fairly powerful reducing agents such as dithionite (hydrosulphite).

Two atoms of hydrogen are taken up in the process, which may be described as follows:

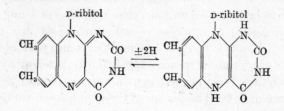

Although reagents such as dithionite are necessary to effect the reduction of the oxidized form, the reduced form is autoxidizable, i.e. it can be oxidized by shaking with molecular oxygen, the oxygen being thereby reduced to hydrogen peroxide. Another point worthy of notice is the presence in this substance not of the pentose sugar, D-ribose, but of the corresponding sugar alcohol, D-ribitol, so that the name riboflavin, suggesting as it does that the molecule contains D-ribose, is a misnomer: a better name would be ribitylflavin.

Riboflavin occurs in the flavoproteins in the form of its 5'-phosphate (see p. 358), a substance which resembles a nucleotide in its general structure. Strictly speaking, however, it is not a nucleotide since, while it does contain a nitrogenous base, it does not contain a pentose sugar, but in view of its importance in cellular metabolism, in which other nucleotides also are intimately concerned, it has become common practice to refer to riboflavin phosphate as *flavin mononucleotide*. The other important nucleotides are *adenine mononucleotide* (adenylic acid) and *nicotinic amide mononucleotide*. The two latter are present in Co I and Co II, and the structures of all three mononucleotides should be compared (see pp. 356–8).

The flavoproteins fall into two classes. In the first of these the prosthetic group consists simply of flavin mononucleotide, in the second of adenineflavin dinucleotide, i.e. the dinucleotide formed by the union of flavin and adenine mononucleotides through their respective phosphate radicals. The mononucleotide can be formed from free riboflavin at the expense of ATP by an enzyme recently obtained from brewers' yeast and called flavo-kinase:

$$\text{riboflavin} + \text{ATP} \longrightarrow \text{riboflavin-5'-phosphate} + \text{ADP.}$$

Adenineflavin dinucleotide can be then formed from the mono-nucleotide by another enzymatically catalysed reaction with ATP:

$$\text{flavin mononucleotide} + \text{ATP} \longrightarrow$$
$$\text{adenineflavin dinucleotide} + \text{inorganic pyrophosphate.}$$

Like free riboflavin, the free mono- and dinucleotides can be reduced by dithionite, the reduced forms being autoxidizable. Similarly, when combined in the form of flavoproteins, these nucleotides can still be reduced, and when in the reduced form are usually though not invariably autoxidizable.

We have already encountered several flavoproteins such, for example, as D-amino-acid oxidase, the prosthetic group of which acts as a built-in hydrogen acceptor for pairs of hydrogen atoms which it takes over from activated molecules of D-amino-acids. That the prosthetic group is so readily reduced by activated substrate molecules when combined with the protein component of the oxidase shows that this protein activates not only its substrates but the prosthetic group as well, just as the dehydro-genases activate their coenzymes as well as their respective substrates.

We now have to consider some other members of the flavo-protein class in which the prosthetic group again acts as a built-in hydrogen acceptor, a pair of hydrogen atoms being taken on in the same manner by the flavin nucleotide as by free riboflavin itself, but this time specifically from the reduced form of Co I or Co II.

Warburg's Flavoprotein ('*Yellow Enzyme*'). Following the dis-covery that the addition of methylene blue to red blood corpuscles causes them to respire, Warburg and Christian set to work to analyse the systems involved in the respiration. They were able to show that the material oxidized is glucose-6-monophosphate, the catalyst being hexosemonophosphate dehydrogenase, which requires Co II as hydrogen acceptor. But in addition to these an additional factor was required to catalyse the transfer of hydrogen from reduced Co II to methylene blue. They subsequently isolated from yeast a flavoprotein which was found to be capable of catalysing this transfer, and gave to it the name of *Gelbferment* or yellow enzyme. The complete system may be written in the following manner:

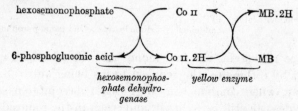

The prosthetic group of the yellow enzyme proved to consist of flavin mononucleotide, and can apparently operate as an intermediary carrier of hydrogen between reduced Co II on the one hand and methylene blue on the other. The mode of action of this flavoprotein is thus comparable with that of D-amino-acid oxidase. The yellow enzyme therefore behaves as an enzyme that catalyses the dehydrogenation of reduced Co II, and, as Warburg himself showed, this 'reduced-coenzyme dehydrogenase' can also catalyse the oxidation of reduced Co I in the presence of methylene blue.

The reduced form of the yellow enzyme can hand on its hydrogen to molecular oxygen, but this is a process that only takes place at an appreciable speed when the partial pressure of oxygen is relatively very high. It was formerly thought that it could transfer its hydrogen to cytochrome c also, suggesting that this flavoprotein constitutes the missing link for coenzyme-specific dehydrogenase systems in general. If this were indeed true (which it probably is not) we could describe oxidation systems involving Co I and Co II in the following general manner:

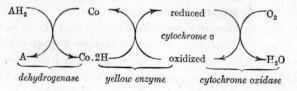

Warburg was of the opinion that this yellow enzyme must be widely distributed in nature since riboflavin, and hence by presumption flavoproteins also, are very widely distributed indeed, while living cells in general undoubtedly contain some factor which links reduced Co I and reduced Co II with cytochrome. Up to the present, however, this yellow enzyme has only been obtained from yeast. Attempts to detect it in animal tissues have not led to evidence for its presence there, but rather to the discovery of new and different flavoproteins. Warburg himself was later reconciled to the view that the yellow enzyme is in reality an artefact, derived in all probability from some other flavoprotein in the course of the procedure used for its isolation.

Cytochrome Reductase. This flavoprotein, discovered by Haas and his co-workers, is the only member of the flavoprotein group at present definitely known to be capable of carrying out the direct reduction of cytochrome *c*. Warburg's yellow enzyme gave some evidence of carrying out this process, but the Haas flavoprotein does so about 100,000 times faster than the yellow enzyme, and it is possible that Warburg's product was contaminated with traces of the Haas enzyme.

Cytochrome reductase resembles the original yellow enzyme in having flavin mononucleotide as its prosthetic group, but differs from it in catalysing the oxidation of reduced Co II only, reduced Co I being quite unaffected. Probably, therefore, we can look upon it as a specific dehydrogenase for reduced Co II, as well as a specific reducing enzyme for cytochrome *c*. The other essential difference between cytochrome reductase on the one hand and Warburg's enzyme on the other lies in the difference between the rates at which they reduce cytochrome *c*. As yet the reductase has only been isolated from yeast, but the existence of another flavoprotein (diaphorase II) has recently been demonstrated in animal tissues. This appears to act in substantially the same way as cytochrome reductase.

Diaphorase I. This flavoprotein has been isolated from heart muscle. Its chief characteristics are that its prosthetic group consists of adenineflavin dinucleotide, that it specifically catalyses the oxidation of reduced Co I, that it reduces methylene blue with great rapidity, but is only very slowly oxidized by molecular oxygen. Diaphorase I is thus qualified to act as a link in the reduction of methylene blue by systems involving Co I, but it does not reduce cytochrome c. Presumably therefore there must be yet another carrier that mediates between reduced diaphorase I on the one hand and oxidized cytochrome c on the other. This additional component of the respiratory chains has not yet been isolated but has been studied in washed heart-muscle suspensions by Slater. It can act as a link between reduced diaphorase I and cytochrome c, but little is known at present about its chemical nature or its mode of action.

Diaphorase II. Evidence has recently come forward for the existence of a second diaphorase which collaborates with reduced Co II. Its prosthetic group, like that of diaphorase I, consists of adenineflavin dinucleotide. Whether, like the cytochrome reductase of yeast, it reacts directly with cytochrome c, or whether, like diaphorase I, it requires the Slater factor, has not yet been determined. In view of its structural similarity to diaphorase I it seems likely that the factor is required.

Functions of the flavoproteins. The functions and mode of action of the flavoprotein oxidases has already been considered. It will be remembered that the prosthetic group in this case acts as a carrier of hydrogen between the substrate of the oxidase and the molecular oxygen which functions as hydrogen acceptor. The flavoproteins with which we are particularly concerned here have similar prosthetic groups, which probably again act as carriers of hydrogen, this time between the reduced coenzymes which constitute their specific substrates and the cytochrome c which is their specific hydrogen acceptor. Only one member of the group is definitely known to react directly with cytochrome c, namely cytochrome reductase, and it follows that our knowledge of the mechanisms of cellular respiration is still incomplete.

We can, however, explain the *reduction of methylene blue* by coenzyme-specific dehydrogenase systems, through the mediation of diaphorase I in cases where Co I is involved, and of cytochrome reductase or diaphorase II where the coenzyme is Co II.

As far as the *reduction of cytochrome* is concerned, dehydro-genases of the succinate type, requiring no coenzyme, now appear to require the participation of two further factors, first cyto-chrome *b*, which is followed by the Slater factor and only then by cytochrome *c*. In the case of systems in which Co I is con-cerned, diaphorase I acts as a dehydrogenase for the reduced coenzyme, passing on its hydrogen to cytochrome *c* through the action of the Slater factor. Systems involving Co II can use cytochrome reductase and this flavoprotein alone suffices to establish contact between the reduced coenzyme and cyto-chrome *c*, but diaphorase II also can collaborate with these systems and may prove to require the Slater factor.

The modes of action of the three known types of dehydrogenase systems can accordingly be summarized in the following manner:

(*a*) *Cytochrome-specific type:*

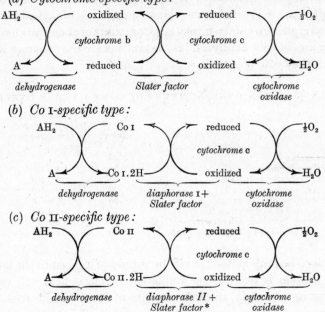

(*b*) *Co I-specific type:*

(*c*) *Co II-specific type:*

The possibility that yet other carriers or 'factors' may be involved cannot yet be ignored.

* Or cytochrome reductase.

REVERSIBILITY AND COUPLING OF
DEHYDROGENASE SYSTEMS

If we consider the complete system involved in the oxidation of lactic acid in animal tissues it is clear that this oxidation is accomplished through the repeated reduction and reoxidation of a chain or series of carrier substances. A single molecule of Co I, for example, might be reduced and reoxidized, say, a thousand times, and thus contribute to the oxidation of a thousand molecules of lactic acid. The oxidation and reduction of these carriers takes place with great rapidity under biological conditions, and Table 13 presents data for the 'turn-over numbers' of some oxidation catalysts, i.e. the number of times they can be reduced and reoxidized under biological conditions in 1 min. at the temperatures stated. It is precisely because their turn-over numbers are so great that very small quantitites of Co I and Co II, for example, can catalyse very large amounts of chemical change. They are, in fact, catalysts, just as truly as are the enzymes with which they collaborate.

TABLE 13. TURN-OVER NUMBERS OF SOME ENZYME SYSTEMS

Enzyme	Temp. °C.	Mol. substrate transformed per mol. enzyme per min. (approx.)
Catalase	0	$2 \cdot 5 \times 10^6$
Cytochrome c	38	$1 \cdot 4 \times 10^3$
Cytochrome reductase	25	4×10^2
Amino-acid oxidase	38	2×10^3
Polyphenol oxidase	20	7×10^4
Alcohol dehydrogenase (Co I)	20	2×10^4
Triosephosphate dehydrogenase (Co I)	20	2×10^4
Carboxylase (diphosphothiamine)	30	1×10^3

It is to be anticipated that if the supply of oxygen to the lactic acid system is cut off, the oxidation of lactic acid will cease almost immediately, since the amount of Co I available to act as hydrogen acceptor is relatively very small. This is in fact true as far as the isolated or reconstructed system is concerned. Yet many cells and tissues, including even mammalian muscle, are capable of functioning in complete absence of oxygen. It is known that metabolic oxidations can still go on in many kinds of cells under anaerobic conditions, and in this section we shall outline the mechanisms whereby these are accomplished. It is clear that, even under anaerobic conditions, the reduced coenzymes must be reoxidized in some way since, so far as we know, they are the only biological substances that can act as hydrogen acceptors for the coenzyme-specific dehydrogenase systems.

As long ago as 1924 it was shown by Quastel and Whetham that the lactic and succinic dehydrogenase systems of bacterial cells can be coupled together in intact cells maintained under anaerobic conditions. Lactic acid is oxidized to pyruvic at the expense of the reduction of fumaric to succinic acid, thus:

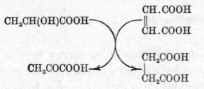

At least two dehydrogenases are involved, the lactic enzyme, which catalyses the dehydrogenation of lactic acid, and the succinic enzyme, which catalyses the reduction of fumaric to succinic acid, acting in this case 'in reverse'. Neither of these requires any known coenzyme. The mechanisms of coupled oxidation-reduction processes of this kind were much studied by Green and his co-workers, who showed that in extracts, as opposed to intact bacterial cells, the coupling can only take place in the presence of a reversibly oxidizable and reducible compound such as methylene blue. Other substances, including cytochrome c, and Warburg's yellow enzyme were also tested, but the only naturally occurring compound found to replace methylene blue as an intermediate hydrogen-carrier was pyocyanine, itself a reversibly oxidizable and reducible dye. In the presence of methylene blue or pyocyanine it was possible to demonstrate separately the reduction of the dye by lactate in the presence of lactic dehydrogenase, and its subsequent reoxidation by fumarate in the presence of succinic dehydrogenase. When the complete system of reactants and catalysts is taken together the conditions of equilibrium are such that a four-point equilibrium is finally attained, and can be modified in accordance with the usual mass-law principles. Thus we may write:

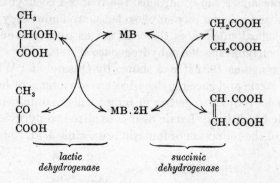

Possibly the natural intracellular carrier here is cytochrome *b*.

Later, working with other systems, Green and his colleagues showed that Co I and Co II can also act as intermediary carriers between pairs of dehydrogenases, *provided that both enzymes are specific for the same coenzyme.* A dehydrogenase that is specific for Co I could not be coupled to one that normally co-operates with Co II. Many coupled pairs of coenzyme-linked dehydrogenases have now been investigated, and the triosephosphate and lactic systems of muscle, the triosephosphate and alcohol systems of yeast, and the triosephosphate and α-glycerophosphate systems, also of yeast, are three of the many pairs that can be linked together through Co I. The L-glutamic and hexosemonophosphate systems of yeast can be similarly coupled together through Co II.

Reactions of this kind are frequently but inaccurately described as 'dismutations' and compared to the well-known Cannizzaro reaction. A true dismutation involves two molecules of one and the same substance, one of which is oxidized at the expense of the reduction of the second. Where such a true dismutation is catalysed by a single enzyme the latter is known as a *mutase*, and is a single entity rather than a pair of coenzyme-linked dehydrogenases.

The part played by the coenzyme in a coupled pair can be very elegantly demonstrated by taking advantage of the absorption band at 3400 A. which is shown by the reduced, but not by the oxidized, form of the coenzyme. Let us consider the coupling between triosephosphate dehydrogenase and alcohol dehydrogenase:

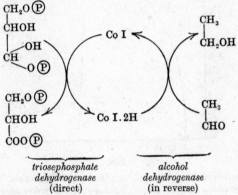

triosephosphate
dehydrogenase
(direct)

alcohol
dehydrogenase
(in reverse)

If triosephosphate is taken together with the oxidized form of Co I in the presence of phosphate, no band is observable at 3400 A. When triosephosphate dehydrogenase is added the coenzyme becomes reduced, and the progress of the reaction can be followed by measurements of the intensity of the band (Fig. 22). The coenzyme is not completely reduced because the reaction does not proceed to completion. The reaction mixture is now boiled to destroy the enzyme and then filtered. The intensity of the band remains unchanged, and is unaffected by the addition of acetaldehyde. If alcohol dehydrogenase is now added the second phase of the process can be observed; the coenzyme is reoxidized and the band fades.

It would be difficult to exaggerate the importance of reactions of this kind and, as we shall see later, they are a very frequent feature of metabolism under anaerobic conditions. Whether they take place when conditions are aerobic it is difficult to say with certainty. They are still *possible* under aerobic conditions, but the rate of reoxidation of a reduced coenzyme by the next member in the oxidative chain is ordinarily so great that these dismutation-like reactions are probably suppressed, if not abolished altogether.

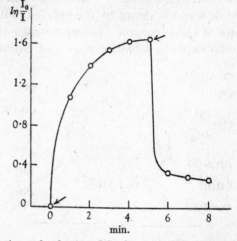

Fig. 22. Oxidation and reduction of Co I in a coupled reaction. Triosephosphate dehydrogenase added at first arrow, alcohol dehydrogenase at second; for rest of explanation see text. Ordinate: relative intensity of band at 3400 A. Abscissa: time. (Modified after Schlenk, 1942.)

We have so far been at pains to think of these as essentially reversible systems which tend towards equilibrium. This they do in isolated systems, but when, as happens under biological conditions, one or other of the reactants undergoes some further change as fast as it is formed, the system as a whole goes in one direction only, and we shall see many examples of this kind in later chapters.

TISSUE RESPIRATION AND THE CAPTURE OF FREE ENERGY

We have so far neglected to consider the possible significance of tissue oxidations as sources of free energy for the organism. We know that, in one or two cases, the dehydrogenation of a substrate leads at once to the appearance of a new energy-rich bond in the product of oxidation. The first reaction of this kind to be investigated in detail was the oxidation of phosphoglyceraldehyde to phosphoglyceric acid under the influence of triosephosphate dehydrogenase. The complete process involves three stepwise reactions:

(a) *Incorporation of inorganic phosphate:*

$$
\begin{array}{ccc}
\mathrm{CH_2O\textcircled{P}} & & \mathrm{CH_2O\textcircled{P}} \\
| & & | \\
\mathrm{CHOH} + \mathrm{HO.\textcircled{P}} \rightleftharpoons & \mathrm{CHOH} \\
| & & |\!\!\diagdown_{\mathrm{OH}} \\
\mathrm{CHO} & & \mathrm{CH} \\
& & \diagdown_{\mathrm{O\textcircled{P}}}
\end{array}
$$

(b) *Dehydrogenation and formation of an energy-rich bond:*

$$
\begin{array}{ccc}
\mathrm{CH_2O\textcircled{P}} & & \mathrm{CH_2O\textcircled{P}} \\
| & & | \\
\mathrm{CHOH} + \mathrm{Co\,I} \rightleftharpoons & \mathrm{CHOH} + \mathrm{Co\,I.2H} \\
|\!\!\diagup_{\mathrm{OH}} & & | \quad{}^{\mathrm{O}} \\
\mathrm{CH} & & \mathrm{C}\!\!\diagup \\
\diagdown_{\mathrm{O\textcircled{P}}} & & \diagdown_{\mathrm{O}\sim\textcircled{P}}
\end{array}
$$

(c) *Transference of energy-rich bond to ADP:*

$$
\begin{array}{ccc}
\mathrm{CH_2O\textcircled{P}} & & \mathrm{CH_2O\textcircled{P}} \\
| & & | \\
\mathrm{CHOH} + \mathrm{ADP} \rightleftharpoons & \mathrm{CHOH} + \mathrm{ATP} \\
| \quad{}^{\mathrm{O}} & & | \quad{}^{\mathrm{O}} \\
\mathrm{C}\!\!\diagup & & \mathrm{C}\!\!\diagup \\
\diagdown_{\mathrm{O}\sim\textcircled{P}} & & \diagdown_{\mathrm{OH}}
\end{array}
$$

The free energy of the new bond has its origin in the intrinsic free energy of the starting material, and the new bond itself arises as a consequence of the redistribution of energy within the molecule brought about by dehydrogenation and the resulting reorganization of the molecular structure.

A new energy-rich bond also appears in reactions in which an α-keto-acid, such as pyruvic, undergoes oxidative decarboxylation. There is still considerable uncertainty about the mechanisms involved in oxidative decarboxylation in animal tissues, but in the micro-organism *Bact. delbruckii* the overall reaction may be tentatively expressed as follows (see p. 422):

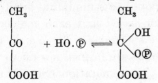

(d)
$$
\begin{array}{ccc}
\mathrm{CH_3} & & \mathrm{CH_3} \\
| & & |\!\!\diagup_{\mathrm{OH}} \\
\mathrm{CO} + \mathrm{HO.\textcircled{P}} \rightleftharpoons & \mathrm{C}\!\!\diagdown_{\mathrm{O\textcircled{P}}} \\
| & & | \\
\mathrm{COOH} & & \mathrm{COOH}
\end{array}
$$

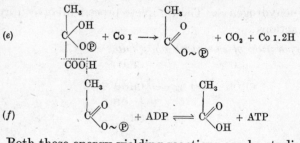

(e)

(f)

Both these energy-yielding reactions can be studied with the aid of purified enzymes in fairly simple systems. But if reactions of this kind are allowed to take place in more complex systems, systems in which the 2H removed by dehydrogenation can be passed on through the appropriate coenzyme, flavoprotein and cytochrome to molecular oxygen, more than one new energy-rich bond always appears. The bond yield can be determined by allowing the oxidation to proceed in the presence of ADP and estimating the ATP formed. Alternatively, in the presence of hexokinase and glucose, traces of ADP or ATP can be used to transfer the newly generated bonds to glucose, yielding glucose-6-phosphate, which may then be estimated. Such methods always give low results, however, because tissue preparations usually contain powerful ATP'ases which tend to decompose ATP as fast as it is formed. Losses through this channel can nevertheless be minimized by the use of finely divided and thoroughly washed tissue, or by working in the presence of fluoride, which is a powerful inhibitor of ATP'ase activity. Quantitative results have been sought in experiments by several groups of investigators.

In one such experiment β-hydroxybutyric acid was used as the substrate and between 2 and 3 molecules of ATP were formed for each atom of oxygen consumed. Now since it is impossible to deal in fractions of an energy-rich bond, and since allowances have to be made for losses of ATP under the experimental conditions, this corresponds to a minimum bond yield of 3 for each atom of oxygen consumed and each molecule of β-hydroxybutyrate oxidized ('P/O ratio' = 3). We do not know exactly where these new bonds are formed nor do we know the mechanisms that lead to their generation. Similar experiments point to a bond yield of 4 for the oxidative decarboxylation of α-keto-glutaric acid, but one bond arises in oxidative decarboxylation itself so that, once again, the transmission of 2H along the reaction chain leads to the generation of 3 new energy-rich bonds.

TABLE 14. APPROXIMATE FREE ENERGIES
OF SOME RESPIRATORY CARRIERS

	$-\Delta F$ (cal.)	Change of ΔF for the step
Coenzyme I	4,000	
Diaphorase I	15,000	$-11,000$
Cytochrome c	31,000	$-16,000$
$\frac{1}{2}O_2$	56,500	$-25,500$

Now as we pass along the chain of carriers from the coenzyme, through diaphorase to cytochrome and finally to molecular oxygen, there is a loss of free energy at each stage. The magnitudes of these losses can be calculated from the known free energies of the carriers themselves, and these can be determined from measurements of their respective oxidation-reduction potentials. This is not the place to enter into a discussion of these potentials and the methods used for their measurement:* we shall merely quote some approximate data which have been obtained in this way. It will be observed from Table 14 that the total loss of free energy between coenzyme I and molecular oxygen amounts to some 52,000 cal. per g.mol., which is sufficient to account for the formation of not more than 4 energy-rich bonds ($= -46,000$ cal.) for each pair of hydrogen atoms (or electrons) carried from Co I to oxygen.

Now the first stage in the oxidation of β-hydroxybutyrate, the transference of 2H from substrate to Co I, entails a loss of only a few thousands of calories of free energy, too small an amount to allow the formation of an energy-rich bond. Since, however, the complete process yields 3 such bonds, it follows that these must arise at later stages in the oxidative reaction sequence. The data of Table 14 show that one new bond ($= -11,500$ cal. per g.mol.) might be generated at the stage between Co I and diaphorase I, and a second between diaphorase I and cyto-

* An excellent and most lucid account is given in M. Dixon's *Multienzyme Systems* (Cambridge, 1949).

chrome c, leaving a third to be produced in the reoxidation of the reduced cytochrome. But while the changes of free energy are large enough to account for the formation of new bonds at these stages, there is as yet no evidence to show precisely at what stages they are formed, nor do we know the mechanisms that lead to their generation. Other experiments have shown that the bond yield of the oxidation of succinate to fumarate is only 2, but here no coenzyme or flavoprotein is involved: cytochrome b is the direct hydrogen acceptor and reduces cytochrome c in its turn.

Although these data are only preliminary and will undoubtedly require modification in the light of future work, it seems certain nevertheless that they represent minimal rather than maximal values because more or less serious losses of ATP are encountered in experiments of the kind carried out in this field. In the meantime they may be used to arrive at estimates of the minimal bond yields of a variety of other processes, and an example may not be out of place here.

Recent years have brought much information about the intermediate stages in the oxidation of pyruvate to water and carbon dioxide, for which the following overall reaction may be written:

$$CH_3COCOOH + 5O \rightarrow 3CO_2 + 2H_2O: \quad \triangle F = -274,000 \text{ cal.}$$

The following table summarizes the estimated bond yields of those intermediate reactions in which new energy-rich bonds are known to be formed:

Reaction	Primary H-acceptor	Estimated bond yield
Pyruvate $\rightarrow$ acetate + CO_2	Co I	4
iso-Citrate $\rightarrow$ oxalosuccinate	Co II	3
α-Ketoglutarate $\rightarrow$ succinate	Co I	4
Succinate $\rightarrow$ fumarate	Cytochrome b	2
Malate $\rightarrow$ oxaloacetate	Co I	3
	Total	16

Thus the minimal bond yield, estimated on the basis of the data considered here, corresponds to 16 per g.mol. of pyruvate oxidized, which is equivalent to an energy-capture of 184,000 cal. out of the 274,000 cal. calculated for complete oxidation. This corresponds to a minimum efficiency of energy-capture of no less than 67 % and, as we have pointed out already, the true efficiency may be higher even than this.

PART II

METABOLISM

CHAPTER VIII

METHODS EMPLOYED IN THE INVESTIGATION OF INTERMEDIARY METABOLISM

GENERAL PRINCIPLES

A GREAT variety of methods is available for the study of metabolic processes and it is necessary to have some idea of their applicabilities and limitations. No attempt will be made in this chapter to compile a list of all the methods that are or have been used, but rather to consider in a general way those which are most usually employed. Ideally, of course, metabolic experiments would be carried out under completely normal conditions, but this is seldom possible. The normal organism under normal conditions is a system which ingests certain materials and excretes others, and the conversion of ingesta into excreta proceeds very smoothly. In order to discover the pathways through which metabolism proceeds it is usually necessary to interrupt the normal processes in some way so as to encourage the formation and accumulation of intermediary products, or else to study the organism piece by piece. In the majority of metabolic experiments, therefore, an element of more or less serious abnormality is necessarily introduced.

In an intact, normal animal, to take a specific example, we cannot obtain much information about the metabolism of proteins by straightforward investigation of nitrogenous substances entering and leaving the organism. If proteins are fed to a mammal we find that the ingoing protein-nitrogen emerges again in the form of urea, or in a bird in that of uric acid. Very little more can be discovered. How the nitrogen is detached from the protein, and how it is built up into urea in the one case and into uric acid in the other, we cannot discover without taking the animal more or less to pieces. If, however, we take a mammal from which the liver has been removed, it will survive for some days provided that proteins are withheld from the diet. If a protein meal is given, however, the animal quickly dies. Urea is no longer formed; instead, ammonia appears in the blood and the urine. Furthermore the presence of unusually large amounts of amino-acids in the blood shows that these products of digestion are being absorbed in the usual manner; the free ammonia arises from amino-acids by deamination, chiefly in the kidneys. De-amination therefore takes place in the hepatectomized animal. But whereas ammonia set free by deamination is converted into urea in the normal animal, urea production ceases with hepat-ectomy. It follows, therefore, that the synthesis of urea must probably be accomplished in the liver, and further evidence regarding the mechanisms involved in that synthesis is therefore to be sought by studying the liver.

An alternative method of approach is that of feeding the intact animal with substances, e.g. amino-acids, isotopically 'labelled', e.g. with heavy nitrogen (N^{15}) in place of some or all of the normal nitrogen. The isotopic form is chemically indistinguishable from ordinary nitrogen and will, we may therefore anticipate, suffer the same metabolic fate. But heavy nitrogen can be recognized and estimated by the use of suitable physical methods, and its trail through the organism can therefore be traced. Whereas in the former procedure we used abnormal animals provided with normal foods, we are now using normal animals provided with modified foods. These, in fact, represent the two fundamental methods of approach to the problems of intermediary metabolism in the intact animal. As a rule both methods are used. But even when the broad, main lines of metabolism have been traced out, there still remains the task of analysing them into their separate stages and steps so that, starting with a whole, intact organism, we find ourselves studying organs, tissues, tissue extracts, groups of enzymes and even single, highly purified enzymes, as the work of analysis proceeds.

In general it must be pointed out that all the methods at present available for metabolic studies, whether in whole cells or in whole organisms, are liable to lead to erroneous conclusions on account of abnormalities introduced by the experimental conditions. The fact that such-and-such a reaction can be demonstrated in a given animal preparation or tissue extract is no guarantee that the reaction is one which normally takes place. Evidence from no one source should be regarded as absolutely conclusive, no matter how convincing it may appear: in every case evidence obtained by one method should be checked against evidence obtained by another with different inherent limitations. The fact that individual workers often tend to develop and adhere to one particular technique is much to be regretted, even though the specialization of biochemical methods is rapidly becoming so intense as to make it virtually impossible for any one worker to master more than one or two techniques.

Studies on Normal Organisms

The chief method in which normal, intact organisms are used consists essentially in the administration, by feeding, injection or otherwise, of the material the metabolism of which is to be investigated, followed by the examination of the tissues and excreta for possible intermediate products.

If we assume that a given compound A undergoes conversion through a series of intermediates, B, C, D, etc., to yield in the end a product X, it will in general be possible to detect, isolate and identify X among the excreta. But even this seemingly simple procedure is beset with pitfalls. The substance X, we will suppose, is found in the urine. Unless the urine is analysed very soon after it has been passed, or else is treated with toluene or some other preservative, there is every prospect of heavy bacterial contamination which may transform X into some other substance or substances. The same danger arises much more acutely in the case of faecal analysis for here, even before the faeces are voided at all, they will already have been incubated for some hours in the presence of a massive bacterial population, and under conditions which are about optimal for bacterial growth. To attain complete faecal sterility is virtually impossible and, in consequence, faecal analysis plays a relatively small part in most metabolic studies. This particular difficulty has been overcome in some cases by opening the upper regions of the intestine to the surface by surgical operation, but the animal cannot then be regarded either as intact or as strictly normal.

The possibility of bacterial involvement is of particular importance in work on herbivorous animals, most of which maintain in their alimentary tract great populations of symbiotic microorganisms upon which they rely for the digestion of much of their food. Any substance fed to such an animal will have to run the gamut of these symbionts before it reaches the blood stream of their host, and may be more or less extensively modified in the process. In experiments upon herbivorous animals, such as the rabbit, it is therefore advisable to inject the material to be studied, whether subcutaneously, intravenously or otherwise. For direct feeding experiments carnivorous animals such as dogs and cats are usually preferred, since the inconvenience of injection can thus be avoided. And this fact alone raises further complications, for herbivorous animals and carnivores may differ considerably in their metabolism. It is necessary therefore to be on one's guard against the temptation to argue from a carnivore to a herbivore, and from one species to another.

We have so far considered only the end-products of metabolism. Several methods may be used to discover the nature and identity of the intermediates B, C, D, etc. One usual procedure is to administer massive doses of A. In a reaction sequence $A \rightarrow B \rightarrow C \rightarrow D \rightarrow$ and so on, the rate of the process as a whole will be limited by that of the slowest reaction in the chain, say $D \rightarrow E$. If the system is overloaded by giving massive doses of A, D will tend to accumulate and may therefore appear in the excreta, blood or tissues, in any or all of which it may be sought. But the administration of massive quantities of A may have consequences that we do not anticipate. It is possible that A may be transformed along more lines than one, so that, when the concentration is high, abnormal side-products begin to accumulate. These may be discovered and mistaken for normal intermediates. Again, if D, which in the ordinary way is converted into E as fast as it is formed, attains any appreciable concentration in the tissues, it, too, may be converted into abnormal side-products which may once more be mistaken for normal intermediates. It is usual, therefore, to administer suspected intermediates in fresh feeding or injection experiments and see whether they yield the same products as normally arise from A itself.

Another possibility is that A may normally undergo conversion into several products, B_1, B_2, B_3 and so on, one of which, say B_2, is excreted without further change. Since the only apparent intermediary we shall detect in such a case is B_2, we may be misled into believing that the whole of A is normally transformed into B_2. It is necessary that these various possibilities should be kept in mind in the interpretation of results obtained in feeding or injection experiments: provided they are realized and that due allowance is made for them, valuable information can usually be obtained. Experiments of this kind have done yeoman service in the past and will doubtless continue to do so in the future.

A further method in which intact, normal animals are used involves the chemical alteration of the substance A in such a manner that it and its products can more easily be detected and recognized. Thus Knoop, in his classical experiments on the metabolism of fatty acids, introduced a phenyl radical into the terminal position of the fatty chain and was able then to find aromatic derivatives in the urine of animals to which these ω-phenylated fatty acids had been administered; ω-phenyl valeric acid, for example, gave rise to hippuric acid when given to dogs:

$$C_6H_5.CH_2CH_2CH_2CH_2COOH \rightarrow C_6H_5.CO-HN.CH_2COOH.$$

It was already known that the administration of benzoic acid to dogs gives rise to the appearance of hippuric acid in the urine, and Knoop was therefore able to conclude that phenyl valeric acid is converted into benzoic acid by the animal's tissues.

This method is open to a number of serious objections. First, we cannot assume that if we modify the starting material we shall not alter its fate in the organism, nor, secondly, can we assume that by feeding abnormal material we shall not induce some completely new series of reactions which, in the ordinary way, play no important part in metabolism.

Valuable information has nevertheless been gained in the past from work of this kind, and the method has its present-day counterpart in the use of isotopes, such as heavy hydrogen, heavy nitrogen, radioactive carbon, phosphorus, sulphur and so on, as 'tracers'. These isotopes are not chemically distinguishable from the normal elements, and it may reasonably be supposed therefore that their metabolism will follow normal lines. The isotope method is used extensively at the present time and is an enormous advance on substitution methods of the kind used by Knoop and others among the earlier workers.

Studies on Abnormal Organisms

Organisms that are intact but suffering from some pathological derangement of metabolism offer valuable experimental material for some purposes. Certain very special metabolic abnormalities occur spontaneously, though rarely for the most part. Albinos, for example, are devoid of the enzyme tyrosinase, and may be used in studies of certain aspects of the metabolism of the aromatic amino-acids. The metabolism of tyrosine goes astray in a number of other curious genetic freaks, notably in alcapto-nuria, a disorder in which the urine becomes dark brown or black when allowed to stand exposed to the air. The blackening is due to the presence of a diphenol, homogentisic acid, which arises from the aromatic amino-acids. When the urine is allowed to stand, bacterial invasion takes place and ammonia is formed from urea by the invading organisms. Like many other diphenols, homogentisic acid undergoes spontaneous oxidation in alkaline solution to yield dark-coloured products.

Cases of alcaptonuria were studied in an attempt to decide whether amino-acids undergo oxidative or hydrolytic deamination. Homogentisic acid is no longer excreted if aromatic amino-acids are excluded from the diet. It is reasonable therefore to suppose that any substance which lies on the route between tyrosine and homogentisic acid will, if administered to an alcaptonuric deprived of aromatic amino-acids, give rise to a renewed excretion of homogentisic acid. Now if tyrosine were hydro-lytically deaminated the deamination product would be *p*-hydroxyphenyl-lactic: if oxidatively, the first product would be *p*-hydroxyphenylpyruvic acid. Both these substances were accordingly prepared and separately administered to human patients suffering from alcaptonuria. It was then found that whereas *p*-hydroxyphenylpyruvic acid was almost quantitatively converted into homogentisic acid, none was formed from the corresponding hydroxy-acid. The relationships of these substances are as follows:

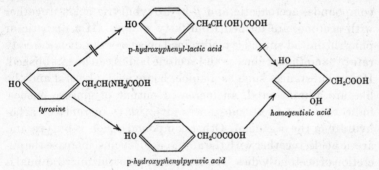

It was concluded that the deamination of tyrosine, and by inference that of other amino-acids, is an oxidative rather than a hydrolytic process.

The danger-points in this argument are, first, the supposition that because *p*-hydroxyphenylpyruvic acid yields homogentisic acid it necessarily lies on the pathway tyrosine → homogentisic acid: it might equally well form homogentisic acid by some independent and possibly abnormal route. Secondly, even if we discount the first objection and take it as established that tyrosine is in fact deaminated with production of the corresponding keto-acid, it is exceedingly dangerous to assume that amino-acids other than tyrosine also undergo oxidative deamination, if only because, in alcaptonuria, the metabolism of tyrosine itself is seriously deranged.

Particularly important among the pathological conditions of which advantage has been taken is the state of diabetes. Spontaneous diabetes, diabetes induced by surgical removal of the pancreas or by injections of alloxan or of the diabetogenic hormone of the anterior pituitary, and the pseudo-diabetes induced by injection of the drug phlorrhizin, have all been put to service, especially in studies of the metabolism of fats and carbohydrates. These animal preparations have two important features in common. First, carbohydrate metabolism is profoundly deranged and glucose, instead of being stored in the liver in the form of glycogen, is eliminated in the urine. Secondly, there is a large-scale excretion of the so-called acetone or ketone bodies. These compounds, acetoacetic and β-hydroxybutyric acids, together with acetone, are formed from fatty sources. If a diabetic or phlorrhizinized animal is maintained on a constant diet, a steady rate of excretion of glucose and acetone bodies can be established. If now substances such as alanine, lactic acid, glycerol and the like are administered, an increased output of glucose ensues, indicating that these substances give rise to or replace carbohydrate in the organism. Other compounds, such as butyric and acetic acids, together with the amino-acid leucine, increase the excretion of acetone bodies. The diabetic or phlorrhizinized animal is thus useful as a device which allows us to detect the formation of carbohydrate and fatty materials from substances of other kinds.

Particularly important among the surgical preparations is the hepatectomized animal. Total removal of the liver is a difficult operation, and the subjects do not survive for more than a few days. An alternative procedure is to establish an Eck's fistula, i.e. to by-pass the liver by leading the portal blood directly into the inferior vena cava. The liver plays a leading part in many metabolic processes, and in its absence these are thrown out of gear or even stopped altogether. Intermediary products tend to pile up and commonly appear in the urine. Mention has already been made of one such case: ammonia produced by the deamination of amino-acids is normally converted into urea by mammalian liver, and into uric acid by the liver of birds, but these synthetic operations cease with removal of the liver or establishment of an Eck's fistula, amino-acids and ammonia accumulating instead. This tells us that urea and uric acid are formed from ammonia and that their synthesis takes place in the liver, but gives no indication of the mode of synthesis. It does, however, serve to show what particular organ we must study in order to elucidate the rest of the story.

The hepatectomized animal is of particular value on account of the central metabolic role of the liver, but pancreatectomized, adrenalectomized, hypophysectomized, thyroidectomized and other preparations have been much employed, especially in attempts to discover the parts played by hormones in the regulation and control of metabolic processes. In all such cases the preparation is abnormal in certain known respects, but it is necessary to realize that processes other than those which we know to be deranged may also be thrown out of gear. Confirmation of results obtained by one method should therefore always be sought, and usually is sought, with the aid of other methods and different preparations.

STUDIES ON PERFUSED ORGANS

It is often possible to study the metabolic activities of a particular organ by providing it artificially with an independent circulation. The organ to be perfused may either be left *in situ* in the animal, or may be removed and kept under conditions that approximate as closely as possible to those which it enjoys under normal physiological conditions. The circulating medium may be the animal's own blood, or blood drawn from another individual of the same species; alternatively, it is possible to use certain physiological salines which we shall discuss presently. The necessary head of pressure may be obtained by means of mechanically operated pumps arranged to imitate the action of the heart, and many types of 'artificial lungs' have been devised for oxygenation of the medium.

The method of artificial perfusion is open to a number of serious objections. It takes time to establish the artificial circulation, and the animal must of course be anaesthetized during the operation. This means that, for the first few minutes, the organ is liable to be influenced by temporary deprivation of oxygen and by the anaesthetic. The choice of anaesthetic has therefore to receive careful consideration. How much damage may be done by the temporary shortage of oxygen is not easy to ascertain but, given speed and skill, damage from this cause can be minimized. If blood is used for the perfusion it is necessary to add an anti-coagulant such as heparin, and the possible action of this upon the organ has to be reckoned with. Care must be taken to ensure that the perfusion medium is kept at the right pressure, temperature, pH and so on, and that it shall be kept well oxygenated, but all these are largely technical matters which can be dealt with, given experience and skill on the part of the operator.

There are, however, other objections that cannot so easily be countered. As long as the organ enjoys its normal blood supply it is exposed to nervous and hormonal influences which cannot be exactly reproduced outside the animal. Thus the liver, a favourite object of study by the perfusion method, plays a great part in the metabolism of carbohydrates, and this, as we know, is profoundly affected by a number of hormones, notably by insulin, adrenaline and certain pituitary and adrenocortical hormones. When the liver is removed from the body the influence of these is withdrawn, and this may be expected to result in abnormal metabolic behaviour. Thus, from the moment at which the normal circulation is replaced by the experimental perfusion system, the organ is exposed to conditions which are abnormal, and probably become progressively more abnormal as time goes on. It is always difficult to be certain that the whole of the organ is actually being perfused, so that parts may be moribund or dead long before the whole. Nevertheless, it does seem that, for the first hour or two, a skilfully manipulated preparation behaves in a manner which approximates fairly closely to normal, and results obtained with such preparations commonly find confirmation by other techniques.

The general procedure, following the successful establishment of the artificial circulation, consists in adding substances of which the metabolism is to be studied to the circulating medium, samples of which are withdrawn from time to time for analysis. Perfusion experiments may be done with liver, muscle, heart, kidney and so on. Large animals are usually preferred since large size facilitates the operative procedure, though it makes considerable demands upon laboratory accommodation at the same time, but the introduction by Trowell of a technique for the perfusion of rat liver may do much to restore the method of liver perfusion to some of its former eminence.

As well-known examples of the successful employment of this method we may refer once more to the classical observation that isolated, perfused dog liver synthesizes urea from added ammonia, goose liver producing uric acid by contrast; and, in addition, to the work of Embden, Friedmann and others on the formation of ketone bodies from fatty acids.

USE OF PHYSIOLOGICAL SALINES

Perhaps the most important single contribution ever made to physiology and biochemistry was the discovery in the early 1880's by Sidney Ringer that simple solutions of the chlorides of sodium, potassium and calcium can maintain the action of the perfused hearts of frogs and tortoises. Subsequent work has shown that with the aid of slightly more complex media the heart-beat of warm-blooded animals also can be maintained for many hours or even days. There is reason to think that, of all the multifarious constituents of mammalian blood, many are specialized features of secondary importance, the ionic constituents alone being absolutely fundamental and essential. Given a supply of well-oxygenated physiological saline at the appropriate temperature, pH and osmotic pressure, it seems that the fundamental physiological requirements even of mammalian tissues can be fulfilled.

Numerous salines have been introduced for specific purposes. They can be used, for example, to replace blood in perfusion experiments, and have been used clinically on a large scale in the past to make up the blood volume after severe haemorrhage. Solutions containing the chlorides of sodium, potassium, calcium and magnesium, together with small amounts of phosphate, are suitable for many purposes, and are best buffered with bicarbonate and carbon dioxide. Glucose is often added to provide 'food' for the tissues. The ionic composition of one such saline is given, side by side with that of the mammalian blood it is designed to imitate, in Table 15; this particular medium has been used extensively by Krebs and others in work involving the use of tissue slices.

TABLE 15. COMPOSITION OF MAMMALIAN BLOOD SERUM AND KREBS'S PHYSIOLOGICAL SALINE

	Mammalian serum (averages)	Physiological saline
Na^+	c. 320	327
K^+	22	23
Ca^{++}	10	10
Mg^{++}	2·5	2·9
Cl^-	370	454
PO_4^-	10	11
SO_4^-	11	11·4
HCO_3^-	54 vol. %	54 vol. %
CO_2 (at 38° C.)	2·5 vol. %	2·5 vol. %
pH	7·4	7·4

All concentrations are in mg. per 100 ml., excepting bicarbonate and carbon dioxide, which are expressed as vol. CO_2 per 100 ml. *Glucose* (0·2%) is also added before use.

.USE OF TISSUE SLICES

In recent years the somewhat messy method of perfusion, making as it does considerable demands upon the surgical skill of the experimenter, has been largely replaced by the use of tissues in the form of thin slices. Provided certain conditions are fulfilled, these slices will survive for some hours, apparently in a manner that approximates closely to the physiological, and are simple to prepare and manipulate. The size of the average cell is such that, although many cells are inevitably damaged when the tissue is sliced, the proportion of damaged to undamaged is very small, while the debris of those that are damaged can be removed fairly completely by washing. Provided the organ to be used is

removed, sliced and washed rapidly, we can obtain small fragments of virtually normal tissue. Their removal from the normal
blood supply of course implies that they are removed also from
the influence of the animal as a whole, just as is the case in
perfusion experiments, but whereas an unknown and often a considerable proportion of the cells in a perfused organ is probably
in a poor if not actually moribund condition, washed tissue slices
contain relatively few cells that are appreciably injured.

Certain conditions must be fulfilled in the preparation and use
of these tissue slices. It is usually convenient to have fragments
one or two centimetres square. Their thickness must be such that
the cells in the middle of the slices, which can acquire oxygen
only by inward diffusion from the medium, do not suffer from
lack of oxygen. Usually, therefore, the medium is kept in equilibrium with an atmosphere containing $2 \cdot 5$–5% of carbon dioxide
for buffering purposes, and $97 \cdot 5$–95% oxygen. If such a gas
mixture is used the slices must not be more than $0 \cdot 3$ mm. thick.
Satisfactory slices can fairly easily be cut free-hand with a sharp
razor.

The usual procedure is as follows. Suitable vessels are filled
with the appropriate saline, through which the gas mixture is
bubbled, the whole being gently shaken in a thermostatic bath
at body temperature. Other samples of the medium are prepared
for washing the slices. The animal is killed, by a blow on the
neck for example, and the organ required is rapidly removed
and placed on clean blotting-paper moistened with warm saline.
Slices are rapidly cut and placed at once in the warm, oxygenated
saline until enough have been accumulated. They are next washed
two or three times and then transferred to the main vessels. The
substances to be studied are added and the whole apparatus is
shaken for a suitable period, during or after which samples of the
medium are withdrawn, deproteinized if necessary, and analysed.

The method is open to several of the criticisms that apply to
the perfusion technique, though others are obviated. No anaesthetic is necessary, and a small animal such as a rat or a guinea-
pig will supply enough material for a number of experiments.
It is possible that the cells may behave abnormally as a result of

their exposure to the high partial pressures of oxygen required to ensure adequate oxygenation of the deeper layers of cells. The method has, however, found wide favour. On account of the small size of the tissue fragments, the method is very suitable for the application of manometric methods which, as is well known, can be used for a very wide range of measurements and estimations on the micro- or semimicro-scale.

USE OF BREIS, HOMOGENATES, EXTRACTS, ETC.

The analysis of a complex series of metabolic events into its component reactions usually provides evidence for the participation of a number of enzymes and accessory catalysts, and for a complete analysis the identification and discovery of the function of each of these is required. To obtain this information it is necessary to separate the enzymes one from another, to destroy some enzymes and preserve others, or in some other way so to disrupt the cellular organization that intermediate products can be discovered. Sometimes this can be done by the use of *specific inhibitors* known to inactivate particular enzymes; in other cases 'trapping' reagents can be employed to fix particular intermediates. More usually it is necessary to extract the enzymes from the tissue, though it sometimes suffices to mince or grind the tissue. The resulting *minces* and '*breis*' contain all the enzymes of the original material, but the normal spatial relationships between them are destroyed by disruption of the cellular architecture.

In recent years the use of *homogenates* has found wide favour. These are prepared by grinding the tissue very finely indeed in a mill consisting of an outer tube and an inner, closely fitting, mechanically driven pestle. The grinding surfaces are roughened by previous grinding with carborundum powder. Complete disintegration of the cells can be easily and rapidly achieved with a good homogenizer. The homogenates contain all the enzymes of the original tissue, and by dilution or washing, which lowers the concentrations of all the substrates, coenzymes and other co-factors, the metabolism of the homogenates can be reduced

to a very low level. The preparations can now be 'fortified' by
the addition of appropriate substrates, co-factors and activators,
so that the activity of one or more particular enzymes is restored
and can be studied independently of the other enzymes present.

The nuclei, mitochondria and other particulate cell-constit-
uents are present intact in homogenates and can be separated
one from another by differential centrifugation. *Washed suspensions of mitochondria* have been much used in studies of
oxidative metabolism since they contain most of the enzymes
involved in cellular respiration and require only to be fortified
with cytochrome c and the necessary coenzymes, usually Mg^{++}
and inorganic phosphate. Co I and Co II are firmly bound to
the mitochondria and are not removed by washing. The further
addition of ADP has been used in studies of coupled phosphorylation, i.e. the synthesis of ATP which is associated with oxidative
metabolism (p. 212).

Many tissue enzymes can be extracted with water or saline, freed
from the general cell debris by filtration or centrifugation, and
later purified. Of the soluble enzymes some tolerate precipitation
with acetone at $0°$ C. and enzymes of this kind can be extracted
with aqueous media, precipitated by means of acetone, and then
extracted again with water or saline from the resulting '*acetone
powders*'.

A fine example of the usefulness of whole *extracts* is found in
the case of yeast juice, which is prepared by macerating the
cells with sand and squeezing the mass in a hydraulic press.
Many of the enzymes extracted in this way require coenzymes,
which can be removed by *dialysis*, and much of our present
knowledge of fermentation has been gained by the use of dialysed
yeast juice, often with supplementary tools in the form of
selective inhibitors. Similarly, the enzymes involved in glycolysis can be obtained in solution by aqueous extraction of
minced muscle, for example.

In the end it is often necessary to have recourse to *purified
enzymes*. Finely divided tissue is allowed to stand with ice-cold
water or isotonic potassium chloride, for example. After centrifugation of the extract to remove the insoluble cell debris it is

possible to purify many enzymes by fractional precipitation, fractional adsorption, and other more specialized procedures, so that highly concentrated preparations are obtained. By further rigorous purification, the details of which vary according to the nature of the enzyme, crystalline preparations are obtainable in many cases. It is well to remember, however, that proteins in general—and enzymes are no exception to the rule—are very prone to the formation of mixed crystals while still far from being chemically pure. Many important enzymes, e.g. cytochrome oxidase and succinic dehydrogenase, are insoluble however. Since they cannot at present be separated from other insoluble enzymes they are usually studied in thoroughly washed and suitably fortified suspensions of finely minced or homogenized tissue. Washed suspensions of mitochondria too are often used.

Detailed knowledge of the processes catalysed by single enzymes often helps us to analyse into several stages a process which seems at first sight to be a single metabolic operation, and information gained by the study of 'built-up' or reconstructed systems, comprising several enzymes and their appropriate accessory catalysts, may give valuable indications of the manner in which the individual stages are organized in the metabolic whole. We shall come across numerous examples of this kind, but for the moment the reader may be reminded of the use of reconstructed systems in the study of the dehydrogenases, and Green's warning apropos of these reconstructions may also be recalled (p. 199).

CHAPTER IX

FOOD, DIGESTION AND ABSORPTION

FOOD

LIVING organisms can be broadly divided into two groups. Some, like the green plants, only require to be provided with simple inorganic materials from which, with the aid of energy drawn from the external world, they can accomplish the synthesis of everything required for their life, growth and reproduction. Others, like the animals, can only live and reproduce if provided with complex, energy-rich, organic materials, collectively designated as food. These two groups of living organisms are known as *autotrophes* and *heterotrophes* respectively.

Predominant among autotrophic organisms are the *green plants*, which are able to fixate and utilize the energy of solar radiation. This is brought to bear, in a manner which is only now beginning to be understood, upon the synthesis of complex energy-rich materials; and, as raw materials for the synthesis, carbon dioxide, water, salts, and some simple source of nitrogen such, for instance, as ammonia or nitrate are all that is necessary. The key substance in photosynthesis, chlorophyll, finds counterparts in the specialized bacterial pigments upon which *photosynthetic bacteria* rely for a comparable fixation of solar energy. In the remaining group of autotrophic organisms, the *chemosynthetic bacteria*, energy is not obtained from the sun but by harnessing the chemical energy of some inorganic process such as the oxidation of ammonia to nitrite or nitrate, the oxidation of hydrogen sulphide to elemental sulphur, or that of ferrous compounds to the ferric state. The autotrophes are in every case competent to synthesize all the structural, catalytic and storage materials they need for growth, maintenance and reproduction: everything their life requires can be produced from the simplest of starting materials, the necessary energy being collected from the external world.

Heterotrophic organisms stand in sharp contrast to the auto-trophes, for not even the most versatile of heterotrophic forms can live except by exploiting the industry and synthetic ingenuity of other organisms. Only by fermenting, oxidizing, or in some other way degrading complex organic material can the heterotrophes obtain the energy required to maintain themselves. It may therefore be said that all heterotrophes require 'food', that is to say oxidizable or fermentable material by the breakdown of which free energy can be released and harnessed for locomotion, chemical synthesis, and other energy-consuming processes.

Many heterotrophic forms of life such, for example, as the *free-living bacteria* and *yeasts*, can live and reproduce in very simple media. Apart from water, salts and some simple source of nitrogen, they need only to be provided with some fairly simple organic compound such, say, as lactate. Given these substances the free-living bacteria can accomplish *de novo* the synthesis of everything their life requires. But many micro-organisms are more exacting. The presence of certain particular compounds in the habitual environment of a given species can lead in the end to the loss within that species of the ability to synthesize the substances in question. Thus many milk-souring bacteria, such as are cultivated for the manufacture of cheese, cannot live or multiply except in media containing riboflavin. Free-living organisms are able to synthesize this important substance for themselves, but these cultivated milk-sourers have lived for so many generations in milk, which is a fairly rich source of riboflavin, that their ability to synthesize it has been lost for lack of employment. For these organisms, riboflavin has become an indispensable accessory food factor; in other words, a vitamin.

The nutritional requirements of many micro-organisms have been carefully investigated in recent years, and there is now abundant evidence that some degree of synthetic disability is a common feature among them. Yeasts which have been carefully nursed and pampered in vineyards and breweries require the provision of a number of the factors that free-living forms can make for themselves, while among bacteria and protozoa many forms, including numerous highly pathogenic strains and species, have been found to have nutritional requirements that are very exacting indeed. Loss of synthetic ability seems to be a step-wise process, for certain bacteria, given β-alanine or nicotinic amide, can synthesize pantothenic acid or Co I respectively, but in other cases it is necessary that these more complicated substances should be given intact; even the ability to join together the constitutional fragments has been lost. The work of Beadle, Tatum and their collaborators and followers on mutant forms of the bread-mould, *Neurospora crassa*, has revealed many examples of step-by-step loss of synthetic ability. This loss of synthetic ability has gone even further in certain micro-organisms than it has in animals, for some of them are unable even to synthesize haematin.

By contrast with green plants, or even with free-living micro-organisms, *animals* are very exacting creatures indeed. In addition to water, salts, and 'food' in the sense of energy-yielding organic substances, animals of every kind need to be provided with certain amino-acids, and with a number of the other indispensable accessory food factors collectively known as vitamins. These include thiamine, riboflavin and nicotinic amide, all three of which are constituents of essential coenzymes. This implies the inability of animals to synthesize many of the tissue constituents and catalysts which they require. More recently evidence has come forward to point to catalytic roles for most of the B group of vitamins including, in addition to those already mentioned, pyridoxal, biotin and pantothenic acid (see Table 16).

These general notions help greatly in the interpretation of the food relationships that exist between living organisms of different kinds. In the words of Charles Elton, 'Animals are not always struggling for existence. They spend most of their time doing nothing in particular. But when they do begin, they spend the greater part of their lives eating. The primary driving force of all animals is the necessity of finding the right kind of food and enough of it.' The 'right kind of food' is largely determined, of course, by the animal's ability to capture and kill other organisms, but on the chemical side we can say that the 'right kind

of food' is that which provides the eater with the energy requirements of its kind and, at the same time, with whatever special
materials are essential to the species in consequence of its
synthetic disabilities.

TABLE 16.   CATALYTIC FUNCTIONS OF SOME MEMBERS
OF THE B GROUP OF VITAMINS

Compound	Present in	Formula see p.
Thiamine	Co-carboxylase; coenzyme of oxidative decarboxylation	351
Nicotinamide	Coenzymes I and II	187
Riboflavin	Prosthetic groups of all flavo-proteins	201
Pyridoxal	Prosthetic groups of transaminases and some decarboxylases	137
Pantothenic acid	Coenzyme A	282
Biotin	Co-factor involved in fixation of CO_2 (bacteria)	—

In any natural animal and plant community we can trace out
what are known as *food chains*. A food chain typically begins
with green plants, which are exploited by herbivorous animals
and these, in their turn, by carnivores. These become the prey of
larger and more powerful carnivores and so on until, in the end,
we arrive at an animal so large and powerful that it has virtually
no enemies except, perhaps, that ubiquitous animal, man. Always
in these food chains the starting-point is with autotrophic
organisms. Herbivorous animals rely at first hand, and carnivores
at second or third hand, upon the autotrophes for supplies of the
numerous essential substances which they require, as well as for
a sufficiency of complex, energy-yielding organic foodstuffs.
Gathered together in the first instance by herbivorous beasts,
these essential materials are passed stage by stage along the food
chains.

The same general ideas are also valuable in the interpretation
of food relationships of other kinds. *Parasitism,* for example,
presents many problems which a thorough knowledge of the
nutritional requirements of parasitic organisms may go far towards solving. We have already seen that the requirements of
a given organism are liable to be influenced by the availability
of particular substances in the environment to which the

organism is accustomed, quite apart from the general physico-chemical properties of the habitat. Many micro-organisms are now confined to particular habitats and have, in fact, become absolutely dependent, i.e. parasitic, upon those habitats because they have lost the ability to synthesize certain substances and can therefore only survive in environments in which those substances are to be found. Very possibly the same will prove to be true of other parasites, such, for instance, as the tape-worms and round-worms that are such a common feature of the intestinal fauna of animals of every kind.

Another important type of nutritional association is *symbiosis*. A cow may harbour large numbers of parasitic worms in addition to the multitude of symbiotic micro-organisms that inhabit its rumen, but the relationships between the cow and the worms on the one hand, and between the cow and its symbionts on the other, are very different. The cow acts virtually as a food-collecting machine for both groups of organisms, but gets nothing in return from its parasitic inhabitants. The symbionts, however, repay their host by breaking down cellulose and other cow-indigestible materials, from which they produce short-chain fatty acids which the cow can utilize. Similar arrangements are found in herbivores of many kinds, from cows to cockroaches. But the host member of the pair stands to gain yet further rewards for hospitality rendered. Some at least of the symbionts can synthesize from very simple materials all the amino-acids and vitamins that they themselves require. These compounds become incorporated in the first instance into the substance of the symbionts, but these organisms are not immortal. When they die and undergo eventual autolysis or digestion by the host's enzymes, their essential amino-acids and vitamins become available to the host, at any rate in part. There can be little doubt that some herbivores depend largely upon their intestinal flora and fauna for supplies of essential accessory food materials, though it may be doubted whether supplies from these sources are ever sufficient by themselves.

Provided that their somewhat exacting nutritional requirements are fulfilled and that sufficient energy-yielding substances are available, heterotrophic organisms such as the mammals are capable of dismantling their food materials and rearranging the component parts in a very versatile manner. From its food proteins, for instance, an animal can build up the species-specific proteins that are characteristic of its own tissues and secretions; carbohydrates and even fats can be produced from the deaminated residues of superfluous amino-acids; carbohydrates can be converted into fats and so on. Herbivorous animals can lay down both carbohydrate and fat at the expense of the short-chain fatty acids produced by the exertions of their intestinal symbionts.

The first steps in this direction consist in the digestion and absorption of the food, and these are followed by storage or metabolism of the ingested materials. By *digestion* we mean the hydrolytic breakdown of food materials, which consist preeminently of relatively large molecules, into simpler compounds from which a given organism can build up its own tissues and food reserves. This definition is one that can be widely interpreted, for the food may be the food eaten by an animal, on the one hand, or, on the other, it may comprise the materials provided in a seed or an egg for the embryonic development of a plant or an animal. A seedling plant is as heterotrophic as any animal until it reaches the daylight and can begin photosynthetic activities on its own account.

The seeds of plants contain considerable reserves of organic foodstuffs from which new plants can develop. At or before the time of germination, enzymes are present which may be said to have digestive functions, since they serve to dismantle the food materials into simpler components which the young plant then oxidizes or rearranges in its own characteristic manner. The seeds of the castor-oil plant, *Ricinus*, are rich in oils and contain a powerful lipase. Barley, which is rich in starch, contains powerful α- and β-amylases and a maltase at germination. More is known, perhaps, about the enzymes of the jack-bean than of any other seed, if only because it has been so much exploited as a source of urease. A veritable army of enzymes has been described here, for apart from urease itself, this bean contains an amylase, a lipase and a pectinase, together with peroxidase, catalase and several others.

Among animals digestion may be accomplished in either of two main ways. The food may be phagocytically ingested and then intracellularly digested, or it may undergo extracellular digestion before being absorbed. Often both mechanisms are used side by side in one and the same animal. Intracellular digestion is probably more primitive than its extracellular counterpart, for phagocytosis is only possible for particles up to a certain order of size. That extracellular digestion arose as an adaptation to the necessity of breaking up relatively large food masses prior to absorption seems very likely, and it is probably significant in this respect that the peptidases involved in the extracellular digestion of proteins in the mammals are known to be qualitatively and quantitatively homospecific with the intracellular peptidases or kathepsins. In some animals it is possible to observe what seems to be a transitional process that is neither entirely intracellular nor wholly extracellular. In certain platyhelminth worms, for instance, the gut is lined with cells endowed with considerable amoeboid activity. When food is taken, these cells absorb water from it and swell up, sending out processes which form a syncytial network that fills the gut cavity and enmeshes the food mass. Digestion takes place within the syncytium, which is later withdrawn. In some cases, however, a syncytium is formed but withdrawn before digestion has proceeded very far, and digestion continues even in its absence. Here it would appear that the function of the syncytium has been discharged once the enzymes it can provide have been liberated.

In many organisms, notably among the protozoa and sponges, phagocytosis followed by intracellular digestion is the only mechanism available for assimilation, but in other phyla it is not uncommon to find both the intracellular and extracellular modes of digestion used together. It usually appears in cases such as these that if an animal is carnivorous its extracellular enzymes are those which act upon proteins; if it is herbivorous the extracellular enzymes are those that act upon carbohydrates. Thus among the coelenterates, which are mainly carnivorous, proteinases are secreted by the walls of the coelenteron while non-protein materials are digested intracellularly. Similarly, the only extracellular digestive enzymes found among lamellibranch molluscs, which are almost exclusively herbivorous, are amylases. The general disintegration of the food mass that results from the action of extracellular enzymes is usually facilitated by mechanical movements of the walls of the digestive cavity, so that the mass is eventually reduced to a particulate dispersion fine enough to allow of phagocytosis, and digestion is subsequently completed within the cells. But when we come to animals as complex and as highly specialized as the mammals we find that digestion is entirely extracellular. Indeed, the only remnant of the phagocytic systems which are so important among invertebrates is that found in the wandering scavenger cells of the reticulo-endothelial system.

Relatively little is known about the digestive processes of invertebrates, but the very large literature of the subject indicates, in a general manner, that animals as a whole are equipped with enzymes competent to break down fats, proteins and carbohydrates into their simple constituents. Proteinases, lipases and carbohydrates have been detected, either in the extracellular digestive juices or in the cells of the digestive glands themselves, in a very large number of cases. It is not always possible to be sure that, because a protein-splitting enzyme is demonstrably present in the cells of a digestive gland, it necessarily has a digestive function. Intracellular proteinases have nevertheless been described having pH optima in rather strongly acid or weakly alkaline media, and thus resembling pepsin and trypsin. In such cases it is possible that the enzymes in question are concerned with digestion. However, other proteinases have been extracted which have optimal proteolytic activity in the region of neutrality, and, in cases like this, it is at least equally likely that their function is akin to that of the kathepsins.

The nature of the chemical operations involved in digestion appears to be substantially the same in all kinds of animals, whether digestion is intra- or extracellular. Most is known about these processes and the enzymes which catalyse them in the mammals, and the ensuing description of digestion will relate mainly to these animals.

It is not unusual to think of digestion as a process which is divisible into a series of nicely defined steps, each of which leads to equally nicely defined products. We find in the text-books an abundance of statements to the effect that pepsin digests proteins thus far and no farther, that trypsin digests them farther to another definite point, and so on. While it is perfectly true that each enzyme, taken by itself, will carry out certain perfectly definite operations and cease acting when these have been accomplished, it must be remembered that digestion is not carried out in this manner. Food that has passed into the small intestine of a mammal, for example, is exposed to the simultaneous activities of all the pancreatic and intestinal enzymes, and its digestion is not separable into a series of discrete steps and stages but is, rather, a continuous process. The fact that the digestive secretions of animals have been resolved into a number of individual catalysts, each of which can be studied separately, has tended somewhat to encourage the step-by-step outlook on digestion as a whole. Perhaps the best way to check this tendency is to think of the enzymes involved in digestion, not as a mere collection of catalysts, but rather as an organized *system* of catalysts, so ordered and regulated as to carry out a long and complex but nevertheless continuous chain of processes.

The products of digestion form the raw materials for the processes of *metabolism*, a general term used to cover all the chemical changes going on in the cells and tissues of living organisms. These changes may result in a chemical simplification of the starting material, in which case we speak of *katabolism*, or in an increase of chemical complexity, when we speak of *anabolism* (cf. Chap. III). Katabolic changes are usually associated with the liberation of a larger or smaller part of the free energy of the starting material and are therefore said to be *exergonic*. A larger or smaller part of this energy can be harnessed by the organism and used for the performance of work of some kind, e.g. in locomotion or chemical synthesis. Anabolic processes, on the other hand, are usually *endergonic*, i.e. they are attended by an uptake of free energy. This energy is drawn from concomitant katabolism or, in autotrophes, from the external world.

Living organisms of every kind appear to be able to accomplish anabolism at the expense of katabolism, but the ability to carry out anabolic changes at the expense of external energy is the prerogative of autotrophic organisms. Thus, when we are studying processes of katabolism we should have constantly in mind the question, how much energy becomes available to the organism? We may also ask in what form it becomes available, and how it is converted into chemical, mechanical, electrical, thermal or osmotic work as the case may be. Similarly, when anabolic changes are being considered, we must inquire whence and in what form the necessary energy is forthcoming, and how it is transferred from its source to its intramolecular destination. These are important questions; questions which, moreover, have remained practically unanswered and unanswerable until very recent times, but at last we have a few clear indications on which we may hope to found a new knowledge of biological energetics.

Before going on to consider metabolism in detail it is desirable to examine the phenomena of digestion, taking our information mainly from the mammals. This task we shall attempt in the rest of this chapter.

Digestion and Absorption of Proteins

Saliva contains no proteolytic enzyme, and the first phase of digestion takes place in the stomach under the influence of pepsin. Pepsin, it will be remembered, is secreted in the form of an enzymically inactive precursor, pepsinogen. This is activated by the hydrochloric acid of the gastric juice, which provides at the same time an acid medium of which the pH is about optimal for the action of pepsin. The latter, which acts more rapidly upon denatured than upon native proteins, opens up certain particular peptide links in its substrates, but whether or not it is able to complete its work depends a good deal on the consistency of the gastric contents. As soon as these have become liquid they are forced through the pyloric sphincter, whether peptic digestion has been completed or not.

After its passage through the pylorus the partially digested food mass, or chyme, is mixed with the pancreatic juice and the bile. Taken together, these secretions contain about enough free alkali to neutralize the acid that has come through from the stomach, and the pH of the intestinal contents is brought nearly to neutrality. It was formerly believed that the pH is about 8·5 at this stage, but more recent measurements show that it usually lies between pH 6·5 and 7.

Trypsinogen and chymotrypsinogen, activated by enterokinase and by trypsin respectively, yield trypsin and chymotrypsin. These enzymes continue the process of hydrolytic disintegration begun by pepsin and open up more, but different, peptide links, to produce peptide fragments much smaller than the original food proteins. Few free amino-acid molecules are produced at this stage. Carboxypeptidases, contributed by the pancreatic juice, and aminopeptidases, secreted by the intestine, take up the task of degrading the polypeptide fragments inwards from the ends, liberating amino-acid molecules one at a time until, when the dipeptide stage is reached, the substrates pass out of their range of specificity and into that of the dipeptidases of the intestinal secretions, and these complete the digestion. Eventually, therefore, the amino-acids which enter into the composition of the food proteins are set free, absorbed into the portal blood stream, and carried away into the general circulation by way of the liver.

In the past there has been considerable discussion as to whether protein foodstuffs are, in fact, completely broken down into their constituent amino-acids before being absorbed. Some favoured this view, while others believed that so long as the protein has been reduced to some soluble form such, for example, as a mixture of peptones, the function of the digestive enzymes has been satisfactorily discharged. There is now evidence in plenty to show that the latter view is erroneous. In the first place it is unlikely that peptones are absorbed as such because, if peptones are injected into the blood stream of mammals, a condition known as 'peptone shock' results, but nothing comparable follows the consumption of a protein meal. Abel, using an ingenious technique known as vividiffusion, showed that amino-acids, but no protein fragments of larger size, can be detected in the blood leaving those regions of the gut from which absorption takes place. This he did by leading off the emergent blood through a series of collodion tubes immersed in warm physiological saline, and returning it then to the circulation. After this performance he was able to isolate several amino-acids from the saline medium and to detect the presence of a number of others by chemical tests, but no trace of products more complex than the amino-acids could be detected. There is, moreover, a large increase in the concentration of free amino-acid nitrogen in the blood while absorption is taking place in a normal animal. It may also be argued, though perhaps the argument savours a little of teleology, that animals do in fact possess a series of enzymes capable of carrying digestion right through to the free amino-acid stage, and that these enzymes would hardly have been perpetuated in the course of evolution unless they were of some use, i.e. survival value, to the organism. Finally, there is the telling fact that certain students have acquired considerable fame for themselves by consenting over considerable periods to the replacement of their dietary protein by mixtures of purified amino-acids without, however, appearing any the worse for the experience.

DIGESTION AND ABSORPTION OF CARBOHYDRATES

Few animals are equipped with enzymes capable of attacking cellulose, although this polysaccharide plays a very large part in the nutrition of herbivorous animals. In these creatures the task of digesting cellulose is usually delegated to vast hordes of symbiotic micro-organisms (p. 99), and the useful products of their activity consist in the main of short-chain fatty acids. The mechanisms of this degradation are complex, if only because many different kinds of micro-organisms are involved. The details of the process are being actively investigated.

Like cellulose, the so-called hemicelluloses (xylans, arabans, mannans, galactans, etc.) and fructofuranosans (such as the levans of grasses and the inulins of the Jerusalem artichoke and other Compositae) are not digestible by the enzymes of most animals, although they can be handled by symbiotic micro-organisms and probably yield products similar to those formed from cellulose.

The digestion of starch and glycogen is initiated by salivary amylase but, unless the eater follows the precept of Mr Gladstone and chews each mouthful of food quite an unbelievable number of times, little digestion takes place in the mouth. The food, more or less intimately mixed with saliva, is swallowed and passes on into the stomach. Although the optimal pH for salivary digestion lies very near to neutrality, the secretion of the strongly acid gastric juice does not put a sudden end to salivary digestion because it takes time for the acid to penetrate into the food bolus. The consistency of the food mass is therefore an important factor. Eventually, however, the free acid of the gastric contents reduces the pH to a value at which the salivary amylase is inactive and is actually destroyed, but in the meantime starch and glycogen alike have been at least partly broken down to yield maltose, together with some maltotriose and, if digestion is not yet complete, some dextrins.

The gastric juice itself contains no carbohydrase, but a notable concentration of free hydrochloric acid is present and contributes something to the digestion of carbohydrates containing fructofuranose units. Fructofuranosides such as sucrose and inulin are hydrolysed with great ease and rapidity by warm, dilute mineral acids, and it is probable, therefore, that substances such as these undergo at any rate a partial hydrolysis during their stay in the stomach. The hydrolytic activities of the hydrochloric acid are cut short when the chyme passes through the pyloric sphincter and into the duodenum, where it encounters the strongly alkaline pancreatic juice and bile. Here the pH rises nearly to neutrality, and under these conditions the amylase of the pancreatic juice has almost its optimal activity. This enzyme finishes the work begun by the salivary amylase, and the conversion of starch and glycogen into maltose is completed. Some free glucose is produced at the same time.

Maltose, however, is only a transitory product, for it is rapidly hydrolysed under the influence of an α-glucosidase, the so-called 'maltase' of the intestinal juice. This secretion also contains a powerful glucosaccharase, which completes the hydrolysis of sucrose, and a β-galactosidase, 'lactase', that deals with lactose. Ultimately, therefore, the digestible carbohydrates of the food are resolved into their constituent monosaccharides and in this form they are absorbed from the gut. It is improbable that appreciable quantities of di- or higher saccharides are absorbed because, as is known from injection experiments, disaccharides present in the blood stream are largely excreted unchanged, and it is only in exceptional and probably abnormal cases that disaccharides appear in the urine, though lactosuria is common during pregnancy and lactation.

The rates of absorption of different monosaccharides vary much more widely than might have been expected in view of the fact that all hexoses have the same molecular weight, while that of the pentoses is not very different. It follows, therefore, that the absorption of sugars from the gut cannot be explained in terms simply of diffusion. The same conclusion follows from the fact that glucose, for example, can be absorbed from very strong solutions, and therefore against large osmotic gradients. Many experiments have been made to discover what mechanisms are involved in the absorption.

The rate of absorption can be determined by opening up an experimental animal such as a rat, and introducing a known amount of the sugar to be studied into a loop of intestine, previously tied off at both ends. The animal is kept for a known length of time, and the contents of the intestinal loop are removed and analysed. The amount of sugar absorbed is then found by difference. While experiments carried out on these lines show that galactose and glucose are absorbed much more rapidly than other sugars, they are open to criticism. There is, in the first place, a definite possibility that direct damage may be done to the gut, and it is also possible that the anaesthetic that must necessarily be used may interfere with the normal processes of absorption. But other methods of investigation are possible and yield substantially the same results. Cori, working on un-anaesthetized rats which he fed by stomach-tube, obtained the results shown in Table 17. Other workers, including Verzár and his co-workers, obtained substantially the same figures, though rather different ratios have been found in different animal species.

TABLE 17. ABSORPTION OF MONOSACCHARIDES FROM THE SMALL INTESTINE OF RATS

(*After* Cori)

Sugar	Relative rate of absorption
D-Galactose	110
D-Glucose	100
D-Fructose	43
D-Mannose	19
L-Xylose	15
L-Arabinose	9

Pentoses are absorbed at the same rate as indifferent substances such as sodium sulphate. Galactose and glucose are absorbed so much more rapidly than the rest that a special mechanism of some kind must be deemed to be involved in their case. Verzár believed that this consists in the phosphorylation of the sugars in the gut mucosa under the influence of a phosphatase which is demonstrably present in the cells. He showed that the selective absorption of glucose and galactose can be abolished by adding iodoacetate or phlorrhizin to the contents of tied-off intestinal loops, and that absorption in the intact animal is much delayed by previous injection of these drugs. Both phlorrhizin and iodoacetate are known to be powerful inhibitors of fermentation and glycolysis, and in both these processes phosphorylation is known to play a fundamental part. Verzár therefore regarded his results as evidence that phosphorylation is involved in the absorption of sugars from the intestine.

Verzár's observations might be regarded as strong evidence in favour of his contention if it were definitely known that iodoacetate inhibits phosphatases specifically, but there is no indication that this is the case. Iodoacetate is known to inhibit several of the enzymes concerned in glycolysis and in fermentation, but there is no reason at present to believe that it directly inhibits enzymes concerned only with phosphorylation. The most probable explanation of the action of iodoacetate lies in the fact, that, for energetic reasons, the phosphorylation of glucose requires the participation of ATP and hexokinase. The provision of ATP depends in turn upon glycolysis and oxidation, which are known to be powerfully inhibited by iodoacetate. The interference of iodoacetate in the normal absorption of glucose is probably due, therefore, to inhibition of ATP formation rather than to any inhibitory effect it might have upon the gut phosphatase, and in any case the phosphorylation of free glucose requires an uptake of *c*. 3000 cal. of free energy per g.mol. and is most unlikely, therefore, to be accomplished by a phosphatase, except possibly by a low-energy transfer reaction of the kind which certain phosphatases are known to catalyse (p. 123).

A point of interest may be added in passing. It is well known that phlorrhizin also abolishes the reabsorption of glucose from the urine by the cells of the kidney tubule, as well as its specific absorption from the small intestine. Phlorrhizin, like iodoacetate, is a powerful inhibitor of glycolysis and oxidation, and the facts suggest that the intestine and the renal tubule alike carry out the work of absorption by essentially similar mechanisms.

DIGESTION AND ABSORPTION OF FATS

Saliva contains no lipase and, while the presence of a lipase in the gastric juice has been reported in a number of cases, the activity of the alleged gastric lipase at the pH of the gastric contents is such that it can be of little importance in digestion. Many authors believe that it must be regarded as pancreatic lipase that has regurgitated from the small intestine. But although no appreciable digestion takes place in the stomach, the fats of the food are warmed and softened, if not actually liquefied. When presently the chyme is somewhat forcibly squirted into the duodenum there is a marked tendency for the fat to become emulsified, a tendency which is emphasized by the presence of bile salts. The commonest representatives of this important group of substances are conjugated derivatives of cholic acid with glycine and taurine. They are remarkable for their property of very greatly reducing the surface tension at fat/water interfaces, and for this reason not only facilitate emulsification but tend to stabilize an emulsion once it has been formed.

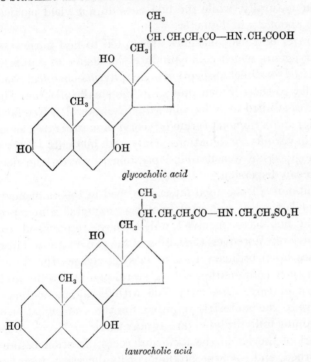

glycocholic acid

taurocholic acid

Until the beginning of the century it was generally believed that finely emulsified fat can be absorbed without previous digestion, but it appears that the bile salts alone cannot produce a sufficiently fine dispersion. Finer emulsions can be prepared with the aid of sodium cetyl sulphate, a synthetic wetting agent, and if emulsions made in this way are introduced into the duodenum of rats, the dispersed fat particles are absorbed. Sodium cetyl sulphate inhibits the action of the digestive lipases, and we have therefore to conclude that direct absorption of unhydrolysed fats can, indeed, take place. Even paraffin can be similarly absorbed, provided only that it is sufficiently finely dispersed. The essential conditions for absorption are, according to Frazer, that the particles shall be less than $0.5\,\mu$ in diameter and that they shall be negatively charged. Sodium cetyl sulphate gives emulsions in which these conditions are fulfilled, but does not occur naturally, while the bile salts do not yield particles less than about $2\,\mu$ in diameter.

Frazer and his colleagues attempted to find natural emulsifying agents which could produce the degree of emulsification required for direct absorption under physico-chemical conditions similar to those which prevail in the small intestine. The substances studied included bile salts, cholesterol, a free fatty acid (oleic) and a monoglyceride (glyceryl monostearate), separately and in various combinations. Only with bile salts + fatty acid + monoglyceride was it found possible to obtain the necessary degree of dispersion.

But not all the food fat is absorbed in the emulsified form. Animals possess powerful lipolytic enzymes, which probably would not have survived unless they were useful to their possessors. Moreover, the action of the pancreatic and intestinal lipases upon ordinary neutral fats disengages the fatty acids from their combination with glycerol one at a time, giving, at first, a mixture of free fatty acids with di- and monoglycerides—precisely the materials required for the emulsification of the remaining unhydrolysed fat. It may therefore be concluded that a part of the fat of the food undergoes digestion before being absorbed, and that the products of its digestion, together with the bile salts, facilitate the emulsification of the remainder, which is then absorbed without previous digestive hydrolysis.

Digestion is carried out in the small intestine under the influence of pancreatic and intestinal lipases. At the pH prevailing in the small gut, the eventual products of hydrolysis are glycerol on the one hand and free fatty acids on the other. It was formerly supposed that the gut contents are alkaline (pH 8–9) in this region, and that the fatty acids are accordingly neutralized to form soaps. These substances are appreciably soluble in water, and their absorption seemed to offer no problems. More recent estimates put the pH at 6·5–7·5 however, and in this range soaps do not exist necessarily as such, but may give rise to free fatty acids. Soaps, moreover, are powerful haemolytic agents, while ulceration of the colon following the use of soap enemata is not an unknown occurrence. Soaps, then, are probably not formed. Free fatty acids, by contrast with the soaps, are characteristically insoluble in water, and the manner of their absorption is therefore more problematical.

Bile salts probably aid the digestion of lipoid materials by facilitating their emulsification and so presenting the digestive lipases with a larger surface upon which to attack their substrates. But bile salts are not essential for digestion. In experimental animals in which the bile duct has been ligated, or in human subjects in whom the bile duct is occluded, e.g. by the presence of gall stones, fat is still digested, as is attested by the presence of free fatty acids in the faeces. Again, if a fat such as olive oil is introduced into a tied-off loop of intestine, with or without the addition of bile salts, no absorption takes place, but if a small amount of lipase is also added, the contents of the loop undergo digestion. But the oleic acid liberated is only absorbed if bile salts were introduced into the loop at the outset. Thus bile salts play some part in the absorption of free fatty acids, as well as in that of unhydrolysed fat.

This is attributed to the so-called hydrotropic action of the bile salts, i.e. their ability to form water-soluble complexes with fatty acids. This effect can be demonstrated readily enough by adding a solution of sodium glyco- or taurocholate to an aqueous emulsion of a fatty acid. If enough bile salt is added, the emulsion becomes water-clear. The simplest and smallest molecular complexes formed in this way are believed to contain one molecule of fatty acid and four of bile salt, but larger aggregates can be formed with fatty acid : bile salt ratios of 2 : 7, 3 : 8, 4 : 9, and so on. The ability of these complexes to pass through a membrane will therefore be determined by the relative proportions of fatty acids and bile salts. If the fatty acid : bile salt ratio is low the particles will be small, and their ability to pass through the intestinal barrier will be proportionately greater. This hydrotropic effect on the part of the bile salts is exerted upon other lipid materials such as cholesterol, but does not extend to unhydrolysed fats.

TABLE 18. ABSORPTION OF FATTY ACIDS
(*After* Verzár)

Contents of intestinal loop	Oleic acid absorbed in 6 hr.
Oleic acid + bile salt	29·3
Oleic acid + glycerol + bile salt	24·9
Oleic acid + phosphate + bile salt	10·3
Oleic acid + phosphate + glycerol + bile salt	48·9
Oleic acid + phosphoglycerol + bile salt	72·7
Oleic acid + phosphoglycerol + bile salt + iodoacetate	0

Many experiments were carried out by Verzár and his colleagues on the absorption of fatty acids, but in discussing them it is well to remember that, at the time, Verzár himself was of the opinion that fats must be fully hydrolysed before they can be absorbed. In his experiments, which were carried out earlier than those of Frazer, use was made of tied-off intestinal loops. Oleic acid and bile salts were introduced into the loops in all the experiments, together with the other substances indicated in Table 18, which is taken from his work. Neither glycerol nor phosphate alone leads to any acceleration of absorption, but if both are present together the rate increases two or three times. This suggests the possible formation of some compound of fatty acids with glycerol and phosphate, i.e. of a lecithin-like substance. Compounds of this type are soluble in water and might therefore be freely absorbed. In lecithin itself, it will be remembered, glycerol is present in combination with phosphoric acid, and the fact that fatty acids are absorbed nearly twice as fast in the presence of phosphoglycerol as when its components are present separately adds considerably to the probability that a phospholipid of some kind is indeed formed.

Like the absorption of sugars, that of fatty acids is inhibited by phlorrhizin and by iodoacetate, probably for the same reasons as in the absorption of glucose. Phosphorylation is probably again involved, for the phospholipid content of the blood is higher during the absorption of a fatty meal than it is at any other time, while the phospholipid content of the intestinal lymph rises from a resting level of about 2·2 to about 7·5 mg. % while fat absorption is taking place. Furthermore, if an animal is fed with fat that has been 'labelled' with iodine or with heavy hydrogen, iodized or deuterated phospholipids can be recovered from the gut mucosa while absorption is in progress. It seems likely, therefore, that fatty acids are transported into the cells of the mucosa, presumably in the form of water-soluble complexes with bile salts, and then condensed with phosphate and glycerol to form substances resembling lecithin.

Phospholipids of the lecithin group typically contain a nitrogenous base, usually choline or ethanolamine, in addition to glycerol, phosphoric and fatty acids, but since some at least of the glycerol and phosphate required for the synthesis of the presumptive phospholipid must probably be provided by the epithelial cells during normal absorption, it is not inconceivable that, if a nitrogenous base is required, it too can be furnished by the cells.

It appears, then, that a part of the food fat is digested by the pancreatic and intestinal lipases, and that the products of partial digestion, aided by bile salts, serve to emulsify the remainder so finely that it can pass through the intestinal wall without previous hydrolysis. How much of the total fat undergoes digestion and how much is absorbed directly is not certainly known. Probably it is reasonable to estimate that from one-quarter to one-third undergoes hydrolysis and that the rest, after emulsification, is directly absorbed.

Fat which is absorbed in the emulsified condition passes into the cells of the gut wall, in which it can be observed in the form of minute droplets which stain with dyes such as Sudan III and have in fact all the histological characteristics of neutral fat. From the cells these droplets, the chylomicrons, make their way into the lacteals and hence, through the lymphatic system and the thoracic duct, into the blood stream, where they are responsible for the condition of post-absorptive lipaemia. That part of the fat which undergoes hydrolysis is ultimately resolved into glycerol and free fatty acids. The latter pass into the intestinal mucosa, apparently in the form of water-soluble complexes with bile salts, and here they appear to be built up into phospholipids of some kind. These too pass into the lymph, for in experiments in which isotopically labelled pentadecanoic acid was administered to experimental animals, the isotope was quantitatively recovered in the effluent from a cannula tied into the thoracic duct.

CHAPTER X

GENERAL METABOLISM OF PROTEINS AND AMINO-ACIDS

FUNCTIONS AND FATE OF PROTEINS AND AMINO-ACIDS

PROTEINS constitute an indispensable article of food for all animals. We have abundant direct evidence from feeding experiments that the usual laboratory animals require supplies of certain amino-acids, notably tryptophan, lysine and histidine, not only for growth while the animal is young, but also for the maintenance of normal physiological condition during adult life. These *essential amino-acids* are only to be found in proteins, and protein foodstuffs are therefore indispensable. In most and probably all herbivores an indirect, secondary source of essential amino-acids is found in the tissue proteins of symbiotic microorganisms inhabiting the gut but, although the value of this supplement may be considerable in some cases, we do not know if it is ever sufficient alone. Evidence regarding the amino-acid requirements of invertebrate animals, unfortunately, is scanty. What information we have relates mostly to insects, but does not give grounds for supposing that their ingenuity in amino-acid synthesis is any greater than our own. Tryptophan, lysine and histidine seem to be essential for animals of every kind.

The naturally occurring amino-acids can be classified as in Table 19. Under the heading of essential amino-acids are some that can be replaced by other members of the essential group; thus tyrosine can be formed from phenylalanine, while cysteine can be produced if methionine is available. But the reverse is not possible. Provided that enough phenylalanine is available to discharge the essential and characteristic functions of phenylalanine itself, *and* to produce at the same time enough tyrosine to fulfil those of tyrosine, tyrosine itself need not be provided. Tyrosine, however, cannot discharge the functions of phenylalanine. Glycine, aspartic and glutamic acids, by contrast, need not be provided at all; these the organism can make for itself from non-protein materials, and of all the amino-acids that enter into the composition of the tissue and other proteins, there are less than ten which the animal organism can produce by its own resources.

TABLE 19. NUTRITIONAL STATUS OF AMINO-ACIDS

| | Essential | |
Non-essential	Irreplaceable	Replaceable
Glycine	Threonine	
Alanine	Valine ✓	
Serine	Leucine ✓	
Aspartic acid	isoLeucine ✓	
Glutamic acid	Methionine	Cysteine : cystine
Proline	Phenylalanine ✓	Tyrosine
Hydroxyproline	Histidine ✓	
Arginine	Tryptophan	
	Lysine ✓	
	Arginine ✓	

The position of arginine, which figures as essential and as non-essential alike, calls for special comment. Adult rats remain alive and healthy, and young rats grow, on diets wholly devoid of arginine. But the growth of young rats on an arginine-deficient diet can be accelerated by the administration of arginine. A similar effect has been observed in chickens. It is therefore probable that, while the growing animal can evidently synthesize arginine to some extent, it cannot do so fast enough to keep pace with the requirements of optimal growth. It may be, indeed, that important substances other than arginine are synthesized slowly enough to limit the growth-rate of young organisms.

Amino-acids, essential and non-essential alike, are required for numerous purposes. Quite apart from the special products to which particular individual amino-acids give rise, new tissue proteins must be synthesized, damaged or wasted tissues must be repaired or replaced, and normal supplies of enzymes and hormones must constantly be maintained. The formation of adrenaline and thyroxine, for example, makes essential the provision of tyrosine (or phenylalanine), to which they are closely related and from which they are in all probability produced, as witness their respective formulae:

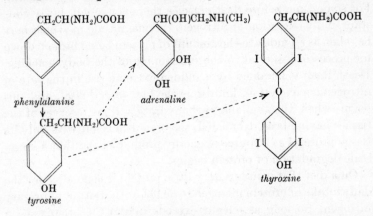

The production of another hormone, insulin, makes particularly heavy demands upon the supplies of essential amino-acids, for it is a polypeptide containing about 16 % leucines, 8 % phenylalanine, 12 % tyrosine, 4 % histidine, 3 % threonine, 2 % lysine and 12 % cystine.

Provided that the food proteins contain enough of all the amino-acids that are essential, the organism can probably make good any deficiency of the rest, although, in the ordinary way, it is not likely to be called upon to do so. The essential amino-acids are, on the whole, the least common, so that an adequate intake of these in the form of protein is necessarily attended by an adequate intake of the rest. It is necessary, however, that the amino-acids required should be presented to the organism all at one time, as they are if an adequate meal of protein is taken. Amino-acids that are not more or less immediately incorporated into tissue or other proteins undergo deamination, be they essential or non-essential, and are therefore lost for purposes of protein synthesis. This has been demonstrated by feeding a variety of mixtures of purified amino-acids simultaneously and at different times.

The elaboration of hormones, enzymes and other special products still goes on even during starvation, when it can only be done at the expense of the tissue proteins. Prolonged deprivation of protein therefore leads to emaciation and eventually to death. For some time before death ensues there is a small, fairly constant, daily excretion of nitrogen, the magnitude of which may be taken as an index to the amount of protein being broken down for processes essential to the functioning of the body machine. Death itself is heralded by a sudden extreme rise in the rate of nitrogenous excretion, known as the 'pre-mortal rise', and this begins when, the available carbohydrate and fat reserves of the tissues having been exhausted, the organism is left with only its tissue proteins as a source of energy production, so that a large-scale degradation of protein begins.

On a diet that contains very little protein it is possible for the daily intake of protein nitrogen to lie below the output of urinary nitrogen. So long as output exceeds intake the organism, on balance, is the loser, and the deficit of nitrogen is withdrawn from the tissues. If, however, the protein allowance is gradually increased, a point is eventually reached at which intake just suffices to balance output. The organism is then said to be in a state of *nitrogenous equilibrium*. The amount of protein required just to attain this equilibrium condition in a given individual is therefore a measure of the *minimum protein requirement* of that individual, and since proteins are among the most expensive articles of food, this is a matter of economic as well as academic interest. Many workers have accordingly investigated the minimum protein requirements of the human organism, and the results obtained have been very variable indeed. Rubner and his colleagues put it at about 100–120 g. protein per diem for an average man, whereas Chittenden, using himself as the experimental animal, found that he could satisfy his personal requirements with only some 30–35 g. per diem, his health improving as a result of the experiment. These large differences do not, as might at first appear, merely reflect differences in individual requirements, but differences rather in the chemical nature of the food proteins chosen. These proteins must supply enough of the essential amino-acids, and no amount of protein, however great, that fails to accomplish this can suffice to establish nitrogenous equilibrium. Animal proteins are, on the whole, much richer than plant proteins in terms of their content of essential amino-acids, and it follows that smaller amounts of protein are required when meat, fish, eggs, cheese, milk and the like are chosen than when the food selected consists largely of cereals and pulses. The maize protein, zein, is notoriously deficient in tryptophan and in lysine, and if zein is taken as the sole protein of a diet, nitrogenous equilibrium can never be established, no matter how much of it is consumed. Gelatin is similarly deficient in tryptophan and in phenylalanine, and, like zein, is a protein of 'poor biological value'.

The primary function of protein food is to supply the amino-acids needed for the growth, repair and general maintenance of the structural and catalytic machinery of living cells. If, as is commonly the case, the proteins of the food provide more amino-acid units than are required for the discharge of these primary and very specific functions, the excess can be degraded and made to subserve the secondary and less specific function of providing fuel for the machine. If excess protein is taken the excess of nitrogen is eliminated, mostly in the form either of ammonia, urea or uric acid, within 24 hr. Proteins and amino-acids are not normally stored to any appreciable extent in the normal adult organism: nitrogen retention on a significant scale is only observed during periods of tissue growth, during childhood and pregnancy, for example, or during periods of protein replacement, as during convalescence after a wasting disease or after protein starvation. The non-nitrogenous residues of surplus amino-acids are retained and serve to contribute to the stores of 'energy-producing' materials, i.e. carbohydrates and fats.

If a meal of protein is administered to a phlorrhizinized or diabetic animal an increased output of glucose and of acetone bodies is observed. Part of the protein must therefore be considered as convertible into carbohydrate derivatives and part into fatty metabolites. If the amino-acids are administered individually it is found that some are *glucogenic*, i.e. give rise to glucose, while others are *ketogenic*, giving rise to acetone or ketone bodies. The known fates of the amino-acids are summarized in

Table 20. It will be noticed that certain amino-acids, including some of the essential group, give rise neither to glucose nor to ketone bodies. Their fate is unknown. It may be that they are incorporated into some sort of protein or peptide which serves as a temporary store, but there is little evidence for the existence of such a store.

TABLE 20. FATES OF AMINO-ACIDS ADMINISTERED
TO A DIABETIC OR PHLORRHIZINIZED DOG

Glucogenic	Ketogenic	Fate unknown
Glycine (2)	Leucine (4)	Lysine
Alanine (3)	isoLeucine (4)	Histidine
Serine (3)	Phenylalanine (4)	Tryptophan
Threonine (3)	Tyrosine (4)	Methionine
Cysteine (3)		
Valine (3)		
isoLeucine (3)		
Aspartic acid (3)		
Glutamic acid (3)		
Arginine (3)		
Ornithine (3)		
Proline (3)		
Hydroxyproline (3)		

Note. The numbers in brackets indicate the number of carbon atoms undergoing conversion in each case.

FATE OF α-AMINO-NITROGEN

Neither glucose nor the ketone bodies contain nitrogen. It follows, therefore, that, at an early stage in their metabolism, the amino-acids suffer the removal of their characteristic α-amino-group. In a typical mammal such as a dog, this α-amino-nitrogen ultimately appears in the urine in the form of urea. In birds, snakes and lizards, by contrast, the final end-product is uric acid, while in most aquatic animals ammonia is excreted instead. The urine of a dog starved of protein contains very little urea, but if a protein meal is taken, urea production soon begins and the protein-nitrogen of the food is almost quantitatively eliminated in the form of urea within 24 hr. or thereabouts. Now we are already aware that the food proteins are broken down by digestive peptidases to yield the component amino-acids, and it is in this form that the food proteins are actually absorbed into the blood stream. We have therefore to discover how, where, and in what form the α-amino-nitrogen is detached from the amino-acid molecules, and how urea is elaborated from the primary nitrogenous product.

A partial answer to these questions is obtained by studying a hepatectomized animal or, alternatively, an animal with an Eck's fistula. An animal of this kind will survive for some days, but dies quickly if it is allowed to eat protein. At death, unusually large amounts of amino-acids are found in the blood, but neither the blood nor the urine contains any urea in the case of a dog, or uric acid in that of a bird. Instead, ammonia is present, and ammonia poisoning is one of the causes of death. These observations show (a) that the amino-groups of the amino-acids are split off in the form of ammonia, and (b) that the conversion of this ammonia into urea or uric acid, as the case may be, normally takes place only in the liver. The latter conclusion is confirmed by liver-perfusion experiments and by experiments on liver slices. If small concentrations of ammonia are perfused through a surviving liver or shaken with liver slices, urea is formed in the case of dog liver, while if a bird's liver is used, the addition of ammonia leads to the production of uric acid.

We shall discuss these processes separately, dealing first with the removal of the amino-groups, a process which is known as deamination.

DEAMINATION

The deamination of amino-acids with production of ammonia might be accomplished in either of two ways, both of which have been considered. It might be a hydrolytic (equation (1)) or an oxidative process (equation (2)):

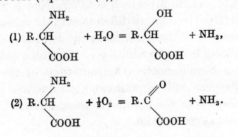

Very little experimental evidence has ever been adduced in favour of hydrolysis as the mode of deamination in animal tissues, though it is known that hydrolytic deamination takes place in some bacteria. The vast bulk of evidence relating to animal metabolism is in favour of oxidative deamination. Early work involving liver perfusion supported this view, for if amino-acids were added to the perfusion medium, traces of the corresponding α-keto-acids could be detected later on. Hydrolytic deamination, on the other hand, would require the production not of the keto- but of the corresponding hydroxy-acids. Further evidence pointing to oxidative deamination was obtained in studies on alcaptonurics, but this is open to serious criticism (p. 222).

The most convincing work on this problem was that carried out by Krebs, who made use of the tissue-slice technique. Slices of various rat tissues were shaken under physiological conditions of temperature, pH, etc., in the presence of various amino-acids. After an hour or two the reaction mixture was deproteinized and the corresponding α-keto-acids were sought and found by taking advantage of the fact that they form very insoluble, characteristic 2:4-dinitrophenylhydrazones. Among mammalian tissues only liver and kidney deaminate amino-acids at all rapidly, and these tissues use more oxygen when they are deaminating than when they are not. These observations give general support to the view that the deamination of amino-acids is essentially an oxidative process.

Surviving liver and kidney deaminate both the common, naturally occurring L-series and the much rarer 'non-natural' D-series of amino-acids, but not all amino-acids are attacked at the same rate. Table 21, which is taken from Krebs's original paper, illustrates the relative differences in the rates of deamination of a number of amino-acids in terms of the extra oxygen uptake resulting from the addition of the amino-acids to kidney tissue slices. Simultaneous determinations of the decrease of α-amino-nitrogen and of ammonia production gave results which, on the whole, ran parallel to those obtained by measurements of the oxygen uptake.

To obtain strictly quantitative evidence in favour of equation (2) is more difficult. If liver tissue is used, the ammonia
set free by deamination is converted more or less completely
into urea, but this difficulty can be obviated by the use of kidney
slices, which do not form urea. But in liver and kidney alike,
the other product of deamination, the α-keto-acid, is liable to

TABLE 21. RATES OF DEAMINATION OF AMINO-ACIDS
BY SLICED RAT KIDNEY TISSUE

(*After* Krebs)

	QO_2	
Amino-acid added	Without amino-acid	With M/100 amino-acid
Glycine	− 21·1	− 21·4
DL-Alanine	− 23·5	− 41·0
DL-*nor*Leucine	− 17·4	− 23·2
DL-Aspartic acid	− 23·5	− 37·0
L-Glutamic acid	− 23·5	− 43·2
DL-Proline	− 18·5	− 37·8
L-Hydroxyproline	− 18·5	− 19·8
L-Lysine	− 21·1	− 25·4
DL-Valine	− 21·1	− 25·0
L-Tryptophan	− 18·9	− 13·5
L-Histidine	− 18·9	− 21·0
DL-Phenylalanine	− 21·1	− 23·3
L-Tyrosine	− 18·7	− 24·4
DL-Leucine	− 23·5	− 29·1
L-*iso*Leucine	− 23·5	− 21·7

be further metabolized, by oxidative decarboxylation in the
first instance. This process, Krebs found, can be prevented by
the addition of arsenious oxide. Working therefore with kidney
slices and in the presence of arsenite, he was able to demonstrate
that, for every molecule of ammonia produced, an extra atom
of oxygen was consumed and a molecule of the corresponding
α-keto-acid formed. Essentially the same results were obtained
with extracts prepared from acetone powders of kidney tissue
(Table 22).

Krebs went on to seek information regarding the mechanism
of the process by studying tissue extracts. Pulp preparations of
liver and kidney alike act upon both the L- and the D-series of
amino-acids, again in an oxidative manner, but as soon as the
pulp is appreciably diluted its ability to attack the naturally

occurring L-acids disappears. The enzyme responsible for the deamination of the D-series, however, is resistant to dilution, and powerful preparations of the D-amino-acid oxidase can be made by extracting fresh, finely divided kidney tissue with water or buffer, centrifuging to remove the tissue debris, and treating the clear extract with 10 vol. of ice-cold acetone under ice-cold conditions. By filtering off the resulting acetone powder and drying it carefully, a stable preparation can be had which retains

TABLE 22. OXIDATIVE DEAMINATION OF AMINO-ACIDS
BY KIDNEY EXTRACT

(*After* Krebs)

Amino-acid added	Mol. $O_2 : NH_3 : $ keto-acid
DL-Alanine	$1 : 1.94 : 1.83$
DL-Valine	$1 : 2.08 : 2.20$
DL-*nor*Leucine	$1 : 1.85 : 1.85$
DL-Leucine	$1 : 2.42 : 2.28$
DL-Phenylalanine	$1 : 2.17 : 1.85$

its activity for some weeks, and from which active enzyme solutions can be made by extraction with water or with phosphate buffer. Preparations made in this way deaminate all the amino-acids of the D-series with three exceptions: glycine, D-glutamic acid and D-lysine. A specific oxidase was later discovered which deals with glycine, but there is reason to think that lysine is never deaminated at all. The D-amino-acid oxidase has been extensively concentrated and finally isolated, and a more detailed description of its nature and properties will be found on p. 162.

So far, however, no evidence had been obtained about the enzyme or enzyme systems involved in the deamination of the L-series of amino-acids. Numerous attempts have been made to obtain enzyme preparations which would act upon the naturally occurring amino-acids, but for a number of years only one such enzyme was known.

This enzyme, which is present in the liver and kidney of mammals, is completely specific with respect to L-glutamic acid. Whereas D-amino-acid oxidase and the specific glycine oxidase are capable of using molecular oxygen as their hydrogen acceptor, the L-glutamic enzyme requires either Co I or Co II, and is, in fact, a typical, coenzyme-specific dehydrogenase, now known as L-glutamic dehydrogenase. A further difference between the two cases lies in the fact that whereas the action of the oxidases seems to be irreversible, that of L-glutamic dehydrogenase is freely reversible.

With the more recent discovery and eventual isolation of an L-amino-acid oxidase from mammalian liver and kidney, we are able to account for the deamination of the majority of L-amino-acids, for the L-oxidase resembles the D-enzyme in being a true oxidase. It is a group-specific enzyme and attacks all the mono-amino-mono-carboxylic amino-acids except glycine and those that contain a hydroxyl radical, but has no action upon the diamino- or dicarboxylic acids. How important this enzyme may be seems uncertain, for even in the rat it acts relatively feebly. It has also been found in other animals in which, however, it is even weaker than in the rat.

Whether it is catalysed by the D- or by the L-amino-acid oxidase, or by L-glutamic dehydrogenase, *deamination is always oxidative and takes place in two stages.* In the first a pair of hydrogen atoms is transferred to the appropriate hydrogen acceptor and the corresponding α-imino-acid is formed:

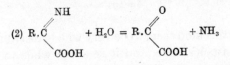

$$(1) \quad R.\underset{\underset{COOH}{|}}{\overset{\overset{NH_2}{|}}{CH}} = R.\underset{\underset{COOH}{|}}{\overset{\overset{NH}{\|}}{C}} + 2H \text{ (to acceptor)}$$

The imino-acid then reacts, apparently spontaneously, with water to yield the α-keto-acid, together with ammonia:

$$(2) \quad R.\underset{\underset{COOH}{|}}{\overset{\overset{NH}{\|}}{C}} + H_2O = R.\underset{\underset{COOH}{|}}{\overset{\overset{O}{\|}}{C}} + NH_3$$

Special non-oxidative mechanisms are probably involved in the deamination of the hydroxy-acids, serine and threonine (p. 113), but an imino-acid is again formed as an intermediate.

TRANSDEAMINATION

In addition to deaminating enzymes, animal and plant tissues contain catalytic mechanisms which catalyse the transference of amino-groups from amino-acids to certain α-keto-acids. If L-glutamic and pyruvic acids are added together to chopped liver or muscle tissue, the α-amino-radical of the glutamic acid is in part transferred to the pyruvic acid, so that α-ketoglutaric acid and alanine are formed. The system tends towards an equilibrium which can be approached equally from either side, and the process, which for obvious reasons is referred to as 'transamination', was attributed by its discoverers to an enzyme which they named 'aminophorase'. This name has now been generally abandoned in favour of 'transaminase':

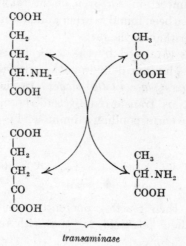

transaminase

Enzymes of this kind seem to be very widely distributed in plant and animal tissues alike, and it is worth while to notice that, unlike the deaminating enzymes, they are not confined to liver and kidney among animal tissues, but are present also in brain, kidney, muscle, and heart, for example. They are specific, moreover, towards amino-acids of the natural L-series. One of these transaminases is specific towards aspartic acid and the corresponding α-ketosuccinic (oxaloacetic) acid, and another towards glutamic and the corresponding α-ketoglutaric acids. The glutamic enzyme seems to predominate in animal tissues and also in many plants.

Braunstein suggested that the deamination of L-amino-acids in general might involve transaminase. It was already known that α-ketoglutaric acid is a common metabolite, arising as it does from carbohydrate as well as from protein sources. Under the influence of glutamic transaminase the α-amino-groups of any incoming amino-acid could, it was suggested, be transferred to α-ketoglutaric acid to yield glutamic acid which then, under the influence of L-glutamic dehyrogenase in liver or kidney, would undergo deamination, α-ketoglutaric acid being regenerated and ammonia set free:

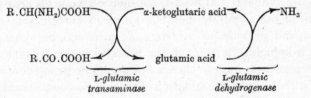

Catalytic concentrations of α-ketoglutaric acid would be all that is necessary, if Braunstein's suggestion is correct, to catalyse the deamination of large amounts of L-amino-acids in tissues containing both glutamic transaminase and the corresponding dehydrogenase. This same scheme could also explain why the dilution of a liver or kidney pulp leads to disappearance of its ability to deaminate the L-series of amino-acids: dilution would mean dilution of the α-ketoglutaric and glutamic acids which play the part of essential coenzymes in the Braunstein scheme.

Braunstein himself showed that L-alanine is oxidatively deaminated by cell-free liver extracts in the presence of catalytic amounts of glutamic acid. He was able also to build up a system capable of deaminating L-alanine by adding glutamic acid, Co I and purified L-glutamic dehydrogenase to partially purified samples of glutamic transaminase.

Recent work (p. 140) has shown that this system can participate in the deamination of amino-acids in general and that pyridoxal phosphate plays the part of co-enzyme, or 'co-transaminase'. Taken together with L-amino-acid oxidase this system enables us to account for the deamination of practically all the naturally occurring amino-acids, and it seems most probable that the transamination machinery is the more important of the two.

Special emphasis must be placed upon the reversibility of transamination, for this process appears to be involved both in the breakdown of amino-acids and in their synthesis from non-protein sources. Since transamination is a reversible process, it follows that new amino-acid molecules can be synthesized at the expense of glutamic acid, provided that the appropriate α-keto-acids are available. At least three such α-keto-acids arise in the course of carbohydrate metabolism, viz. α-ketoglutaric, oxalo-acetic and pyruvic acids. Glutamic acid can be synthesized from α-ketoglutaric through the reversed action of L-glutamic dehydrogenase, and can then act as an amino-group donator for the synthesis by transamination of aspartic acid and alanine from oxaloacetic and pyruvic acids respectively. These mechanisms thus enable us to account for the production from non-protein sources of three of the relatively few amino-acids that animal tissues are capable of synthesizing for themselves.

There can be little doubt that, on account of its reversibility, transamination plays a part of fundamental importance in the anabolism as well as in the katabolism of nitrogenous compounds. Schoenheimer and his co-workers kept a group of young rats on a low protein diet and added heavy ammonium citrate to their food. The idea was to see whether the animals could utilize the heavy nitrogen, N^{15}, for the synthesis of nitrogenous compounds, and a low protein diet was used in order to increase the chances of its utilization. Later the animals were killed and creatine, glutamic acid, aspartic acid, histidine, arginine and lysine were isolated from the carcasses and analysed for heavy nitrogen. With a single exception in the case of lysine, all these compounds were found to contain significant quantities of N^{15}, showing that the heavy ammonia had, in fact, been used. The fact that N^{15} had found its way into all these substances serves to show (a) that ammonia can be used for the synthesis of amino-acids, and (b) that the α-amino-group of a given amino-acid is not simply a static feature of the amino-acid molecule, but that it must be undergoing a constant, dynamic interchange with other —NH_2 groups. That lysine fails to acquire N^{15} suggests that this particular amino-acid never undergoes biological deamination at all. Again, the N^{15} of arginine was found to be located almost entirely in the amidine part of the molecule, suggesting that arginine, and probably ornithine too, therefore, do not undergo deamination. The close structural relationship between ornithine and lysine seems to be in accordance with this view. Schoen-heimer's work provides important circumstantial evidence for the central importance of transamination in amino-group meta-bolism, and serves also to underline the importance of its reversi-bility. A reversible system in metabolism is not merely to be regarded as something that goes one way at one minute and the other way the next, but as a process that goes on simultaneously in both directions at one and the same time, so that the process as a whole is one that is essentially dynamic.

STORAGE OF AMINO-GROUPS

It will be realized that if amino-acid synthesis is to proceed in living tissues, amino-groups must be forthcoming. These might be taken from incoming amino-acids by transamination or, alter-natively, ammonia itself might be utilized, if available. But ammonia is a very toxic metabolite, and concentrations of the order of 1 : 20,000 in the blood are lethal to mammals (rabbits). Since non-essential amino-acids can be produced by animals, even under conditions of protein starvation, it follows that ammonia or amino-groups must in some way be stored in the tissues in an innocuous form. Further evidence that such a storage takes place is found in the fact that any tendency towards acidaemia is counteracted in the mammal by the secre-tion of a more than usually acid urine, the excess acid present being neutralized more or less extensively by ammonia produced in the kidney. This process of ammonia production can still go on in animals temporarily deprived of protein foodstuffs.

No clue to the manner of this storage was found until, in the course of his experiments on deamination, Krebs observed that, of the ammonia produced by the deamination of added amino-acids, a part sometimes failed to put in an appearance. The disappearance of ammonia in liver tissue could be attributed to its conversion into urea, and it might have been thought that some of this urea is later broken up by a tissue urease to furnish ammonia when the latter is required for amino-acid synthesis or for ammonia production by the kidney. In fact, however, there is not a shred of evidence for the occurrence of urease in mammalian tissues, although this enzyme is known to be present in the tissues of numerous invertebrates. If 'heavy' urea is administered to a mammal, preferably by injection so as to avoid possible bacterial intervention, the heavy nitrogen is quantitatively eliminated in the urine, still in the form of urea.

Even in the case of kidney tissue, which forms no urea, Krebs found that substantial amounts of ammonia could disappear on occasion and accordingly set himself the task of discovering its fate. He discovered that, in fact, ammonia can react with glutamic acid to form glutamine. This is now known to be an endergonic reaction involving the participation of ATP (see p. 134):

$$
\begin{array}{ccc}
\begin{array}{l}
\text{COOH} \\
| \\
\text{CH}_2 \\
| \\
\text{CH}_2 \\
| \\
\text{CH.NH}_2 \\
| \\
\text{COOH}
\end{array}
&
+ \text{NH}_3 + \text{ATP} \longrightarrow
&
\begin{array}{l}
\text{CONH}_2 \\
| \\
\text{CH}_2 \\
| \\
\text{CH}_2 \\
| \\
\text{CH.NH}_2 \\
| \\
\text{COOH}
\end{array}
& + \text{ADP} + \text{HO} \textcircled{P}
\end{array}
$$

$\qquad$ *glutamic acid* $\qquad\qquad\qquad$ *glutamine*

It is known too that many tissues, including even the blood, contain considerable quantities of glutamine, and it would seem that glutamine can be synthesized by many tissues at times when ammonia is available, and broken down again by glutaminase, a widely distributed hydrolytic enzyme, to furnish ammonia when the latter is required.

Glutamine has long been known as an important constituent of plant materials, as also has the corresponding amide of aspartic acid, asparagine. The function of the latter as a storage depot for ammonia had been demonstrated many years earlier in studies of etiolated seedlings of the tree-lupin, *Lupinus luteus*. If the protein-rich seed of this plant is allowed to germinate in the dark, a seedling develops which is devoid of chlorophyll. Its development fairly soon comes to an end, and a study of the nitrogen distribution in the plantlet shows that some 80% of the protein-nitrogen of the original seed has been converted into asparagine. The remaining 20% has been transferred to the tissue proteins of the seedling. If the seedling is now allowed access to light, asparagine begins to disappear and new protein is synthesized at the expense of the asparagine-nitrogen.

These changes can be accounted for if we suppose, as is undoubtedly true, that the processes of photosynthesis can give rise in one way or another to α-keto-acids corresponding to all the amino-acids required for protein synthesis. It is necessary also to suppose that transamination in the plant allows the transfer of amino-groups from aspartic acid to any α-keto-acid. In the etiolated seedling, oxaloacetic acid arises in the course of carbohydrate breakdown and can function as an amino-group receptor with respect to amino-acids formed by hydrolysis of the seed proteins. This allows the de-aminated residues of the amino-acids to be utilized as fuel at a time when the organism is as yet unable to derive solar energy through chlorophyll and photosynthesis. The aspartic acid formed by transamination can react with more ammonia, produced by direct deamination of amino-acids, to yield asparagine, and the process can continue as long as the protein reserves hold out, subject only to the limitation imposed by the fact that the tissues, even of an etiolated seedling, contain some protein.

When presently the plant gains access to light, chlorophyll makes its appearance and photosynthesis begins. This leads to the production of α-keto-acids, among other substances and, as the concentration of these begins to increase, they begin to undergo transamination at the expense of aspartic acid so that new amino-acids are formed. The utilization of aspartic acid and the consequent fall in the concentration of the latter leads, in its turn, to the breakdown of more asparagine. This gives rise to more aspartic acid, which can be used for transamination, and to ammonia, which can be employed in direct amination of more

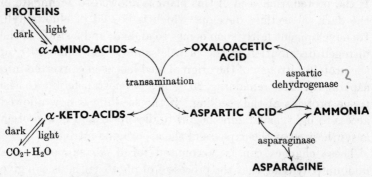

Fig. 23. Nitrogen metabolism in seedlings of *Lupinus luteus*.

of the α-keto-acids: alternatively, the free ammonia can be used to synthesize more aspartic acid from oxaloacetic, the latter arising as an intermediate in the oxidative breakdown of carbohydrate. The whole cycle of events can be summarized as in Fig. 23.

Asparagine and aspartic acid seem, therefore, to play in this plant a part parallel to that of glutamine and glutamic acid in many other plants and in animal tissues. Aspartic acid and its amide have long interested plant biochemists, and with good reason. In more recent times aspartic acid has been brought again into prominence by claims that the primary amino-acid synthesized by the symbiotic root-nodule bacteria of leguminous plants is aspartic acid.

CHAPTER XI

SPECIAL METABOLISM OF THE AMINO-ACIDS

GENERAL

Glycogenesis and ketogenesis

As has been pointed out (p. 260), certain amino-acids give rise to glucose if administered to diabetic or phlorrhizinized animals, or to glycogen in the livers of starving animals, and are accordingly said to be *glucogenic* or *glycogenic*. Others yield acetoacetic acid and the other ketone bodies and are said to be *ketogenic*, while a few give rise to neither.

If alanine is administered to a diabetic animal, all three of its carbon atoms are transformed into glucose. To state categorically that the extra glucose excreted has been formed from the alanine is not strictly accurate, for it may only be that the deaminated residues of the amino-acid molecules were metabolized in place of glucose, and that an equivalent quantity of glucose or glycogen was therefore spared the fate of oxidation. Nevertheless, if the deaminated material replaces glucose or glycogen it presumably does so because it joins the metabolic pathway of glucose and glycogen, so that, for all practical purposes, it suffices to say that the amino-acid is convertible into glucose or glycogen.

Glucose and glycogen are formed from amino-acids by way of reaction chains which are often of considerable length. Many simple organic substances are known to be convertible into glucose or glycogen, and in some cases, e.g. lactic acid, pyruvic acid and glycerol, we know fairly precisely what the intermediate stages are. In the case of propionic acid the following are among the intermediate reactions:

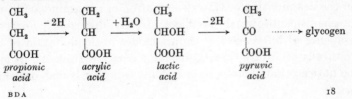

propionic / acrylic / lactic / pyruvic
acid / acid / acid / acid

In this chapter we shall content ourselves with tracing, as far as we can, the routes of conversion of amino-acids into substances which, like propionic, lactic and pyruvic acids, are known carbohydrate-formers. The rest of the stages are common to the metabolism of carbohydrates and carbohydrate derivatives, and will be considered in later chapters.

The amino-acids are classified as essential or non-essential according as they can or cannot be synthesized in the animal body. If the reader will refer again to Tables 19 and 20 (pp. 256 and 260) several interesting points will be noticed. First, *all the non-essential amino-acids are glycogenic*, which probably indicates that their conversion into carbohydrate is a reversible operation. *Of the essential amino-acids only a few are glycogenic*, and the fact that they are essential presumably indicates that the reaction chains through which they are transformed into carbohydrate include some irreversible step or steps. Thus carbohydrate can contribute to the synthesis of some amino-acids, but not of all. *All the ketogenic amino-acids are essential.* They give rise to fatty metabolites, but the fact that they are essential, i.e. cannot be synthesized by the animal organism, shows that their conversion into ketone bodies is not a reversible performance. Thus fat, unlike carbohydrate, contributes little or nothing towards the synthesis of amino-acids or of protein. These general points may be summarized as follows:

$$Proteins \rightleftharpoons Amino\text{-}acids \begin{cases} Non\text{-}essential \rightleftharpoons Carbohydrate \\ \\ Essential \longrightarrow Ketone\ bodies \end{cases}$$

The first step in the transformation of the amino-acids consists in the deamination or transdeamination of the amino-acids, the mechanisms of which we have already discussed. For convenience of reference the known modes of deamination of the naturally occurring L-acids are summarized in Table 23. It may be noticed that there is serious doubt whether lysine, ornithine and arginine undergo biological deamination (p. 269). It is known that serine, and perhaps threonine too, can be atypically deaminated by a non-oxidative enzyme present in rat liver (p. 113), which, in the absence of any other name, we may call 'serine deaminase'.

TABLE 23. DEAMINATION OF AMINO-ACIDS OF THE NATURALLY OCCURRING L-SERIES IN ANIMAL TISSUES

Amino-acid	L-Amino-acid oxidase	Specific enzyme
Glycine	−	Glycine oxidase
Alanine	+	.
Serine	−	'Serine deaminase'
Threonine	−	? 'Serine deaminase'
Cysteine	+	.
Methionine	+	.
Valine	+	.
Leucine	+	.
isoLeucine	+	.
Aspartic acid	−	
Glutamic acid	−	L-Glutamic dehydrogenase
Arginine	−	.
Ornithine	−	.
Lysine	−	.
Phenylalanine	+	.
Tyrosine	+	.
Tryptophan	+	.
Histidine	+	.

Most and probably all can be transdeaminated except arginine, ornithine and lysine.
Note. The use of a negative sign indicates only that the amino-acid is not at present known to be deaminated by the system concerned.

Bacterial Attack and Detoxication

Bacteria of many kinds possess powerful and specific amino-acid decarboxylases, and although these do not fall within the scope of this book they must be mentioned here because they have considerable interest for animal metabolism. The alimentary canal of animals is always densely populated with bacteria at some region or other, and the activities of the members of this population lead to the production of materials which may be later absorbed by the animal itself. The extent of this absorption depends upon the region in which bacterial activity takes place.

In herbivorous animals, of course, micro-organisms play a very large and important part in the digestion of the food, but even in animals that do not delegate their digestive operations to symbiotic bacteria, the metabolism of the micro-organisms has to be taken into account.

The bacterial inhabitants of the intestine have access to the food, or to the products of digestion of the food, among which amino-acids are included; and certain bacteria decarboxylate one or more of these to produce the corresponding amines:

$$R.CH(NH_2)COOH = R.CH_2NH_2 + CO_2.$$

Some of these products are intensely poisonous and, when they are absorbed into the animal's blood stream, undergo what is known as *detoxication*. This is accomplished by oxidation, reduction, acetylation, methylation, or in some other manner. Furthermore, by progressive bacterial degradation of the side-chains of acids containing aromatic rings, poisonous phenolic substances are formed, and these, like the amines, undergo detoxication in the animal body. We shall deal individually with individual cases, and we shall also comment upon the parts played by the amino-acids themselves, since several of them act as important detoxicating agents.

In addition to amino-acids, many other substances play a part in detoxication, and these may be briefly mentioned at this point. Acetylation (p. 143) is a common fate among aromatic substances containing —NH$_2$ groups, and the administration of aniline, substituted anilines, sulphonamide drugs and the like, is followed by their excretion, partly or wholly in the acetylated form. Amines are commonly oxidized, yielding harmless aldehydes or acids, by the amine and diamine oxidases of the tissues (pp. 165–6). Phenolic substances are frequently excreted in conjugation with glucuronic acid or with sulphuric acid, the latter being probably derived from sulphur-containing amino-acids.

This book does not contain a special chapter on detoxication or, as it is often termed, protective synthesis; it has seemed more suitable to the author to dispense with such a chapter, since a large part of the subject can be dealt with under the special functions of individual amino-acids, while the foregoing remarks, together with a judicious use of the index, will fill in most of the gaps that will remain when the present chapter has been studied.

OPTICAL ISOMERISM AND NOMENCLATURE

With the single exception of glycine, the simplest member of the group, all the amino-acids which occur in proteins are optically active. As a rule only one of the possible optical antipodes occurs naturally on the large scale and this is usually referred to as the 'natural' form, even though the other antipode may also occur on occasion. Similarly among the sugars, one isomer always preponderates in natural materials, the other being encountered rarely if at all.

The simple monosaccharides can all be regarded as derivatives of glyceraldehyde, which is itself optically active and is, in fact, a triose sugar conventionally formulated thus:

$$\beta \quad \text{CHO} \qquad \beta \quad \text{CHO}$$
$$\alpha \quad \text{H.C.OH} \quad \text{or} \quad \alpha \quad \text{HO.C.H}$$
$$\text{CH}_2\text{OH} \qquad \qquad \text{CH}_2\text{OH}$$
$$\textit{dextro}\text{-isomer} \qquad \textit{laevo}\text{-isomer}$$

Tetroses, pentoses, hexoses and higher sugars can be regarded as being derived from glyceraldehyde by the interposition of additional radicals—usually $>$CHOH—between the α-carbon and the reducing group.

One form of glyceraldehyde is dextro- and the other laevo-rotatory and in accordance with the practice current until recently, these were ordinarily described as d- and l-glyceraldehyde respectively. Now the stereochemical arrangement about the α-carbon atom of $\textit{dextro}$-glyceraldehyde is present also in the preponderant, i.e. the 'natural', form of all naturally occurring sugars and because of this structural resemblance, which extends to ketoses as well as to hexoses, it became usual in biochemical circles, where structure is on the whole more important than optical rotation, to refer to them all as d-sugars. This practice was however not universally adopted in more purely chemical circles and thus led to considerable confusion. Fructose, for example, is a d-sugar in biochemical parlance but, being laevorotatory, remained l-fructose to many chemists, and is still sometimes referred to as 'laevulose'.

In an endeavour to overcome this difficulty the prefixes -(+)- and -(−)- were introduced to signify dextro- and laevo-rotation respectively, d- and l- being retained in their purely structural signification. Thus the 'natural' form of glucose became d-(+)-glucose and 'natural' fructose became d-(−)-fructose. But this system, too, failed to achieve universal acceptance. Accordingly d- and l- have now been abandoned, and replaced by D- and L- by general agreement (at any rate between Great Britain and the United States of America) and we shall use this nomenclature here. *These small capital letters have purely structural significance and give no indication whatsoever of optical rotation.* When it is necessary to specify rotation as well, the supplementary symbols, -(+)- or -(−)-, or the supplementary prefixes, *dextro-* or *laevo-*, are employed in addition to D- and L-.

Returning now to the sugars, we recall their structural relationships to what is now officially recognized as D-glyceraldehyde and refer to the 'natural' forms as D-sugars. L-Sugars do occur in natural products but are relatively rare. By the same token the 'natural' amino-acids are all members of the L-series; D-amino-acids, though they do occur, are uncommon. This time, however, the standard of reference is not glyceraldehyde, a triose sugar, but an amino-acid, serine. Actually, however, D-serine is structurally related to D-glyceraldehyde and L-serine to L-glyceraldehyde:

$$\begin{array}{cc} & \text{COOH} \\ \alpha & \text{H}_2\text{N}.\text{C}.\text{H} \\ \beta & \text{CH}_2\text{OH} \\ & \textit{L-serine} \end{array} \qquad \begin{array}{cc} \beta & \text{CHO} \\ \alpha & \text{HO}.\text{C}.\text{H} \\ & \text{CH}_2\text{OH} \\ & \textit{L-glyceraldehyde} \end{array}$$

Now it is conventional to use D- and L- with reference to the spatial relationships prevailing about the α-*carbon atom* of an optically active substance, but unfortunately the α-position is differently defined in different groups of compounds. In amino-acids the standard of reference is the carboxyl radical, so that the immediately adjacent carbon atom is the α-carbon. In carbo-hydrates, however, the standard of reference is the carbon atom most remote from the reducing group, e.g. carbon 6 in glucose or fructose, so that in this case the α-carbon is the most remote but one in the chain.

This difference of convention has led to difficulties in some cases, notably with the amino-acid, threonine, so-named because it is structurally related to the tetrose sugar, D-threose. Re-garded as a sugar derivative, the 'natural' form of threonine can be formulated as follows:

$$
\begin{array}{llllll}
\gamma & \text{COOH} & & \gamma & \text{CHO} \\
\beta & \text{H}_2\text{N.C.H} & & \beta & \text{HO.C.H} \\
\alpha & \text{H.C.OH} & & \alpha & \text{H.C.OH} \\
& \text{CH}_3 & & & \text{CH}_2\text{OH} \\
& \textit{threonine} & & & \text{D-}\textit{threose}
\end{array}
$$

If we consider threonine as a sugar derivative it must be called D-threonine because the configuration at the α-carbon atom is the same as in D-threose. But regarded as an amino-acid, threonine must be described thus:

$$
\begin{array}{llllll}
& \text{COOH} & & & \text{COOH} \\
\alpha & \text{H}_2\text{N.C.H} & & \alpha & \text{H}_2\text{N.C.H} \\
\beta & \text{H.C.OH} & & \beta & \text{CH}_2\text{OH} \\
\gamma & \text{CH}_3 & & & \\
& \textit{threonine} & & & \text{L-}\textit{serine}
\end{array}
$$

and from this point of view it must be called L-threonine because the configuration at the α-carbon atom is the same as in L-serine. The difference here is due simply to the use of two different conventions.

Cases like this do not often arise but, when they do, order can be produced out of the apparent chaos by using subscripts to the usual D- and L-. Where a structure is referred back to that of glyceraldehyde, to which all carbohydrates are referred in the end, $_g$ is used; where the structure is referred back to that of serine we use $_s$. Thus the 'natural' form of threonine can be written as D_g-threonine or as L_s-threonine, and the two terms are synonymous.

SPECIFIC METABOLISM

GLYCINE, $H_2N.CH_2COOH$

(non-essential: glycogenic), is the simplest of the naturally occurring amino-acids and is the only member of the group that does not contain an asymmetric carbon atom. It gives rise on deamination by the specific *glycine oxidase* to glyoxylic acid,

$$CHO.COOH,$$

the metabolic fate of which is not fully known. We do not know how it undergoes conversion to carbohydrate in the animal body, but it is interesting to notice that there is a considerable delay between the administration of glycine to a diabetic or phlorrhizinized animal and the ensuing excretion of glucose in the urine.

Glycine gives rise to two methylated derivatives, *sarcosine*, a monomethyl glycine which can be formed by the biological methylation of glycine itself, and *glycine betaine*, in which three methyl radicals are present. The distribution and functions of these substances are described elsewhere (p. 334). Glycine also

$(CH_3)H_2N^+.CH_2COO^-$ $(CH_3)_3N^+.CH_2COO^-$ $H_3N^+.CH_2COO^-$
     sarcosine   *glycine betaine*   *glycine (zwitterion)*

enters into the formation of *creatine* (pp. 141–2): it is believed to be convertible also into *serine* and *ethanolamine*. Experiments with isotopic glycine have shown that this amino-acid enters into the formation of uric acid and other *purines* (p. 327) and into that of *porphyrins* too. Again the details of the reactions are unknown at present. Glycine is also present in certain *bile salts* formed by the union of glycine with cholic and other bile acids (p. 249).

It occurs again in combination in the peculiar tripeptide *glutathione*, which has the constitution of γ-glutamyl-cysteinyl-glycine: the peculiarity here lies in the fact that it is the γ- and not the α-carboxyl radical of the glutamic acid unit that is engaged in forming the peptide linkage:

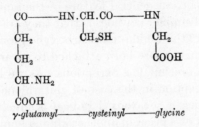

γ-glutamyl————cysteinyl————glycine

Finally, glycine plays an important part in the *detoxication* of aromatic acids such, for instance, as benzoic and phenylacetic acids, and also in that of nicotinic acid. These acids are excreted in the urine in the form of conjugates with glycine:

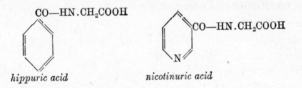

hippuric acid   nicotinuric acid

ALANINE, $CH_3CH(NH_2)COOH$

(non-essential: glycogenic), is the simplest of the optically active amino-acids. Two forms are known, one of which has the same spatial configuration as D-serine and D-(−)-lactic acid and is now usually called D-alanine, while the other, with the spatial configuration of L-serine and L-(+)-lactic acid, is known as L-alanine; the latter is the predominant or 'natural' form in biological structures and systems.

It is an interesting fact that, while all the naturally occurring amino-acids can exist in both the D- and the L-forms, the D-isomers occur only rarely in nature; so rarely, in fact, that the prefix L-, which refers to the common forms, has been omitted throughout this book except where it is necessary for the sake of clarity. Chemical synthesis of the amino-acids ordinarily yields racemic products, i.e. mixtures of the D- and L-forms. Biological synthesis, on the other hand, yields only the L-form

in the ordinary way on account of the stereochemical specificity
of the enzymes involved.

Another important general feature of the amino-acids found
in proteins and simpler peptides is that they are all members of
the *α-series*, i.e. the amino- and carboxylic groupings involved
in peptide formation are both attached to α-carbon atoms. To
this rule there are but few exceptions. As we have just seen,
there is an exception in the case of glutathione, a natural tripeptide in which a γ-carboxyl radical is involved in peptide
formation. An exception of another kind is found in the occurrence of *β-alanine*,

$$H_2N.CH_2CH_2COOH,$$

in the dipeptides *carnosine* and *anserine* (p. 344). β-Alanine also
occurs in a member of the B_2 group of vitamins, viz. *pantothenic
acid*, a constituent of coenzyme A:

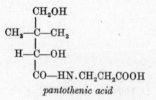
pantothenic acid

α-Alanine yields pyruvic acid on deamination or transdeamination. The product is known to lie on the direct line of
breakdown and synthesis of glucose and glycogen, and we shall
deal with its intermediary metabolism in a later chapter. For
our present purposes it suffices to point out that alanine, since it
yields pyruvic acid on deamination, is convertible into glycogen
or glucose.

(non-essential: glycogenic), is one of the less common amino-
acids, and not much is known about its metabolism. It can be
deaminated anaerobically by an enzyme ('serine deaminase',

p. 113) that is present in cell-free extracts of liver, to yield pyruvic acid, a known glucose-former:

$$
\underset{\substack{|\\ \text{COOH}}}{\overset{\substack{\text{CH}_2\text{OH}\\ |}}{\text{CH.NH}_2}} \xrightarrow{-\text{H}_2\text{O}} \underset{\substack{|\\ \text{COOH}}}{\overset{\substack{\text{CH}_2\\ ||}}{\text{C.NH}_2}} \longrightarrow \underset{\substack{|\\ \text{COOH}}}{\overset{\substack{\text{CH}_3\\ |}}{\text{C}=\text{NH}}} \xrightarrow{+\text{H}_2\text{O}} \text{NH}_3 + \underset{\substack{|\\ \text{COOH}}}{\overset{\substack{\text{CH}_3\\ |}}{\text{CO}}} \longrightarrow \text{glycogen}
$$

Probably the first of these reactions is catalysed by the enzyme, the remainder as far as pyruvate being perhaps spontaneous. It is not known, however, whether the conversion of serine into glycogen normally follows this or some other pathway.

Serine has been isolated from acid hydrolysates of casein in the form of the difficultly hydrolysable *phosphoserine*, suggesting that the organically bound phosphorus, which is a characteristic constituent of casein and other phosphoproteins, may find attachment to the protein molecule through the hydroxylic side-chains of serine residues.

In addition, it has recently been shown that serine can exchange its hydroxyl radical for the sulphydryl group of homocysteine to yield *cysteine* (p. 285). There is some reason to think that serine itself can be formed from glycine, perhaps by way of *ethanolamine*: alternatively the latter might conceivably be formed by the decarboxylation of serine:

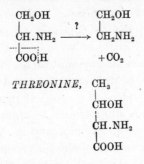

$$
\underset{\substack{|\\ \text{COOH}}}{\overset{\substack{\text{CH}_2\text{OH}\\ |}}{\text{CH.NH}_2}} \xrightarrow{\;?\;} \underset{\substack{|\\ +\text{CO}_2}}{\overset{\substack{\text{CH}_2\text{OH}\\ |}}{\text{CH}_2\text{NH}_2}}
$$

$$
THREONINE, \quad \underset{\substack{|\\ \text{COOH}}}{\overset{\substack{\text{CH}_3\\ |\\ \text{CHOH}\\ |\\ \text{CH.NH}_2}}{}}
$$

(essential: glycogenic), like serine, is a hydroxylic amino-acid, but its functional importance and the mode of its conversion into carbohydrate are still unknown. It is possible that threonine, like serine, is deaminated by 'serine deaminase', giving rise to propionic acid and thence to glycogen:

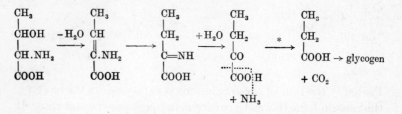

Threonine is one of the few essential amino-acids that are glycogenic, and it seems probable that, if the reactions suggested here correspond to reality, the reason that threonine cannot be synthesized in the body is that oxidative decarboxylation (*), a general reaction to which all α-keto-acids are liable, is irreversible under the conditions obtaining in animal tissues.

$$CYSTEINE, \quad \begin{matrix} CH_2SH \\ | \\ CH.NH_2 \\ | \\ COOH \end{matrix} \quad and \quad CYSTINE, \quad \begin{matrix} CH_2S\text{——}S.CH_2 \\ | \qquad\qquad | \\ CH.NH_2 \quad CH.NH_2 \\ | \qquad\qquad | \\ COOH \qquad COOH \end{matrix}$$

(essential but replaceable by methionine: glycogenic), are the commonest sulphur-containing amino-acids. How they are converted into carbohydrate is not known: conceivably they may yield up the characteristic —SH group to some other substance and give rise in this way to serine, which is also glycogenic.

That dietary cysteine and cystine can be replaced by *methionine* argues that they can be derived from it, and it has recently been shown that this is indeed the case. If methionine containing radioactive sulphur is administered to animals, radioactive sulphur can be recovered in cysteine and in cystine isolated from the tissues. The mechanism of the conversion has recently been discovered. Cysteine does not arise directly from methionine but from its demethylated product, *homocysteine*. If sliced rat liver is incubated with homocysteine in the presence of *serine*, cysteine is formed by a transthiolation reaction in which an —SH group changes place with an —OH. An intermediary reaction complex, *cystathionine*, is formed:

$$
\begin{array}{c}
\text{CH}_2\text{SH} \\
| \\
\text{CH}_2 \\
| \\
\text{CH.NH}_2 \\
| \\
\text{COOH} \\
\textit{homocysteine}
\end{array}
+
\begin{array}{c}
\text{CH}_2\text{OH} \\
| \\
\text{CH.NH}_2 \\
| \\
\text{COOH} \\
\textit{serine}
\end{array}
\xrightarrow{-\text{H}_2\text{O}}
\begin{array}{c}
\text{CH}_2\text{S}\!\!-\!\!-\!\!-\!\!\text{CH}_2 \\
| \qquad\qquad | \\
\text{CH}_2 \qquad \text{CH.NH}_2 \\
| \qquad\qquad | \\
\text{CH.NH}_2 \quad \text{COOH} \\
| \\
\text{COOH} \\
\textit{cystathionine}
\end{array}
\xrightarrow{+\text{H}_2\text{O}}
\begin{array}{c}
\text{CH}_2\text{OH} \\
| \\
\text{CH}_2 \\
| \\
\text{CH.NH}_2 \\
| \\
\text{COOH} \\
\textit{homoserine}
\end{array}
+
\begin{array}{c}
\text{CH}_2\text{SH} \\
| \\
\text{CH.NH}_2 \\
| \\
\text{COOH} \\
\textit{cysteine}
\end{array}
$$

Cysteine and cystine are particularly important because of the ease with which a *pair of* —SH *groups* of cysteine can be oxidized to give the —S—S— bond of cystine, and vice versa. This property extends to many compounds into the composition of which cystine enters. Thus it is present in *glutathione*, which we may represent as G.SH. This compound is very readily oxidized, e.g. by molecular oxygen in the presence of traces of heavy metals, to give the oxidized form, G.S—S.G, and it is upon this behaviour that the functional importance of glutathione appears to depend.

Linkages of the —S—S— type also play an important part in the intramolecular structure of *hair keratin* and other sclero-proteins. Hair contains about 7·3 % of cystine and it is believed that —S—S— bonds are formed between adjacent molecular fibres, and that the tensile strength and other mechanical pro-perties of the hair fibre as a whole are largely due to these linkages. The —SH group is important also among *enzymes*, many of which are active only so long as their —SH groups are in the free state. If these are oxidized to give —S—S— bonds, catalytic activity disappears, but can be recovered by the addi-tion of reduced glutathione. Although this is not by any means a universal property of enzymes, certain dehydrogenases in particular are reversibly inhibited by mild oxidation, and irreversibly by iodoacetate, which reacts with and blocks —SH groups in the following manner:

$$\text{—SH} + \text{I.CH}_2\text{COOH} = \text{HI} + \text{—S.CH}_2\text{COOH}.$$

A considerable number of war gases (cf. p. 192), including lachry-mators and vesicants, act by blocking the —SH groups of enzymes which can, however, be 'protected' or reactivated by certain dithiols, in particular by British anti-lewisite ('BAL').

Cysteine is the mother substance of *taurine*, a compound which is very widely distributed, often in remarkably large amounts (p. 346). It is found in the bile of many vertebrates as a conjugant in the *bile salts* (p. 249). Taurine is known to arise from *cysteic acid* through the agency of a specific cysteic acid decarboxylase, one of the few 'straight' decarboxylases known to occur in animal tissues (liver and kidney). Cysteic acid itself is believed to be formed from cysteine by oxidation, though the responsible enzyme has not so far been discovered. That the reaction takes place cannot be seriously doubted, however, for the administration of methionine containing radioactive sulphur can be followed by the isolation, not only of radioactive cysteine and cystine from the tissues, but by that of radioactive taurine also. The formation of taurine is therefore believed to take the following course:

$$
\begin{array}{ccc}
\mathrm{CH_2SH} & \mathrm{CH_2SO_3H} & \mathrm{CH_2SO_3H} \\
| & | & | \\
\mathrm{CH.NH_2} \longrightarrow & \mathrm{CH.NH_2} \longrightarrow & \mathrm{CH_2NH_2} + \mathrm{CO_2} \\
| & \cdots\cdots|\cdots\cdots & \\
\mathrm{COOH} & \mathrm{COO\,H} & \\
\textit{cysteine} & \textit{cysteic} & \textit{taurine} \\
& \textit{acid} &
\end{array}
$$

The oxidation of cysteine to cysteic acid may represent a step in the oxidative degradation of cysteine and cystine, the sulphur of which ultimately appears in the urine of mammals in the form of *inorganic sulphates*. Perhaps cysteine is also the source of the so-called *ethereal sulphates* which appear in the urine following the absorption of phenolic substances into the body: their conjugation with sulphuric acid is one of several devices involved in the *detoxication* of phenols. Examples of ethereal sulphates are the following:

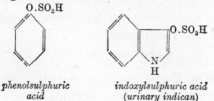

phenolsulphuric   indoxylsulphuric acid
acid   (urinary indican)

Unlike cysteic acid and taurine, these ethereal sulphates are true sulphates and not sulphonic acids: the direct carbon-to-sulphur linkage characteristic of the sulphur-containing amino-acids is absent from the ethereal sulphates.

Cysteine also contributes to the formation of *mercapturic acids*, which are the products of detoxication of certain aromatic substances. A classical example of this is seen in the fate of bromobenzene administered to dogs. The substance is eliminated in conjugation with N-acetylcysteine in the form of p-bromophenyl-mercapturic acid, a remarkable achievement on the part of an animal that is never likely to meet bromobenzene except through the medium of the laboratory. Napthalene also is converted in part into a mercapturic acid:

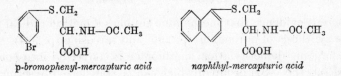

p-*bromophenyl-mercapturic acid*   *naphthyl-mercapturic acid*

In addition to the inorganic and ethereal sulphates, mammalian urine contains a third fraction, the so-called '*neutral sulphur*'. This comprises a mixed bag of sulphur compounds, including traces of thio-alcohols (mercaptans) and mercapturic acids. Not much is known about this fraction, but there is no doubt that much of it arises from the sulphur-containing amino-acids. There exists, however, a rare condition known as *cystinuria*, in which the neutral sulphur fraction is very large and consists mainly of cystine itself. The administration of cystine to a cystinuric does not, however, increase the output of urinary cystine, showing that the cystine excreted is not directly derived from that of the food.

$$
\begin{array}{l}
\textit{METHIONINE,} \quad \mathrm{S.CH_3} \\
\qquad\qquad\quad\ \ \, | \\
\qquad\qquad\quad\ \ \mathrm{CH_2} \\
\qquad\qquad\quad\ \ \, | \\
\qquad\qquad\quad\ \ \mathrm{CH_2} \\
\qquad\qquad\quad\ \ \, | \\
\qquad\qquad\quad\ \ \mathrm{CH.NH_2} \\
\qquad\qquad\quad\ \ \, | \\
\qquad\qquad\quad\ \ \mathrm{COOH}
\end{array}
$$

(essential), is not known to give rise either to glucose or to ketone bodies. Its main known function is that of a *biological methylating agent*. Thus it completes the biological synthesis of *creatine* by the transfer of a methyl group to glycocyamine (p. 142). Very probably it is the methylating agent involved in the *detoxication* of pyridine and certain pyridine derivatives, including nicotinic acid, for pyridine itself is excreted in the form of N-methylpyridine, and nicotinic acid partly as trigonelline:

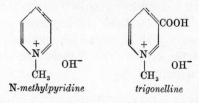

N-*methylpyridine*   *trigonelline*

There is evidence that methionine supplies a methyl radical for the synthesis of adrenaline (p. 296) and sarcosine (p. 334). By undergoing demethylation, methionine is converted into *homocysteine*, the —SH group of which can be transferred to serine in the synthesis of *cysteine* (p. 285). On account of the ease with which homocysteine can be remethylated at the expense of the methyl radicals of choline, methionine perhaps plays a part of some importance in the *metabolism of phospholipids* by converting ethanolamine into choline and vice versa. Homocysteine can be remethylated at the expense of choline, glycine betaine and possibly of sarcosine, but not at that of creatine.

$$\text{VALINE,} \quad \begin{array}{c} \text{CH}_3\,\text{CH}_3 \\ \diagdown\diagup \\ \text{CH} \\ | \\ \text{CH.NH}_2 \\ | \\ \text{COOH} \end{array}$$

(essential: glycogenic), was formerly believed to be ketogenic, in common with the other branched-chain amino-acids. Very little is known about the metabolism of this and the other amino-acids containing branched chains. To explain its conversion into glycogen it is necessary to suppose that one of the methyl groups of the deaminated product can be removed, though whether this can be accomplished, and if so how, we do not know. There is no reason to suppose that this group can be transferred to homocysteine to yield methionine. Oxidative decarboxylation of the demethylated product would then give propionic acid, which is a known glucose-former:

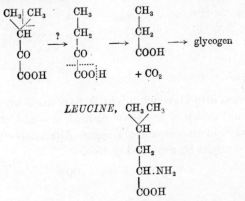

(essential: ketogenic). Its conversion into ketone bodies can be explained if we suppose, as in the case of valine, that one of the terminal methyl groups of the deaminated product can be removed in some way. If this were followed by the usual process of oxidative decarboxylation we should get butyric acid, which would be expected to undergo β-oxidation in the usual manner to give acetoacetic acid:

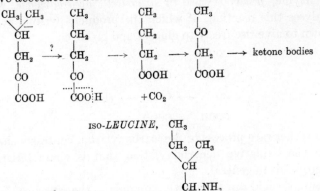

(essential: glycogenic *and* ketogenic), might be converted into acetoacetic acid by mechanisms similar to those postulated for valine and leucine, i.e. by the removal of a terminal methyl radical, followed by the usual further chemical changes:

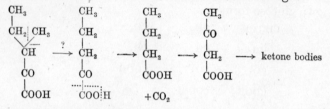

Its conversion into glycogen might be explained by the removal of the methyl group of the ethyl radical, to yield valine, which is known to yield glucose and glycogen. Alternatively, the whole ethyl group might be removed *en bloc*.

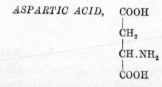

ASPARTIC ACID,

(non-essential: glycogenic), yields oxaloacetic acid on deamination or transdeamination. This product is somewhat unstable and undergoes slow, spontaneous β-decarboxylation under physiological conditions of temperature and pH. The liver contains an enzyme, β-carboxylase or *oxaloacetic decarboxylase*, which catalyses this reaction, of which the product, pyruvic acid, is known to give rise freely to glucose and glycogen:

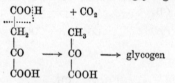

This rather rare process of β-decarboxylation contrasts sharply with the oxidative decarboxylation that is characteristic of α-keto-acids in general.

Aspartic acid can react with ammonia in the presence of ATP and under the influence of an enzyme to form *asparagine*, which is itself non-essential and glycogenic. This system plays an important part in the *storage of amino-groups* in the tissues of certain plants (p. 269). Finally, aspartic acid plays a central part in *transamination and transdeamination* in some animal and plant tissues and plays a part also in ureogenesis by donating its amino-group to citrulline to yield arginine (p. 140).

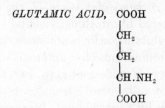

$$GLUTAMIC\ ACID,\quad \begin{matrix} COOH \\ | \\ CH_2 \\ | \\ CH_2 \\ | \\ CH.NH_2 \\ | \\ COOH \end{matrix}$$

(non-essential: glycogenic), yields α-ketoglutaric acid on deamination. The product, an α-keto-acid, undergoes oxidative decarboxylation in the usual way, giving rise to succinic acid. Succinic is converted into fumaric acid by dehydrogenation, catalysed by succinic dehydrogenase, and fumaric acid, under the influence of fumarase, takes on water to give malic acid. Malic acid is dehydrogenated in its turn by the action of malic dehydrogenase and Co I, to give oxaloacetic acid. The latter, on β-decarboxylation, yields pyruvic acid and hence gives rise to glycogen:

$$\begin{matrix} COOH \\ | \\ CH_2 \\ | \\ CH_2 \\ | \\ CO \\ \overset{....|....}{COOH} \ +CO_2 \end{matrix} \longrightarrow \begin{matrix} COOH \\ | \\ CH_2 \\ | \\ CH_2 \\ | \\ COOH \end{matrix} \overset{-2H}{\longrightarrow} \begin{matrix} COOH \\ | \\ CH \\ \| \\ CH \\ | \\ COOH \end{matrix} \overset{+H_2O}{\longrightarrow} \begin{matrix} COOH \\ | \\ CH_2 \\ | \\ CHOH \\ | \\ COOH \end{matrix} \overset{-2H}{\longrightarrow} \begin{matrix} COO\!:\!H \\ \overset{....|....}{CH_2} \\ | \\ CO \\ | \\ COOH \end{matrix} \begin{matrix} +CO_2 \\ CH_3 \\ | \\ CO \\ | \\ COOH \end{matrix} \longrightarrow glycogen$$

The existence of a *glutamic-α-decarboxylase* in animal tissues accounts for the formation of *γ-aminobutyric acid*, which occurs in brain tissue and elsewhere:

$$H_2N.CH_2CH_2CH_2COOH.$$

Like β-alanine this is a somewhat uncommon and thoroughly atypical amino-acid and perhaps it is worth noticing that β-alanine might conceivably arise by the action of an analogous enzyme upon aspartic acid.

Glutamic acid together with glutamic dehydrogenase plays a central part in *transamination and transdeamination*, and is a constituent of *glutathione*, while its amide, *glutamine*, occurs in considerable quantities in many plant and animal tissues, in which it represents a *store of amino groups*. Glutamic acid is also involved in urea-formation; by reaction with carbon dioxide and ammonia it yields *carbamylglutamic acid*, the carbamyl radical of which is transferred to ornithine, yielding citrulline (p. 322).

Glutamine, like glutamic acid, is non-essential and glycogenic, giving rise to glutamic acid and free ammonia under the influence of *glutaminase*. There is evidence too (p. 140) that it can lose its amido-group and simultaneously transfer its α-amino-group to certain α-keto-acids by a special kind of transamination process. In addition, glutamine plays a special part in the *detoxication* of aromatic acids, though only among Primates, according to present information. Phenylacetic acid is excreted in the form of a conjugate with glycine by most animals, but in man and the chimpanzee it gives rise to phenylacetylglutamine:

$$
\begin{array}{l}
CO.NH_2 \\
| \\
CH_2 \\
| \\
CH_2 \\
| \\
CH.NH\!-\!OC.CH_2\!\!-\!\!\bigcirc \\
| \\
COOH
\end{array}
$$

phenylacetylglutamine

$$
ARGININE, \quad HN\!=\!C\!\!\begin{array}{l} NH_2 \\ NH \\ | \\ (CH_2)_3 \\ | \\ CH.NH_2 \\ | \\ COOH \end{array}
$$

('half-essential', see p. 256: glycogenic), can lose its amidine group under the hydrolytic influence of *arginase* to yield *ornithine*, which is also glycogenic. How arginine itself gives rise to glycogen we do not know: perhaps it is a long and somewhat

tortuous process, for the rate at which arginine can be synthesized in the body appears to be slow enough to act as a limiting
factor for the rate of growth of young animals kept on arginine-
deficient diets. Indeed, there are indications that arginine does
not normally undergo deamination (p. 269).

Arginine can also part with its amidine radical by participating
in group-transfer reactions, i.e. by *transamidination*. It plays
a vital part in the synthesis of urea by the so-called *ornithine
cycle* of Krebs; the mechanisms leading to its resynthesis from
ornithine are considered elsewhere (pp. 322–3). Arginine occurs
much more extensively in invertebrates than among vertebrates,
for it forms the guanidine base of the *invertebrate phosphagen*
(p. 339): in addition, arginine is probably the parent substance
of some at least of the peculiar guanidine bases found in invertebrate tissues such, for example, as *octopine* and *agmatine*
(Chap. XIII).

$$CITRULLINE, \quad O=C\begin{array}{l} NH_2 \\ NH \\ | \\ (CH_2)_3 \\ | \\ CH.NH_2 \\ | \\ COOH \end{array}$$

(non-essential: glycogenic), does not, so far as is known, enter
into the composition of proteins, but occurs as an intermediary
between ornithine and arginine in the '*ornithine cycle*' (p. 319).

$$ORNITHINE, \quad \begin{array}{l} NH_2 \\ | \\ (CH_2)_3 \\ | \\ CH.NH_2 \\ | \\ COOH \end{array}$$

(non-essential: glycogenic), has not been isolated from protein
hydrolysates, but arises from the action of arginase upon
arginine, and participates in the '*ornithine cycle*'. It yields
citrulline by accepting a carbamyl radical ($-CO.NH_2$) from
carbamylglutamic acid. There is some doubt whether it undergoes biological deamination (cf. lysine, p. 269).

Among birds, ornithine discharges a special function in the *detoxication* of aromatic acids such as benzoic: the latter is excreted in the urine of birds in the form of dibenzoylornithine, or *ornithuric acid*:

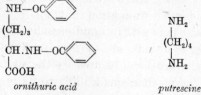

ornithuric acid   *putrescine*

By bacterial decarboxylation in the intestine and elsewhere, ornithine can give rise to the toxic diamine *putrescine*. Small amounts of this substance are absorbed by animals and are *detoxicated*, probably undergoing oxidation at the hands of diamine oxidase (p. 166).

LYSINE,

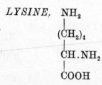

(essential: not known to be glycogenic or ketogenic), is the next higher homologue of ornithine. It is believed not to undergo deamination in the body (p. 269). Very little is known about the specific functions which, as an essential amino-acid, it must be presumed to discharge in the organism. Under the influence of bacterial enzymes it can yield *cadaverine*,

$$H_2N(CH_2)_5NH_2,$$

which, like putrescine, is highly toxic and can be oxidatively detoxicated by diamine oxidase.

PHENYLALANINE, $CH_2CH(NH_2)COOH$

(essential: ketogenic), and

TYROSINE, $CH_2CH(NH_2)COOH$

(replaceable by phenylalanine: ketogenic). It may be presumed that phenylalanine is irreversibly convertible into tyrosine (p. 255), but we have no certain knowledge of the mechanisms involved. These important amino-acids are known to be ketogenic and it is usually considered that the ring must be opened in the process because the side-chain contains only three carbon atoms whereas four are required for the production of acetoacetic acid. Work with isotopically labelled phenylalanine and tyrosine indicates that the α- and β-carbon atoms of the side chain and two more from the ring furnish the four carbon atoms of acetoacetate. Recent experiments suggest that the following reactions are involved, though the intermediate stages have not yet been completely worked out:

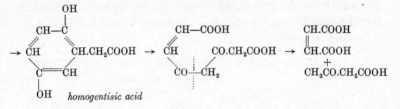

homogentisic acid

Transdeamination and oxidative decarboxylation precede these reactions, which account for the incorporation of the α- and β-carbon atoms of the original side-chain and two more from the ring into the resulting acetoacetic acid.

The metabolism of these aromatic acids goes astray in a group of interesting 'inborn errors of metabolism'. A peculiar form of mental deficiency known as imbecillitas (oligophrenia) phenylpyruvica owes its name to the curious fact that the urine of the afflicted regularly contains small amounts of phenylpyruvic acid. In albinism the enzyme tyrosinase is completely lacking, and the dark-coloured melanic pigments (p. 159) are characteristically absent from the skin, hair, eyes and other usual situations. A single case of tyrosinosis has been reported, the urine in this disorder containing traces of tyrosine as a regular feature. Alcaptonuria is another disorder in which the metabolism of the aromatic amino-acids appears to be blocked, and homogentisic acid is found in the urine (p. 223).

Phenylalanine and tyrosine are believed to be of particular importance in animal metabolism as the parent substances of two hormones, *adrenaline* and *thyroxine*. This belief has been confirmed by the use of isotopes. *Tyramine* can be formed from tyrosine by the action of a weak, specific tyrosine decarboxylase that occurs in the kidney and liver of mammals, and may possibly be an intermediate in the elaboration of adrenaline. If so, it must presumably be attacked by the monophenol oxidase component of tyrosinase to yield the amine corresponding to dihydroxyphenylalanine ('dopa'). It is known, however, that dopa can be formed from tyrosine by the action of tyrosinase and, moreover, that there exists a specific dopa decarboxylase which, acting upon dopa itself, could yield the same amine once more. Little is known about the remaining stages on the route to adrenaline, but the possible stages just described may be summarized in the following manner:

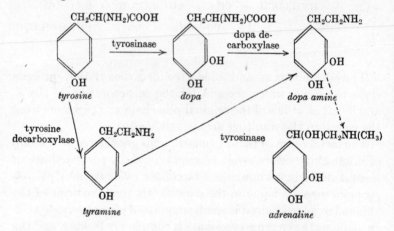

The *N*-methyl group of adrenaline is probably transferred from methionine, for administration of methyl-labelled (C^{14}) methionine leads to the production of *N*-methyl-labelled adrenaline in the adrenal medulla.

Thyroxine is a heavily iodinated derivative of tyrosine. It occurs, together with *di-iodotyrosine*, in the thyroid tissue of vertebrates. Di-iodotyrosine, together with the corresponding *dibromotyrosine*, has also been described as a constituent amino-acid of the skeletal protein material of a coral, *Gorgonia*, for which reason these halogenated tyrosines are sometimes called iodogorgoic and bromogorgoic acids respectively.

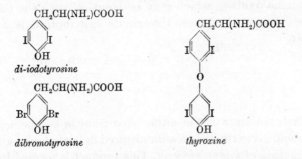

di-iodotyrosine

dibromotyrosine

thyroxine

Phenylalanine and tyrosine give rise to a series of toxic products when submitted to bacterial attack. These include phenol, *p*-cresol, tyramine and phenylethylamine. The amines are probably oxidatively *detoxicated* by amine oxidase, and the phenols by conjugation, usually with sulphuric acid.

$$HISTIDINE, \quad \overline{}CH_2CH(NH_2)COOH$$

(essential: neither glycogenic nor ketogenic), occurs in combination with β-alanine in the dipeptide *carnosine* (p. 344), which is present in the muscles of vertebrates of most kinds, though invariably absent from invertebrate tissues. The analogous compound *anserine* (p. 345) is similarly distributed and also contains β-alanine, but histidine is here replaced by its 1-*N*-methyl derivative. The methyl group is believed to arise by transference from methionine.

Comparatively little is known about the metabolism of histidine, though there are hints that it may be concerned in the *synthesis of purines* (p. 326). Animal tissues are known to contain a *histidase*, which is said to open the imidazole ring and yield, through a series of reactions, glutamic acid and succinic semi-aldehyde, both of which are strongly glucogenic, unlike histidine itself.

Histidine is the mother substance of *histamine*, being attacked by a specific *histidine decarboxylase*, traces of which are present in liver and kidney. Histamine can also be produced by bacterial activity in the intestine and elsewhere, and is *detoxicated* by a histamine oxidase, which may be identical with the diamine oxidase of animal tissues, though its distribution is a little peculiar.

TRYPTOPHAN,

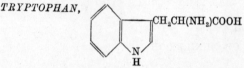

(essential: not known to be either glycogenic or ketogenic). This amino-acid gives rise, when administered in fairly large doses, to the excretion of *kynurenic acid*. This product is formed by way of *kynurenin*, apparently through the following reactions:

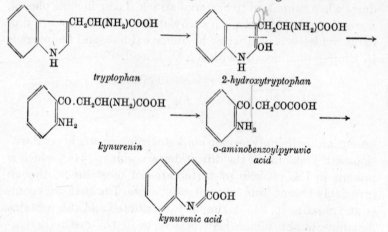

tryptophan

2-hydroxytryptophan

kynurenin

o-aminobenzoylpyruvic acid

kynurenic acid

There is evidence that kynurenic acid may be further metabolized to yield *nicotinic acid* in the animal; this is the only known case in which a vitamin can be produced from an essential amino-acid.

Bacterial decarboxylation of tryptophan leads to the formation of a poisonous amine, *tryptamine*, which is probably destroyed by amine oxidase, like other amines. Further degradation of the side-chain by bacteria is also possible and leads to the formation of a pair of foul-smelling compounds, *indole* and *skatole*; these are said to be largely responsible for the odour of faeces. Indole undergoes biological conversion into the corresponding alcohol, *indoxyl*, which, if absorbed, is *detoxicated* by conjugation with sulphuric acid and excreted in the urine in the form of the corresponding ethereal sulphate:

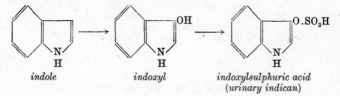

indole   indoxyl   indoxylsulphuric acid
(urinary indican)

Finally, mention may be made of two natural pigments that are of some historical interest and are related to tryptophan, viz. *natural indigo*, from the woad and indigo plants, and the Royal or *Tyrian purple* of the ancients, which can be prepared from a variety of marine gastropod molluscs, the classical source being *Murex* spp. Natural indigo arises from a β-glycoside of indoxyl that is present in the plant juices and undergoes decomposition when the tissues are bruised; free indoxyl is thus formed and undergoes oxidative coupling in the presence of oxygen to yield indigo. Tyrian purple is similarly formed from a derivative, thought to be a mercaptan, of 4-brom-indoxyl:

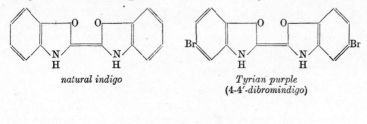

natural indigo   Tyrian purple
(4-4′-dibromindigo)

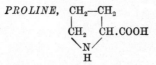

(non-essential- glycogenic), is, strictly speaking, an imino- rather than an amino-acid. Little is known about its metabolism, apart from the fact that *proline oxidase*, which is present in kidney tissue, can open the ring and give rise to glutamic acid. This may perhaps be a preliminary to the deamination of proline. The ring opening is not a hydrolytic but essentially an oxidative process. Since glutamic acid is glycogenic, the formation of glucose and glycogen from proline can be understood:

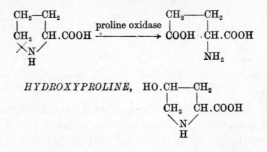

(non-essential: glycogenic), like proline, is an imino-acid. How it is converted into carbohydrate we do not know: conceivably it might first be reduced to proline and then attacked by proline oxidase. Alternatively, it might perhaps be attacked directly by proline oxidase to give γ-hydroxyglutamic acid, which occurs in nature and is known to be glycogenic.

CHAPTER XII

EXCRETORY METABOLISM OF PROTEINS AND AMINO-ACIDS

NATURE OF THE NITROGENOUS END-PRODUCTS

THE great bulk of all the nitrogen entering a typical animal arises from the α-amino-nitrogen of its food proteins. In mammals, at any rate, this is split off by deamination or transdeamination in the form of ammonia. Small quantities of ammonia also arise from other sources, such as the deamination of aminopurines and aminopyrimidines, but the great mass originates in the food proteins. The tissues have little capacity to store proteins or amino-acids as such, but considerable amounts of ammonia can undoubtedly be stored in animal tissues in the form of the amide-N of glutamine. The storage capacity with respect to ammonia-N is, however, small compared with the average daily turnover of protein and amino-acid nitrogen. In plants, which have no excretory apparatus, larger quantities of nitrogen can be stored, either in the form of asparagine or glutamine or both, according to the species, but in animals, which possess efficient excretory machinery, the superfluous nitrogen is excreted and the excreta of animals contain a remarkable variety of nitrogenous substances of varying degrees of complexity (Table 24).

Only among invertebrates do we find significant amounts of amino-acid nitrogen being excreted as such, and in certain invertebrate groups as much as 20–30 % of the total ingested nitrogen may be excreted in the form of unchanged amino-acids (see Table 24). Whether this is due simply to leakage of amino-acids from the body fluids of these animals, or whether it indicates some sort of metabolic disability we do not know. In marine animals, at any rate, it is known that the surface membranes are permeable to water, to ions and to small molecules, and it is therefore possible that amino-acid molecules might be lost by diffusion to some extent.

TABLE 24. NITROGEN PARTITION IN EXCRETA OF VARIOUS ANIMALS

(*From* data collected by J. Needham)

Phylum	Class and Order	Animal	Habitat	Ammonia	Urea	Uric acid	Amino-acids, creatine, etc.
Annelida	Chaetopoda	Sea-mouse (*Aphrodite aculeata*)	SW	80·0	0·2	0·8	.
	Hirudinea	Leech (*Hirudo officinalis*)	FW	76·4	5·4	None	3·2
Gephyrea	Sipunculoidea	Worm (*Sipunculus nudus*)	SW	50·0	9·7	None	16·6
Arthropoda	Crustacea	Crab (*Carcinus maenas*)	SW	67·8	2·9	0·7	8·7
		Spider-crab (*Maia squinado*)	SW	42·9	5·2	2·7	20·2
		Crayfish (*Astacus fluviatilis*)	FW	59·6	11·2	0·8	10·1
	Insecta	Silkworm (*Bombyx mori*)	T		None	85·8	.
		Clothes-moth (*Tinea pellionella*)	T	10·2	17·6	47·3	10·0
Mollusca	Gastropoda	Sea-hare (*Aplysia limacina*)	SW	33·5	8·7	4·6	13·0
		Land-snail (*Helix pomatia*)	T	13·7	20·0	10·7	6·0
	Lamellibranchiata	Clam (*Mya arenaria*)	SW	21·5	4·5	Trace	18·0
		Pond-mussel (*Anodonta cygnea*)	FW	63·0	.	.	.
	Cephalopoda	Octopus (*Octopus vulgaris*)	SW	41·7	15·0	.	20·7
		Cuttle-fish (*Sepia officinalis*)	SW	67·0	1·7	2·1	7·8
Echinodermata	Asteroidea	Star-fish (*Asterias rubens*)	SW	39·3	11·7	Trace	23·8
	Echinoidea	Sea-urchin (*Paracentrotus lividus*)	SW	28·1	7·5	1·0	28·0
	Holothuroidea	Sea-cucumber (*Holothuria tubulosa*)	SW	40·0	6·0	Trace	.

Group	Species					
Vertebrata						
Pisces: Teleostei	Goose-fish (*Lophius piscatorius*)	SW	36·8	16·2	0·0	15·8
	Sole (*Solea vulgaris*)	SW	53·0	16·6	·	13·8
	Sea-horse (*Hippocampus*)	SW	63·1	8·9	0·2	10·6
	Carp (*Cyprinus carpio*)	FW	56·0	5·7	·	7·0
Dipnoi	Lung-fish (*Protopterus aethiopicus*)	FW	41·2	18·5	·	·
Elasmobranchii	Dog-fish (*Mustelus canis*)	SW	7·3	80·7	0·8	·
	Dog-fish (*Scyllium canicula*)	SW	3·8	80·0	0·2	·
	Electric ray (*Torpedo*)	SW	·	91·4	0·0	0·8
Amphibia	Frog (*Rana temporaria*)	FW/T	15·0	82·0	Trace	·
	Frog (*Rana virescens*)	FW/T	3·2	84·0	0·4	·
	Toad (*Bufo vulgaris*)	FW/T	16·1	84·5	Trace	·
Reptilia: Chelonia	Turtle (*Chelone mydas*)	SW	15·3	45·1	19·1	11·5
	Turtle (*Chrysemis pinta*)	FW	8·7	39·0	18·8	·
Sauria	Snake (*Boa constrictor*)	T	Trace	·	80·0	·
	Snake (*Python*)	T	·	·	89·0	2·3
	Grass-snake (*Tropidonotus natrix*)	T	20·0	Trace	80·0	·
	Lizard (*Lacerta viridis*)	T	·	·	91·0	·
	Horned lizard (*Phrynosoma cornutum*)	T	·	None	98·0	·
Aves	Fowl (*Gallus domesticus*)	T	17·3	10·4	62·9	9·4
	Duck (*Anas*)	T	3·2	4·2	71·9	·
	Goose (*Anser*)	T	13·5	·	80·0	·
Mammalia	Spiny ant-eater (*Echidna aculeata*)	T	6·9	81·2	None*	·
	Dog (*Canis vulgaris*)	T	3·0	89·0	1·0	·
	Cat (*Felis vulgaris*)	T	4·9	68·1	0·1	·
	Whale (*Balaena mysticetus*)	SW	1·5	90·0	3·0	·
	Bat (*Xantharpyia collaris*)	T	0·6	77·8	1·2	·
	Camel (*Camelus bactrianus*)	T	4·1	62·7	1·0	18·5
	Llama (*Auchenia huanacos*)	T	2·2	67·7	0·8	10·0
	Man (*Homo sapiens*)	T	4·3	87·5	0·8	·

All figures refer to nitrogen in terms of % of total nitrogen excreted.
SW = sea water; FW = fresh water; T = terrestrial.
* Uric acid is replaced by allantoin in almost all mammals (see pp. 161, 361).

Up to the present we have dealt mainly with the nitrogenous metabolism of mammals, chiefly because so much more is known about them than about any other group of animals. But there is reason to think that animals of every kind possess digestive enzymes capable of dismantling their food proteins completely to yield the component amino-acids. Although an excretion of unchanged amino-acids is observed among many invertebrates, the greater part of the ingested nitrogen is excreted in the form of ammonia, even among these animals. It is probable that all animals deaminate at any rate the greater part of their incoming amino-acids with production of ammonia. Whether the deaminating machinery is always the same or even of the same general kind we do not at present know, but the evidence points to a large-scale production of ammonia by deamination in all animals.

Now ammonia is a very toxic substance. Just how toxic it is can be appreciated if we consider some experiments carried out by Sumner, who injected crystalline urease into rabbits. The blood of the rabbit contains a small amount of urea, and from this urea ammonia was formed by the hydrolytic action of the enzyme. The animals died as soon as the concentration of ammonia in the blood rose to about 5 mg. per 100 ml., i.e. about 1 part in 20,000, a very high order of toxicity indeed. Death occurred before any change in the pH of the blood could be detected, and it is therefore probable that the toxicity of ammonia is due to some specific property of the ammonium ion rather than to the basicity of ammonium hydroxide. It is extremely improbable that death was due to any toxic properties of the enzyme itself, for urease was also injected into birds, the blood of which does not contain urea, and in this case the animals were unharmed; but fatal results followed the injection of urease together with urea.

If we examine the excreta of many different kinds of animals, representing as many different phyla and classes as possible, we find that among the nitrogenous substances present, some one compound always predominates. Over and above the traces of assorted odds and ends such as creatine, purine bases, betaines and the like, we find either ammonia, urea or uric acid accounting as a rule for two-thirds or more of the total nitrogen excreted (see Table 24). In a few special cases, some compound other than these predominates, but such cases are rare and, in fact, animals as a whole may be divided rather sharply into three groups according as their main nitrogenous excretory product is ammonia, urea or uric acid. These three groups are respectively said to be *ammonotelic*, *ureotelic* and *uricotelic*. This discovery raises several important problems. First we must inquire why some animals are content to excrete their waste ammonia unchanged, and why others convert ammonia, the primary product of deamination, into secondary products in the form of urea and uric acid. Then we must ask why it is that, among animals that do elaborate these secondary products, some produce urea and others uric acid. Finally, we have to inquire into the mechanisms whereby these ultimate end-products are synthesized.

The nature of the predominant end-product in any particular case seems to be conditioned by the nature of the habitual environment of the particular organism, and the known facts are best explained on the supposition that *the conversion of ammonia to other products is an indispensable adaptation to limitation of the availability of water.*

If we consider the invertebrates first of all it may be said at once that they fall into a very large group of ammonoteles on the one hand, and a much smaller group of uricoteles on the other. Aquatic invertebrates, almost without exception, are ammonotelic. Ureotelism seems not to have been developed by members of the invertebrate phyla, while uricotelism is found only among terrestrial representatives of groups which, like the insects and the gastropod snails, have succeeded in colonizing the dry land. Animals living in water have at their disposal a relatively vast reservoir into which they can discharge waste ammonia, a relatively diffusible substance, without running any grave risk of being poisoned by their own excrement. Terrestrial invertebrates, on the other hand, are often hard put to it to find enough water for their essential needs, and the impossibility of disposing of ammonia fast enough to avoid toxaemia is overcome by the biological conversion of ammonia, a very soluble and highly poisonous material, into the insoluble and relatively innocuous uric acid. Terrestrial woodlice, however, are ammonotelic, and in their case adaptation to terrestrial existence has been achieved, not by uricotelism, but by an over-all reduction in protein metabolism. The daily turnover of nitrogen here is of the order of only 10 % of that of related marine and freshwater species, and this suppression of protein metabolism is certainly the simplest and probably the most primitive device for combating the dangers of ammonaemia.

The general picture appears particularly clearly among the vertebrates, as the data of Table 24 make clear. Taking the fishes first, it must be remembered that they fall into two main classes, the teleosts, or bony fishes, and the elasmobranchs, or cartilaginous fishes. Each of these classes is well represented in fresh and in salt water alike. To appreciate their position in the matter of water supply must involve a short digression.

The lives of aquatic animals are complicated by a factor which terrestrial creatures like ourselves have little reason to appreciate. The fact that an animal is aquatic does not necessarily mean that it enjoys an unlimited supply of water. Among *marine invertebrates* the membranes bounding the body surface are, as a rule, more or less permeable to water and to small molecules. Ammonia formed in the body of such an organism can therefore escape comparatively readily by diffusion into the external environment. In *fresh-water invertebrates*, however, the boundary membranes are much less permeable: indeed, the main part of the body surface is impermeable to salts, and not very permeable even to water. This impermeability is important because the cells and tissues can only survive in the presence of considerably higher concentrations of salts than are present in the surrounding water, and surface impermeability is a device that serves to prevent leakage of salts out of the animal. But even so, the animal not only lives in water, it *breathes* in water, and this means that, in certain organs specialized for the purposes of respiration, the animal's blood comes into very close proximity to the surrounding water. In these respiratory organs, oxygen is taken into the blood and carbon dioxide eliminated, and the membranes of these organs have necessarily to be freely permeable to dissolved gases. It seems that the necessary degree of permeability to dissolved gases is inseparable from an appreciable degree of permeability to water. In the respiratory organs of a fresh-water animal, therefore, we find membranes that are permeable to water, though impermeable to salts; they are, in fact, approximately semi-permeable. On the outer side of these membranes we have fresh water, which is virtually free of dissolved salts, and on the other lies the animal's blood, which contains on the average about 1% of dissolved salts. For this reason there is a considerable osmotic force tending to drive water into the animal from outside. The entry of this water leads to dilution of the salts of the blood, but aquatic animals possess elaborate salt-absorbing and excretory organs which enable them to turn out the unwanted water, while maintaining at the same time a constant internal salinity. A fresh-water invertebrate may therefore be pictured as having a constant, osmotically-driven current of water passing through its body. Any ammonia formed in the cells and tissues can diffuse into the blood of such an animal and be carried away with the water in the form of a copious but very dilute urine.

The position is substantially the same for *fresh-water teleosts*. Ammonia formed in the tissues escapes rapidly and readily by way of the urine, and here, as in aquatic invertebrates, there is no danger of toxaemia due to the accumulation of ammonia. For *marine teleosts*, however, the position is considerably more difficult. The gill membranes and the mucous membranes of the mouth are appreciably permeable to water, as they are in the fresh-water forms. But sea water contains about 3% of salts as against the 1% or thereabouts present in the blood, and the osmotic flow of water in this case is therefore away from the fish, instead of towards it. Marine teleosts, therefore, although they inhabit a watery medium, are nevertheless poorly supplied with water. They lose water constantly to their environment and are liable to die of desiccation, unlike their fresh-water relatives, whose lives are constantly imperilled by the imminent threat of flooding.*

The nitrogenous excretion of marine teleosts has been investigated in a very ingenious experiment devised by Homer Smith. A wooden box is divided into two compartments by a watertight rubber dam pierced by a hole large enough to fit closely round the belly of a fish. The animal is placed in the apparatus, which is filled with sea water, in such a way that the head and the gills are accommodated in one compartment and the tail and the excretory aperture in the other. After a suitable time, samples of water from either compartment are withdrawn and analysed for nitrogenous compounds, and it then appears that 80–90 % of the total nitrogen excreted is found in the forward compartment and must therefore have been excreted by way of the gills, only a small part of the whole being evacuated by way of the kidneys. About two-thirds of all the nitrogenous material excreted consists of ammonia, indicating that, although the fish has a comparatively poor water supply, it can, nevertheless, dispose of most of its ammonia by diffusion across the gill membranes, without previously converting it into any less noxious nitrogenous compound. The remaining third is not present in the form of urea, not yet as uric acid; indeed, it defied identification for some time, but turned out in the end to be trimethylamine oxide, $(CH_3)_3N \rightarrow O$. This, a practically neutral, soluble and innocuous material, is probably formed from ammonia, which it partially replaces in the excreta of marine, but not of freshwater, teleosts. It seems, then, that the marine teleosts eliminate ammonia as far as possible, but that the water supply is not sufficiently abundant to allow all the nitrogenous waste matter to be excreted in this form. Detoxication by the production of trimethylamine oxide is perhaps a device which removes, or at least reduces, the danger of toxic ammonaemia in these fishes.

In support of the general validity of this argument it may be pointed out that, although not many fishes have been studied,

---

* For further information regarding the osmotic regulation of aquatic animals, see Baldwin, *An Introduction to Comparative Biochemistry*; also Krogh, *Osmotic Regulation in Aquatic Animals*, for detailed information.

there is no record of the occurrence of significant amounts of trimethylamine oxide in the tissues or in the excreta of fresh-water teleosts, though its presence in the tissues and excreta of marine forms has been abundantly confirmed.

The elasmobranch fishes present a slightly more difficult problem. *Marine elasmobranchs* produce and retain within their bodies large amounts of urea. Retention of urea in the blood and tissue fluids of these fishes is possible because the gills are impermeable to urea, while the kidney possesses a specialized mechanism that can control the loss of urea from the body. Enough urea is always retained to keep up a concentration of 2–2·5 % of urea in the blood; over and above this concentration, urea is excreted, and the elasmobranch fishes are, in fact, ureotelic. The presence of so much urea in the blood raises the total osmotic pressure of the blood to a level slightly higher than that of the surrounding sea water, and these fishes therefore escape the constant loss of water which threatens the existence of the marine teleosts. Instead of losing water to their environment, they constantly receive an osmotically driven stream of water from the sea. By resorting to ureotelism, therefore, the marine elasmobranchs are not only protected against toxaemia due to ammonia but, by retaining some of the urea they produce, now find themselves in a very favourable position as regards water supply.

Like marine teleosts, the marine elasmobranchs excrete a part of their waste nitrogen in the form of trimethylamine oxide. This suggests that they have at some time in the past experienced the same osmotic difficulties as confront the marine teleosts of the present day, and that they faced them in the same way, i.e. by converting a part of their waste ammonia into trimethylamine oxide. But subsequently, it appears, they evolved the still better trick of making urea, which is even less toxic than trimethylamine oxide, and, by retaining enough of it in their tissues, managed in the end to turn the osmotic gradient to their advantage instead of their detriment.

The *fresh-water elasmobranchs* are believed to be descended from their marine cousins, which they resemble in being ureotelic, although in their case the amount of urea retained is only of the order of 1 %. Thus, even among the fishes, an essentially aquatic group, we find ureotelism already well developed.

But no discussion of the fishes would be complete without some mention of the Dipnoi, or *lung-fishes*. These creatures inhabit swamps and rivers in tropical regions. During the hot season the water dries up, and the lung-fishes shut themselves up in cocoon-like structures in the mud to wait until the rains come. As long as water is available, these fishes behave like fresh-water teleosts and are essentially ammonotelic. But during the period while they lie dormant and cut off from the water, they switch over to ureotelism and, when the rains come and the rivers fill again, almost their first act on emerging is to excrete a mass of urea that has accumulated during their aestivation. This case is a particularly interesting one, since it constitutes a test case of the validity of our general hypothesis—that the detoxication of ammonia is essentially an adaptation to restriction of the water supply.

Going on now to the *Amphibia*, the frogs, toads, newts and the rest, we are in the company of animals which are able to spend longer or shorter periods away from the water. We should expect, in the terms of our hypothesis, that no animal could live long away from water without exposing itself to the hazards of ammonia-poisoning and, indeed, that the colonization of dry land could hardly have been begun until some mechanism had been evolved by means of which ammonia could be detoxicated. The Amphibia would be expected, then, to be either ureotelic or uricotelic. We get some very interesting evidence here by studying the humble tadpole. Tadpoles are aquatic and ammonotelic. Later, the tadpole undergoes the metamorphosis that changes it from a wholly aquatic animal into a true amphibian and, at the same time precisely, it also undergoes a chemical metamorphosis and abandons ammonotelism in favour of ureotelism. The adult frog, in common with the adult forms of other Amphibia, is ureotelic, and it seems as though, in the course of its development, it recapitulates some of the essential features of its evolutionary past. There is one special case that deserves mention;

Xenopus, an animal that possesses the morphological features of a true amphibian, is exceptional in that, although it undergoes metamorphosis, it remains throughout its life an aquatic, and an ammonotelic, organism.

TABLE 25. NITROGEN EXCRETION OF SOME
CHELONIAN REPTILES

(Averages, *after* V. Moyle)

Habitat	% of total N as		
	Ammonia	Urea	Uric acid
Wholly aquatic	20–25	20–25	5
Semi-aquatic	6	40–60	5
Wholly terrestrial:			
Hygrophilous	6	30	7
Xerophilous	5	10–20	50–60

The rest of the vertebrates are generally considered as having evolved from some primitive kind of amphibian stock which, we suppose, must have been ureotelic. Leading from the Amphibia we find two main, diverging lines of evolution, one leading to the mammals and the other to the reptiles and the birds. There exists among the reptiles one group, the Chelonia (tortoises and turtles) which are of rather particular evolutionary interest as a transitional group, at any rate from the chemical point of view. Probably the original chelonian stock was terrestrial or amphibious, but to-day we find wholly aquatic, semi-aquatic and wholly terrestrial species. Table 25 presents some recent data relating to the nitrogen excretion of some of these animals. Those which are terrestrial but favour marshy surroundings are essentially ureotelic; little ammonia or uric acid is produced. In wholly aquatic species a significant degree of ureotelism is still retained, but the ratio of urea-N to ammonia-N is much lower, suggesting that these forms tend to revert towards an ammonotelic habit. But in the dry-living and wholly terrestrial forms we find that, although urea formation still persists, the bulk of the total N is now excreted in the form of uric acid.

Other dry-living reptiles, the Sauria (snakes and lizards), together with the birds, have altogether abandoned ureotelism in favour of uricotelism. The mammals, however, have continued in the amphibian manner and clung to the more primitive ureotelic habit.

Joseph Needham considers that the choice between ureo- and uricotelism is determined by the conditions under which embryonic development takes place. The case of the Chelonia has not been very thoroughly studied, but in certain species at least the eggs are laid in wet sand or in mud, and if urea were formed during development it could probably escape into the water of the immediate surroundings fast enough to avoid interference with the processes of ontogenesis, at any rate in some species. Ammonia, probably, could not escape fast enough under these conditions, and ureotelism presumably allows the embryo to get safely through its development. In one species the female lays her eggs in dry situations, but then goes to the trouble of wetting them very thoroughly with water from a supernumerary bladder, and this suggests that wetness of the environment must be an important factor in chelonian ontogenesis.

The position is much clearer in the other ureotelic group, the *mammals*. There still remain a few egg-laying mammals, e.g. *Echidna*, and their eggs are incubated always in wet situations. Not much is known about the water relationships of these eggs, but it has nevertheless been established that the adults are ureotelic. The rest of the mammals undergo embryonic development in intimate contact with the maternal circulation. Food materials diffuse from the maternal blood stream across the placenta to the embryo, and waste products can likewise diffuse back across the placental barrier to be excreted by the maternal kidneys. The mammalian embryo, with the entire water resources and the excretory apparatus of the maternal organism at its disposal, has no need to do otherwise than remain ureotelic and excrete its waste nitrogen by proxy.

Conditions are very different in the eggs of certain tortoises and all *snakes, lizards and birds*. These eggs are laid with a supply of water just sufficient to see them through development, and no more is to be had, apart from metabolic water formed by the oxidation of food reserves as development proceeds, because the eggs are surrounded by tough membranes or hard shells which are practically impermeable to water. In such a system the production of ammonia could be nothing short of disastrous. Urea would be a more suitable end-product if only because it is relatively harmless, but apart from the elasmobranch fishes, no organisms are known that can stand up to more than a very mild uraemia without more or less serious disturbances of normal physiological function. Needham has calculated that, if the waste nitrogen actually turned out during the embryonic development of the chick were converted into urea, the resulting uraemia, by human standards, would be sufficient to give the embryo a bad headache at the very least. 'In which case', as Needham says, 'natural selection would hardly have preserved it for our entertainment.' Embryos which develop in these closed-box, or 'cleidoic', eggs solve their problems by the conversion of waste ammonia, not into urea, but into uric acid, and the habit of uricotelism which they acquire during embryonic existence persists into, and throughout, their adult life. Whereas urea is a very soluble compound, the excretion of which requires a comparatively liberal supply of water, uric acid, which is almost equally innocuous, is exceedingly insoluble and can simply be dumped in the solid form. It is carried away from the embryo proper and deposited in a little membranous bag, the allantois, the contents of which include solid nodules of uric acid at the end of development.

Finally, mention may be made of a case of chemical recapitulation comparable to that already mentioned in the case of the frog. Needham has studied the nitrogenous excretory products of chick embryos at different stages throughout development. His results, which are shown graphically in Fig. 24, show that at the very beginning of development the chick produces ammonia, like an aquatic animal. This is quickly switched off in favour of urea, the embryo behaving for a time like an amphibious animal. Finally, the chick appears in its true colours, as a truly terrestrial, uricotelic organism, developing inside a cleidoic egg.

To summarize, we may make the following statements. Among invertebrates, the ammonotelic type of metabolism is found in aquatic animals; ureotelism appears not to be employed, while uricotelism is confined to organisms that have become adapted to life under terrestrial conditions. Among vertebrates, ammonotelism is confined to animals that are entirely aquatic and, even among these, ureotelism and perhaps trimethylamine oxide formation have been exploited by animals which, though aquatic, experience considerable shortage of water. With the conquest of the land, ureotelism appears to have been generally adopted and

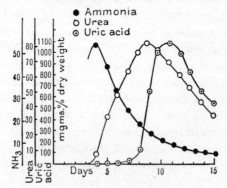

Fig. 24. Nitrogenous excretion of developing chick embryo (after Needham).

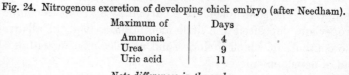

Maximum of	Days
Ammonia	4
Urea	9
Uric acid	11

Note differences in the scales.

is still found to-day among the Amphibia. It has been retained by a group of reptiles the eggs of which develop under conditions of comparative humidity, and in the mammals, whose embryos have the water of the maternal blood-stream at their disposal. The dry-living reptiles, together with the birds, have abandoned ureotelism in favour of uricotelism, a change which is associated with embryonic development under the conditions of acute water shortage implied by the cleidoicity of the egg. Thus the detoxication of ammonia by conversion to urea or uric acid appears in every case to be intimately associated with limitation of water supply. A more pictorial form of summary is given in Table 26.

TABLE 26. NITROGEN EXCRETION OF VERTEBRATES IN RELATION TO WATER SUPPLY

Group	Environment	Water supply	$(CH_3)_3N \rightarrow O$	NH_3	Urea	Uric acid
Pisces:						
Teleostei	FW	Abundant	–	+	–	–
	SW	Poor	+	+	–	–
Elasmobranchii	FW	Abundant	–	–	+	–
	SW	Good	+	–	+	–
Dipnoi	FW	Abundant	–	+	–	–
	T*	None	–	–	+	–
Amphibia:						
Urodela	FW	Abundant	–	+	–	–
Anura: Tadpole	FW	Abundant	–	+	–	–
Frog	FW/T	Good/poor	–	–	+	–
Reptilia:						
Chelonia	FW	Abundant	–	+	+	–
	FW/T	Good/poor	–	–	+	–
	T	Poor	–	–	+	+
Sauria	T	Poor	–	–	–	+
Aves	T	Poor	–	–	–	+
Mammalia	T	Poor	–	–	+	–

Key. FW = fresh water; SW = sea water; T = terrestrial.
* During aestivation.

SYNTHESIS OF THE END-PRODUCTS: UREA

Most of the early work on the biological synthesis of urea was, not unnaturally, carried out on mammalian materials. It will be recalled that hepatectomy in the dog leads to cessation of urea production, an observation that points to the liver as the sole seat of urea synthesis in the mammalian organism. Work with perfused mammalian liver confirmed this conclusion, for a synthetic formation of urea from added ammonia was readily demonstrated. Little was known about the mechanisms of the synthesis for many years, but several theories were expounded, two of which were widely held in their day.

According to the classical view, ammonia reacts with carbon dioxide in the blood to form ammonium carbonate which, under the influence of the liver, was believed to undergo two successive dehydrations to yield ammonium carbamate and finally urea:

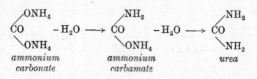

This view was eventually abandoned, numerous attempts to demonstrate urea production from ammonium carbamate having failed. A second theory was based upon the fact that the oxidation of nitrogenous organic substances under laboratory conditions often gives rise to traces of cyanic acid. If cyanic acid were similarly formed under biological conditions it could react with ammonia to form ammonium cyanate which, it was supposed, could subsequently undergo intramolecular rearrangement, after the manner of the classical synthesis accomplished by Wöhler, to yield urea:

$$NH_4CNO \rightleftharpoons CO(NH_2)_2.$$

This scheme, too, was abandoned. Not only is cyanic acid toxic, but little evidence was forthcoming in favour either of its formation in the animal or of the supposed biological conversion of ammonium cyanate into urea.

The existence of a urea-producing enzyme in mammalian liver was suspected at the end of the last century, following the discovery that, if liver tissue is allowed to autolyse, urea is produced. Kossel and Dakin showed that this urea originates in arginine (set free by autolysis of the tissue proteins) under the influence of a hydrolytic enzyme which they called arginase, and which catalyses the following reaction:

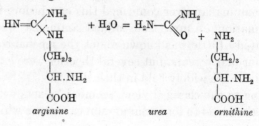

This enzyme can be extracted with water, saline, glycerol, etc., is activated by Mn^{++}, and has been studied extensively.

It was Clementi who first drew attention to the striking fact that, while *arginase occurs in high concentrations in the liver of ureotelic animals*, it is present in traces at most in the liver of those which are uricotelic (Table 27). It was already clear that arginase could be held responsible for the production of some of

TABLE 27. DISTRIBUTION OF ARGINASE IN LIVER
AND KIDNEY OF VERTEBRATES

(*Data from* Clementi)

Class	Species	Liver	Kidney
Mammalia	Dog	+	−
	Ox	+	−
	Pig	+	−
	Guinea-pig	+	−
	Rat	+	−
	Monkey	+	−
	Man	+	−
Aves	*Gallus domesticus*	−	+
	Columba livia	−	+
	Turtur turtur	−	+
	Fringuilla cloris	−	+
Reptilia:			
Chelonia	*Emys europae*	+	−
Sauria	*Lacerta agilis*	−	−
	Anguis fragilis	−	−
	Coronella austriaca	−	−
Amphibia	*Rana esculenta*	+	−
	Rana temporaria	+	−
Pisces:			
Elasmobranchii	*Torpedo ocellata*	+	.
	Raia clavata	+	.
Teleostei	*Perca fluviatilis*	+	−
	Abramis brama	+	−
	Barbus fluviatilis	+	−

the urea excreted by mammals, inasmuch as arginine occurs in considerable amounts in most proteins. Arginine arising from the food proteins could therefore account for some, though not by any means for all, of the urea formed.

Later, Krebs, using the tissue-slice technique, showed that surviving slices of rat liver can convert added ammonia into urea, thus confirming earlier observations made by the perfusion method. When amino-acids are added to the slices, the ammonia set free by deamination undergoes approximately quantitative conversion into urea. Different amino-acids are deaminated at different rates as we have already noted, and the rate of urea formation from amino-acids therefore varies from one to another. In one case, however, the rate of synthesis exceeded all expectation. It was to be anticipated that when ornithine was used, not more than one molecule of urea could be formed from each molecule of ornithine used, one-half arising from the α- and one-half from the δ-amino-group. In fact, however, ten or more molecules of urea were found for each molecule of ornithine added. This suggested that ornithine must act catalytically in the synthesis of urea.

Following up this clue, the effect of arginine also was investigated, and again it was found that the rate, as well as the amount of urea synthesized from added ammonia, was greater than could be accounted for. Krebs therefore concluded that ornithine must react with ammonia and carbon dioxide to form arginine which, under the influence of the liver arginase, could give rise to urea, ornithine being regenerated and used over and over again as a carrier, thus:

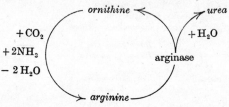

The formation of arginine from ornithine must evidently be a complex process, and Krebs sought to discover possible intermediate compounds. It was known that there exists in the water-melon, *Citrullus vulgaris*, a substance which, chemically speaking, lies midway between ornithine and arginine. This substance, known as citrulline, has been tested, and evidence has been obtained that, like ornithine and arginine, citrulline can act catalytically in the synthesis of urea from added ammonia, though the results obtained with citrulline are usually less dramatic.

Krebs therefore proposed the so-called 'ornithine cycle', the outline of which is illustrated in Fig. 25. This scheme explains the catalytic behaviour of ornithine, citrulline and arginine and, involving as it does the participation of arginase as an integral part of the system, provided for the first time a rational basis for the empirical rule enunciated by Clementi, that arginase is always present in the livers of ureotelic animals.

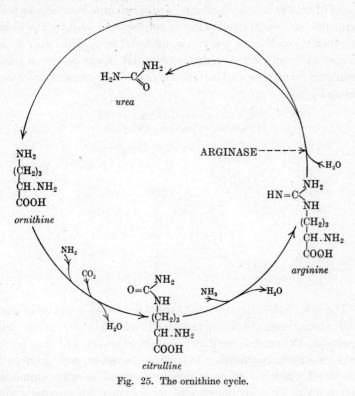

Fig. 25. The ornithine cycle.

Certain points must be noticed in connexion with Krebs's original observations. The synthesis of urea from ammonia would not take place, even in the presence of ornithine, unless the liver cells were intact and some oxidizable material such as glucose or lactate was available. The dependence of the synthesis upon intact cellular architecture might be attributed to a breakdown of some one or other of the enzymes concerned, or to the loss of some essential coenzyme, when the cells are disrupted, while the necessity for the provision of some kind of oxidizable material could be attributed to the fact that, being as it is an endergonic process, the synthesis of urea requires the provision of energy from concomitant oxidative reactions.

Krebs's original work on rat liver has been extended to the livers of other ureotelic animals, and it has now been shown that ornithine acts catalytically in the synthesis of urea by the livers of other mammals, of a tortoise, and of a frog. Bird and snake livers, as would have been anticipated, form no urea when ammonia, ornithine and lactate are provided: uric acid is formed instead.

TABLE 28. ARGINASE CONTENTS OF VARIOUS
TISSUES (ARBITRARY UNITS)

(*Data from* Hunter and Dauphinee)

Species	Liver	Kidney	Heart	Muscle
Cat	1280	2·7	.	.
Rabbit	369	0·9	.	.
Hen	0	.	.	.
Pigeon	0	18·3	.	.
Mud-turtle	14·2	0	.	.
Dog-fish	319	31	109	2·2
Herring	181	7	8·8	0·9
Other teleosts	8–110	1–5	.	.

The case of the fishes (Table 28) calls for some special comment. Teleostean fishes are characteristically ammonotelic rather than ureotelic, although their livers contain arginase. The rest of the ornithine cycle mechanism is lacking, however, and no urea is produced when ornithine is provided, together with ammonia and lactate. The elasmobranchs, by contrast, are ureotelic and here, unlike other ureotelic organisms, arginase is present in considerable concentrations in practically every part of the body. As yet the effect of ornithine on the synthesis of urea seems not to have been studied in elasmobranch tissues. Presumably the study of urea synthesis in such tissues is difficult since, to ensure survival of the tissues, it is necessary to work in a medium which resembles elasmobranch blood, and the latter already contains a high proportion of urea. That arginase is present all over the elasmobranch body suggests that the synthesis of urea may not be confined to the liver, as it is in other ureoteles, and it is perhaps significant that, whereas hepatectomy in the dog is followed by cessation of urea production, the hepatectomized dog-fish maintains its normal high level of uraemia.

As far as the invertebrates are concerned there is, as has been stated, little reason to believe that ureotelism has ever been exploited. Arginase, however, is present in many such organisms, usually in traces, but occasionally in concentrations as high as those in mammalian liver. One can only suppose that here, as among the teleostean fishes, the *tour de force* necessary for the acquisition of the rest of the ornithine cycle has not been achieved.

In general confirmation of Krebs's hypothesis we may again refer to the observations of Schoenheimer, who fed animals on a diet containing heavy ammonia. Arginine was subsequently isolated from the carcasses and found to contain heavy nitrogen (N^{15}). The isotopic nitrogen was confined to the amidine group, for on alkaline hydrolysis the ornithine formed was free from N^{15}, the whole of the heavy nitrogen being present in the urea. Moreover, the heavy nitrogen content of the arginine was practically equivalent to that of samples of urea isolated from the urine of the same animals. More recently still it has been shown that N^{15}-labelled ornithine does not give rise to labelled urea whether the isotope is incorporated into the a- or the γ-NH_2 radical, whereas citrulline labelled with N^{15} in the carbamyl group yields correspondingly labelled urea.

More recently still the mechanisms that underlie the ornithine cycle have been worked out in considerable detail. The first step in this direction came with the discovery that ureogenesis is markedly stimulated by glutamine or glutamate, and the second with the further discovery that urea can be synthesized in whole homogenates of mammalian liver, provided that ATP is added to furnish the free energy required for this endergonic synthesis. If liver homogenates are incubated with ammonia, bicarbonate, ornithine, glutamate and ATP, urea is slowly formed and citrulline accumulates. The second stage of the process, the conversion of citrulline to urea, requires magnesium ions and, if these are added, urea is more rapidly formed and citrulline no longer accumulates.

The first stage, in which citrulline is formed, is a 'particle bound' process and has not yet been achieved except in the presence of solid, particulate tissue, but the second stage, leading to the formation of arginine from citrulline, proceeds well in the presence of watery extracts of acetone powders prepared from liver tissue. The final stage, the decomposition of arginine to give urea and regenerate ornithine, is catalysed, as has long been known, by arginase.

We know least about the first stage of ureogenesis. The prevalent belief is that glutamate reacts with carbon dioxide and ammonia to form carbamylglutamate, a process which requires ATP at some stage. The carbamyl radical is believed then to be transferred to ornithine, yielding citrulline and regenerating glutamate:

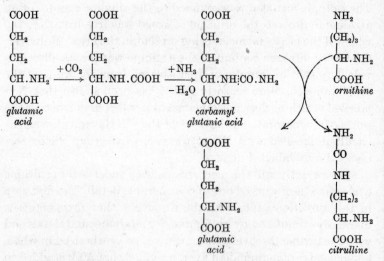

This stage of the synthesis can be carried out by suitably fortified, washed homogenates, and carbamylglutamic acid can replace free glutamic acid.

The conversion of citrulline to arginine can take place in extracts prepared from acetone liver powders and again requires ATP. Magnesium ions are also necessary. This stage of the process involves an unusual kind of transamination (p. 140) and it has been established that citrulline reacts with aspartic acid to form a complex, which is then decomposed to give arginine and malic acid and has been isolated in crude form. Two enzymes are required here and have been partially separated by ammonium sulphate fractionation of the extracts. The reactions appear to be the following:

```
NH2          NH          COOH          NH    COOH        NH          COOH
|            ||          |             ||  H: |          ||          |
CO           C.OH    H2N.CH            C — N:—CH          C.NH2   HO.CH
|            |          |             |      |     +H2O  |          |
NH           NH         CH2     ATP    NH     CH2    ——>  NH         CH2
|     ⇌      |       +  |    ——————>   |      |          |       +  |
(CH2)3       (CH2)3     COOH    -H2O   (CH2)3  COOH       (CH2)3     COOH
|            |          aspartic       |                 |
CH.NH2       CH.NH2     acid           CH.NH2            CH.NH2
|            |                         |                 |
COOH         COOH                      COOH              COOH
keto-        enol-                     intermediate      arginine    malic
  citrulline                           complex                        acid
```

The products of the reaction, arginine and malate, have been positively identified. It is not known what part ATP plays in the process but, since malate rather than oxaloacetate is formed, it seems likely that citrulline reacts in its enolic and not in its ketonic form, and it may be that ATP phosphorylates the enolic hydroxyl group.

The final stage, the fission of arginine by arginase, is well known. Evidently the synthesis of urea is a complex process and one, moreover, that calls for the expenditure of a good deal of energy, so that the animal has to pay a fairly heavy price for the advantages it can derive from ureotelism.

As an illustration of what appears to be a general principle (which might be called 'the principle of multiple function'), mention may be made here of the presence of the complete ornithine cycle mechanism in certain strains of the bread-mould, *Neurospora crassa*. It is difficult indeed to see what advantage can conceivably be gained by this organism from ureotelism as such. Krebs, however, has grappled with this problem and produced what appears to be a satisfying if not a satisfactory solution. The synthetic side of the ornithine cycle, he suggests, may be very widely distributed in living organisms, perhaps as a mechanism for the synthesis of citrulline and of the 'half-essential' amino-acid arginine. Perhaps this is its *primary* function. Animals which, by developing this system on a large scale and supplementing it with a powerful arginase activity, become ureotelic, can obtain advantages which are of enormous survival value under conditions of acute water shortage. This, according to Krebs's view, is no 'new' invention but a case rather of putting 'old' mechanisms to new uses. A somewhat similar notion had already been propounded by Hopkins many years earlier in his studies of certain butterfly pigments thought at the time to be formed from uric acid: here, it appeared, a nitrogenous compound primarily of excretory significance was being secondarily employed for purposes of personal adornment. The formation of uric acid by birds and xerophilous reptiles fits in with the same general proposition, for all living organisms, probably, are able to synthesize the purines required for the production of their indispensable nucleotides and nucleoproteins. Uricotelism could, however, arise by placing heavy emphasis on purine production, with the addition, perhaps, of purine deaminases and xanthine oxidase, to produce uric acid on the large scale. Biochemically, as otherwise, it seems that there is nothing new under the sun.

Synthesis of the End-products: Uric Acid

Uric acid is just as important an excretory product among uricotelic animals as is urea in those that are ureotelic, but very little is known about its mode of synthesis. Hepatectomy in the dog is followed by cessation of urea production, and hepatectomy in the goose is similarly followed by cessation of the synthesis of uric acid. In both these cases hepatectomy leads to the accumulation of ammonia in the blood, and it follows that, just as urea is synthesized from ammonia in the liver of the dog, so too is uric acid synthesized from ammonia in that of the bird.

Early experiments with perfused goose liver confirmed this conclusion, and showed convincingly that the uric acid excreted by birds can be formed from ammonia.

The suggestion was made quite early that uric acid might be synthesized by way of urea, two molecules of the latter combining with one of some 3-carbon material to form the purine ring system, perhaps as follows:

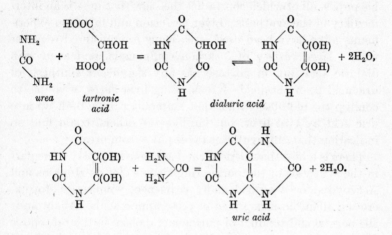

Perfusion experiments were performed on goose liver in which urea was added to the perfusion medium and, in some cases, small yields of extra uric acid were obtained, but a statistical analysis of the results has shown that the yields are not significant. Other experiments which gave results in favour of the hypothesis were carried out by feeding urea, together with 3-carbon compounds, to birds. In this case substantial yields of extra uric acid were recorded, but here, too, more recent work has shown that the results are not valid, for if urea is injected instead of being fed, there is no increase in the output of uric acid. The urea administered is quantitatively excreted in the urine, and the earlier results must therefore be attributed to bacterial activity in the gut. Acting upon urea, the intestinal micro-organisms presumably liberate ammonia, which is absorbed and, as we know, can be converted into uric acid by the liver.

Quite apart from other considerations, it is known that the liver of birds and other uricotelic animals contains little or no arginase and, unless it can be established that urea can be synthesized through mechanisms not involving that enzyme, there seems little probability that urea could be produced in the avian liver, let alone be further converted into uric acid.

Numerous experiments have been performed by Clementi and his pupils, all of which contradict the view that urea is an intermediary in the synthesis. Liver perfusion and injection experiments alike have been used, urea being administered together with a large variety of 3-carbon compounds, and even with dialuric acid, but in no case has any significant synthesis of uric acid been obtained. Krebs, using liver slices, was able to confirm the old observation that ammonia can be built up into uric acid by bird liver, but he, like the others, could find no indication that any synthesis takes place from urea.

There is a hint that histidine and arginine may play some part in the synthesis of the purine ring system, for as Hopkins and Ackroyd showed a good many years ago, young rats stop excreting allantoin if deprived of these amino-acids. Allantoin is the normal end-product of purine metabolism in the rat, and is formed by the enzymatic oxidation of uric acid. The rat, however, is a ureotelic animal, and we cannot necessarily argue from this to the case of a purely uricotelic organism.

Some further knowledge was gained by taking advantage of the fact that, whereas the livers of most birds, e.g. the domestic hen and the goose, form uric acid from added ammonia, that of the pigeon does not yield uric acid but a precursor of some kind which, under the influence of an enzyme present in the kidney, undergoes conversion into uric acid itself. Schuler and Reindel were the first to study this problem. Working with pigeon-liver slices they demonstrated that, whereas small amounts of uric acid are formed by liver or kidney alone, much more is produced when both tissues are allowed to act simultaneously, or when the action of the liver is followed by that of the kidney. Krebs and his co-workers collected enough of the intermediary body for identification, and showed that it is hypoxanthine. Schuler and

Reindel confirmed this result, inasmuch as they, too, isolated a purine body, which they believed to be xanthine, while subsequent repetition of their work by Krebs confirmed his original finding of hypoxanthine. The reason for this interesting dissociability of uricogenesis in the pigeon is that, whereas the livers of most birds contain xanthine oxidase, that of the pigeon does not. In this bird, xanthine oxidase is present in the kidney, and hypoxanthine formed in the liver is passed on to the kidney and there catalytically oxidized to uric acid, presumably by way of xanthine.

The administration to birds of isotopically labelled glycine, acetate or formate and CO_2, followed by systematic degradation of the uric acid formed, has made it possible to specify the probable origins of some of the atoms which go to make up the purine ring. The results available to date may be summarized as follows:

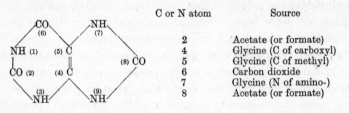

C or N atom	Source
2	Acetate (or formate)
4	Glycine (C of carboxyl)
5	Glycine (C of methyl)
6	Carbon dioxide
7	Glycine (N of amino-)
8	Acetate (or formate)

The three N atoms at 1, 3 and 9 are believed to be drawn from the general pool of amino-groups and ammonia molecules at the disposal of the organism.

At present, however, we are still as far as ever from knowing how the purine-ring system is synthesized: all we can say for certain is that the nitrogenous starting materials are ammonia and probably glycine, and that hypoxanthine, and by presumption xanthine also, are intermediaries in the synthesis. It is worthy of note that purine synthesis has recently been achieved *in vitro* with the aid of dialysed liver extracts. In the presence of glutamic acid or glutamine, a source of ribose-1-phosphate and boiled liver extract to supply necessary coenzymes, the following reactions were demonstrated:

$$2NH_3 + CO_2 + 2 \text{ glycine} + 2 \text{ formate} + \text{ribose-1-phosphate} \rightarrow$$
$$\text{inosine-1-phosphate} \rightarrow \text{inosine} \rightarrow \text{hypoxanthine} + \text{ribose-1-phosphate},$$

These changes take place aerobically in the presence of a source of energy (glycolysis) but no purine intermediates were detected apart from inosine, itself a derivative of hypoxanthine.

Little work has been done on uricogenesis in the reptiles. As far as the uricotelic invertebrates are concerned, a good deal of work has been done, but the results are, at best, inconclusive. The outlook in this field has been much prejudiced by the view, now abandoned in so far as it affects uricotelic vertebrates, that urea is an intermediary in the synthesis. The best attitude to adopt at the present time is one of ignorance.

SYNTHESIS OF OTHER END-PRODUCTS: TRIMETHYLAMINE OXIDE

Feeding experiments have been carried out with young salmon to elucidate the origin of this compound. These fishes are euryhaline and were kept at first in fresh water on a diet of fresh, ground ox liver, when no trimethylamine oxide was produced. They were then transferred to sea water, still on the same diet, but still no trimethylamine oxide appeared until food containing preformed trimethylamine oxide was given in place of the ox liver. This would seem to indicate that this compound is wholly exogenous in origin, but the excretion in some cases of nearly 50 % of the total nitrogen in the form of trimethylamine oxide by marine fishes suggests that this substance must have a synthetic origin in these fishes, to some extent at least. Probably a part originates as such in the food, for many marine organisms, including the small crustaceans which form an important article of diet for many fishes, contain substantial amounts of trimethylamine oxide, which is taken over by the feeder and excreted unchanged. Another possible source is glycine betaine. This substance occurs abundantly in some animals and in many plants. It is known that if cows are fed on sugar-beet residues, which are a rather rich source of glycine betaine, trimethylamine oxide appears in the milk. But although betaine gives rise to trimethylamine oxide when administered to cows, it is generally believed that the conversion is not due to the tissues of the cow itself, but rather to the activities of the symbiotic micro-organisms which inhabit its rumen. Animal tissues do not, in general, appear to be capable of converting betaine into trimethylamine oxide, though trimethylamine itself is oxidized by mammalian tissues to yield the oxide, and a trimethylamine oxidase has been discovered in fish muscle. One can do little more at present than guess at the extent to which such a conversion can take place in fishes, and in any case there remains to be explained the excretion of trimethylamine oxide by marine yet not by fresh-water fishes, for there is no reason to think that the food of fresh-water species contains less precursors than that of marine forms.

It is conceivable that trimethylamine itself might first be formed by the biological methylation of ammonia, and subsequently oxidized to the oxide in animal tissues; mechanisms for methylation are known (p. 142), and it is known too that trimethylamine can be oxidized to its oxide in the tissues of some animals.

Guanine (2-amino-6-oxypurine). Special mention must be made of guanine, for this purine appears to replace uric acid in the excreta of spiders. In spite of the popular belief to the contrary, the spiders constitute a group that is morphologically quite distinct from the insects: they demonstrate their independence chemically, too, by excreting guanine in place of uric acid. Guanine, if anything, is even less soluble than uric acid, and contains one amino-group per molecule over and above the four ring-bound nitrogen atoms of the purine ring. Evidently, therefore, guanine is well qualified to take over the excretory functions of uric acid.

The manner of its synthesis is unknown: conceivably it might arise from xanthine by amination, but there is no experimental evidence whatever on this point.

CHAPTER XIII

SOME SPECIAL ASPECTS OF
NITROGEN METABOLISM

NITROGENOUS substances of many different kinds have been isolated from time to time from various animal materials, and although their origins, functions and metabolic fates are known in only a few cases, some mention of these compounds and their distribution seems desirable here. We shall consider first a group of compounds chemically related to choline, then a group of betaines, a rather large group of derived guanidines, and some iminazole bases.

DISTRIBUTION OF CHOLINE, TETRAMETHYL AMMONIUM HYDROXIDE, TRIMETHYLAMINE AND TRIMETHYLAMINE OXIDE

Many different animal tissues have been found to contain larger or smaller amounts of highly methylated nitrogenous compounds such as trimethylamine oxide and various betaines, and the suggestion has often been made that they must arise from choline. At the present time, however, it seems less probable that they arise directly from choline than that they are formed by the methylation of other substances, choline entering into the picture only as a source of methyl groups.

$$CHOLINE, \quad (CH_3)_3N^+.CH_2CH_2OH,$$
$$OH^-$$

is probably universally distributed as the basic constituent of phospholipids of the lecithin type. Traces of free choline have been isolated from animal tissues of many kinds, but it is doubtful whether it occurs in the free state to any great extent. Probably it arises by autolysis, for, to take only one example, dog liver worked up as rapidly as possible after the death of the animal contains only 0–43 mg. free choline per kg., rising to 136–164 mg. per kg. if the tissue is allowed to stand for 5 hr. before being worked up.

In addition to its importance as a constituent of the lecithins, choline is important as the raw material from which *acetylcholine*, the neuro-hormone of the parasympathetic nervous system, is synthesized by acetylation (see p. 143). In comparatively recent times it has been discovered that the methyl groups of choline can be transferred to homocysteine to yield methionine which, in its turn, acts as a biological methylating agent (see p. 142):

$$
\begin{array}{cccc}
(CH_3)_3 & SH & & S.CH_3 \\
| & | & & | \\
N^+....OH^- & CH_2 & NH_2 & CH_2 \\
| & | & | & | \\
CH_2 & + 3\,CH_2 & \rightleftharpoons CH_2 & + 3\,CH_2 & + H_2O \\
| & | & | & | \\
CH_2OH & CH.NH_2 & CH_2OH & CH.NH_2 \\
& | & & | \\
& COOH & & COOH \\
choline & homo- & ethanol- & methionine \\
& cysteine & amine &
\end{array}
$$

The other product, ethanolamine (cholamine), it will be remembered, replaces choline in phospholipids of the cephalin type.

The metabolic importance of choline may be judged from the fact that it appears to be an essential dietary constituent, usually classified with the B_2 group of vitamins: it is perhaps essential as a source of $-CH_3$ groups. Little is known about its metabolism however. The discovery of a choline dehydrogenase in mammalian liver indicates that choline can be oxidized, the product being betaine aldehyde, and there is a possibility that the latter may then be further oxidized to betaine itself, e.g. by the group-specific aldehyde oxidase of the liver:

$$
\underset{\substack{|\\ OH^- \\ choline}}{(CH_3)_3N^+.CH_2CH_2OH} \xrightarrow{-2H} \underset{\substack{|\\ OH^- \\ betaine\ aldehyde}}{(CH_3)_3N^+.CH_2CHO} \xrightarrow[+H_2O]{-2H} \underset{glycine\ betaine}{(CH_3)_3N^+.CH_2COO^-}
$$

TETRAMETHYLAMMONIUM HYDROXIDE ('tetramine'), $(CH_3)_4N^+....OH^-$, has been isolated from only one animal source, the coelenterate *Actinia equina*, from which it was obtained in remarkably high yield, some 12 g. of the chloride being obtained from 33 kg. of the fresh material. Like most quaternary ammonium bases it has a powerful paralysant action and may, it is thought, be responsible for the paralysing 'sting' which many coelenterates are capable of inflicting.

TRIMETHYLAMINE, $(CH_3)_3N$, and
TRIMETHYLAMINE OXIDE, $(CH_3)_3N \rightarrow 0$,

have been obtained from many animal sources, vertebrate and invertebrate alike. As a rule the oxide occurs in quantities that completely overshadow those of the free base and, in general, it seems that trimethylamine arises from its oxide through bacterial action. The characteristic odour of dead marine fishes, which incidentally is not observable in fresh-water species, is largely due to free trimethylamine formed by the action of putrefactive bacteria upon trimethylamine oxide present in the tissues. The isolation of free trimethylamine from fish muscle has been reported by several workers, but it seems highly probable that such results are attributable to the use of stale material. Perfectly fresh fish muscle contains traces at most of the free base.

Free trimethylamine has long been known as a trace constituent of mammalian urine, and it has also been detected in human menstrual blood. Little is known about its metabolic origin and fate except that it is almost quantitatively converted into its oxide when fed to mammals (cow, man).

Perhaps the most striking fact that has emerged in connexion with trimethylamine oxide is that, while it is present in a great variety of marine animals, it seems never to occur on a substantial scale among fresh-water organisms. Its function in the fishes has been studied a good deal. That it occurs only in marine species suggests that it might play a part, analogous to that of urea in marine elasmobranchs, in the regulation of the osmotic pressure of the blood, for it resembles urea in being nearly neutral and relatively innocuous. Elasmobranch bloods contain about 100–120 mM per litre, as compared with about 330–440 mM of urea. It accounts therefore for 20–25 % of that part of the total osmotic pressure not due to salts. Further, the concentration of trimethylamine oxide in the urine of marine elasmobranchs is only about one-tenth as great as that present in the blood, so that this substance, like urea, is actively retained by the elasmobranch kidney. Probably, therefore, it plays a significant part in osmotic regulation in these fishes.

Among teleosts, however, matters are different. The trimethylamine oxide content of fresh cod muscle, for example, has been estimated at about 20 mM per kg., i.e. only about one-fifth of the amount present in elasmobranch muscle. Furthermore, there is no reason to believe that the substance is retained, for it is one of the major nitrogenous constituents of the excreta of marine teleosts. It is therefore unlikely that trimethylamine oxide plays any significant osmotic role in marine teleosts; it is far more probable that it is essentially an excretory product and represents a detoxicated form of ammonia (p. 308). Its origin has been discussed in an earlier section (p. 328).

DISTRIBUTION OF BETAINES

Betaines of various kinds are widely distributed among animals and plants alike, but their mode of formation is still somewhat obscure. It has usually been supposed that they are formed by the methylation of simpler substances, glycine betaine arising from glycine for example:

$$H_3N^+.CH_2COO^- \longrightarrow (CH_3)_3N^+.CH_2COO^-$$
glycine (zwitterion)   *glycine betaine*

In cases in which a given betaine is known as a constituent both of plant and animal materials it is, of course, always possible that the animal derives the substance from plant food, either directly or indirectly, according as it is herbivorous or carnivorous. Several of the known betaines, however, appear to be peculiar to animal tissues.

GLYCINE BETAINE

This is very widely distributed in plants and has been found in quantities of the order of 0·2 % in the muscles of many invertebrates. Little is known about its origin or function unless, indeed, it arises from plant foods. There is evidence that it can be formed in mammals by the oxidation of choline (p. 331).

As a rule, large amounts of the betaine are found in association with small quantities of free glycine and vice versa, suggesting that the two are metabolically interconvertible. In one case, at least, glycine has been found side by side with sarcosine,

$$(CH_3)H_2N^+.CH_2COO^-,$$

suggesting that the methylation of glycine is a step-wise process. If sarcosine is fed to rats together with betaine or methionine labelled at the methyl groups with C^{14}, sarcosine can be isolated from the urine with C^{14} in its own methyl radical: this suggests that there is perhaps a free interchange of methyl groups between methionine, glycine betaine and sarcosine itself. That glycine and its betaine are interconverted by an exchange of methyl radicals seems very probable in view of the discovery that the methyl groups of glycine betaine can be transferred, like those of choline, to homocysteine; but if glycine betaine is fed to cats, dogs or rabbits it is largely recoverable from the urine. Traces of trimethylamine are found at the same time, but this, according to prevailing opinion, is formed by bacterial intervention.

γ-*BUTYROBETAINE*, $(CH_3)_3N^+.CH_2CH_2CH_2COO^-$,
CROTONBETAINE, $(CH_3)_3N^+.CH_2CH{=}CH.COO^-$, and
CARNITINE, $(CH_3)_3N^+.CH_2CH(OH)CH_2COO^-$,

are closely related one to another, and all three are in part inter-convertible, as has been shown by subcutaneous administration to dogs. Their origins, functions and fates are obscure. Unlike glycine betaine, these substances are not known to occur in plant tissues and are therefore supposed to arise *de novo* in animals. It is possible that γ-butyrobetaine arises by methylation from γ-aminobutyric acid; the latter has been found in animal materials, in which it can arise by the action of glutamic α-decarboxylase upon glutamate.

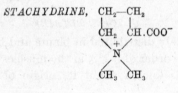

STACHYDRINE,

a cyclic compound, has been isolated only from one animal
source, the Noah's Ark mussel, *Arca noae*, an animal that contains a remarkably rich collection of nitrogenous compounds.
Stachydrine is well known as a constituent of plant materials,
and, since *Arca noae* is herbivorous, we may suppose until more
information is forthcoming that its presence in this animal is
dietary in origin. It might however be formed by the methylation
of proline.

TRIGONELLINE,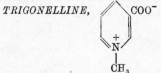

has been isolated from mammalian urine. It arises to some
extent, no doubt, in plant foodstuffs, but can arise also as an
end-product of the metabolism of a member of the B_2 group of
vitamins, viz. nicotinic acid. If large doses of the latter are
given to mammals, a part is excreted unchanged, a part is conjugated with glycine to form nicotinuric acid, and a part undergoes
N-methylation and gives trigonelline. This appears to be but
one instance of a rather general phenomenon, for it has been
known for many years that the mammalian organism is able to
accomplish N-methylation of the pyridine ring, and pyridine
itself suffers this fate.

HOMARINE,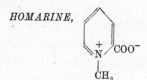

appears to be peculiar to animals, and has been found in a few
invertebrates, including *Arca noae*. It is a methylated picolinic
acid, isomeric with trigonelline, and may conceivably arise by
biological methylation of picolinic acid, though the latter does
not appear to have been discovered as a product of animal
metabolism.

DISTRIBUTION OF BASES RELATED TO GUANIDINE

The predominant members of this group are arginine and creatine. These bases are mainly confined to muscular tissues, in which they are present in the form of their very labile phosphates, the *phosphagens* (p. 76). With certain notable exceptions to which we shall refer later it may be said that creatine phosphate is found only among vertebrates, and arginine phosphate only among invertebrates.

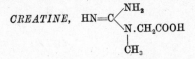

is an amino-acid, though not of the usual α-amino-type, nor does it occur in proteins. The fact that it replaces arginine in the muscles of vertebrates led to the belief that it must be formed metabolically from arginine, a view which received some support from the common presence of an amidine radical in both substances.

Creatine itself does not usually appear in mammalian urine, but undergoes slow, spontaneous conversion under physiological conditions of temperature and pH into its internal anhydride, *creatinine*,

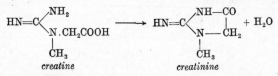

Creatinine is a normal excretory product among mammals, and its origin in creatine has been demonstrated by feeding experiments in which creatine, 'labelled' with heavy nitrogen, was administered. When heavy nitrogen was introduced into the amidine group, the isotope was recoverable in the same position in the amidine residue of creatinine isolated from the urine.

If small doses of creatine are administered to normal animals the substance is temporarily accommodated in the muscles, as may be demonstrated by comparing the muscles of animals thus fed with those of controls. Later, increased outputs of creatinine are observed. Larger doses of creatine give rise to a definite creatinuria, however, together with an increased excretion of creatinine. In certain pathological conditions of the muscles, the muscular dystrophies, which are characterized by extensive wasting of the muscular tissues, creatine is still produced in the organism at the usual rate, but, as the muscles are no longer able to accommodate it, it is excreted in the urine. Creatine is also excreted after the amputation of a limb. Evidently, therefore, creatine is made elsewhere than in the muscles, and is excreted if the muscles cannot make use of it. Animals suffering from muscular dystrophy, or from which some major muscle masses have been removed, have therefore played an important part in studies of creatine formation.

For many years it was believed that creatine must arise from arginine, for reasons that we have already mentioned. Little evidence could be found in favour of this hypothesis, but it was discovered that glycocyamine, a compound which is intermediate in structure between arginine and creatine, gives rise to creatine in feeding experiments. Glycocyamine requires only to be biologically methylated to yield creatine:

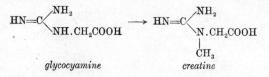

glycocyamine   *creatine*

Many other nitrogenous substances have been tested in a search for precursors of creatine, and it has been shown that several amino-acids can lead to a greater or less formation of creatine. Outstanding among these compounds is glycine, which yields creatine more freely than does arginine. In recent years it has been found that if kidney slices are allowed to act simultaneously upon glycine *and* arginine, glycocyamine is formed. By the subsequent action of liver tissue upon glycocyamine in the presence of methionine, creatine is produced. The synthesis of creatine therefore involves three amino-acids: first *glycine*, which is transamidinated at the expense of *arginine* and yields glyco-cyamine, which is then transmethylated at the expense of *methionine* and ATP (for equations see pp. 141–2).

The correctness of this scheme has been demonstrated in feeding experiments involving the use of isotopic 'markers'. If arginine containing N^{15} in its amidine group is administered to animals, heavy nitrogen can be recovered from the amidine radical of creatine isolated from the muscles. Similarly, if glycine containing N^{15} is fed, heavy nitrogen is again recoverable from creatine isolated from the muscles but not, this time, in the amidine radical. Similarly, the administration of trideutero-methionine, i.e. methionine of which the methyl group contains heavy hydrogen, gives rise to a creatine which also carries deuterium in its methyl group.

Nearly related to creatine is another base, known as *creatone*. This substance has been isolated from many vertebrate materials but not from invertebrate sources. It is an artefact derived from creatine during the processes of isolation. The methods used in working up the nitrogenous bases of biological materials usually involve the use of mercuric salts as precipitants, and it has been shown that, in the presence of mercuric compounds, creatine readily undergoes atmospheric oxidation to creatone:

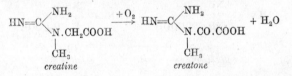

Creatone itself is readily hydrolysed to give oxalic acid and another artefact, *methylguanidine*:

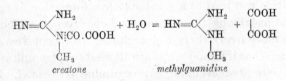

Methylguanidine, like creatine and creatone, has been isolated from numerous vertebrate muscles but not, so far at any rate, from any invertebrate source. *Guanidine* itself has been obtained from a few animal sources, and may perhaps arise by the further degradation of creatine, arginine, or some other guanidine derivatives.

ARGININE

This is a relatively common amino-acid and is present, probably, in all proteins. Quite apart from the special part it plays in the muscle metabolism of invertebrates, arginine enters into the composition of the tissue proteins of animals of every kind. It will be recalled that the rate at which arginine can be synthesized *de novo* in young rats and chicks appears to be limited and can act as a limiting factor upon their growth-rate. Its synthesis from ornithine forms a major part of the 'ornithine cycle' (pp. 322–3). Whether invertebrates are less or more adept at the synthetic production of arginine we do not know: for present purposes we may reasonably assume that it is normally forthcoming in sufficient quantities in their diet.

Distribution of the Phosphagens. Although arginine has been detected in, and in many cases actually isolated from, the tissues of representative members of almost every phylum and class among the invertebrates (excepting the polychaete annelids, from which it is absent), there is no reason to believe that it occurs in vertebrates except, of course, as a constituent of proteins, and also in small concentrations, as a transitory metabolic intermediate.

Just as non-protein arginine is confined to members of the invertebrate phyla, so too is creatine confined to the vertebrates. Arginine and creatine alike occur mainly in the muscles, and in the form of their phosphates, the phosphagens; the following discussion refers to these latter substances and the free guanidine bases arising by their decomposition.

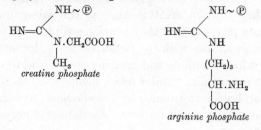

creatine phosphate   *arginine phosphate*

22-2

Creatine has been isolated from representative members of every vertebrate group but never, except occasionally and in traces, from invertebrates. To these generalities, however, there are a few noteworthy exceptions, as is shown in Table 29. Of all the invertebrate types studied, the Echinodermata are exceptional in that they alone include species in which the presence of creatine has been satisfactorily demonstrated. In the echinoids (sea-urchins) arginine and creatine occur side by side, while in the ophiuroids (brittle-stars) only creatine could be detected.

No comparable cases have been found in the Vertebrata proper, but among the Protochordata, a group of creatures which resemble the true vertebrates in their possession of a primitive notochord, one similar case has been recorded. The Protochordata comprise three groups, the Tunicata (sea-squirts), the Enteropneusta (a small group of worm-like animals) and the Cephalochorda (lancelets). These Protochordata are of special interest since they are regarded on morphological grounds as lying on the border-line between the true Vertebrata on the one hand and the invertebrate phyla on the other.

Of the Cephalochorda it may be said that they resemble the vertebrates rather than the invertebrates, for not only do they possess a well-developed notochord but, chemically speaking, the relationship is clear from the fact that they contain creatine but not arginine. The Tunicata resemble the invertebrates rather than the vertebrates, for, quite apart from their general appearance and mode of life, their tissues contain arginine but not, so far as we know, creatine. In the Enteropneusta, however, we find a case in which there is evidence for the presence of arginine and creatine side by side in the musculature.

The Enteropneusta thus appear to be related to the Vertebrata in that they contain creatine and, at the same time, to the invertebrate phyla in that they contain arginine. In particular, they show an affinity with the Echinodermata, for only in these two groups have arginine and creatine been found to co-exist in significant quantities. Similar relationships were established on purely morphological grounds by the classical investigations of Müller, Metschnikow and Bateson. As Bateson showed, in addition to their gill-slits the Enteropneusta possess a short but well-defined notochord, features which establish their relationship to the Vertebrata. But in their larval forms the Enteropneusta so closely resemble the echinoderms that their larvae were classified with those of the Echinodermata before the adult forms were

TABLE 29. DISTRIBUTION OF ARGININE AND CREATINE
IN THE ANIMAL KINGDOM

Phylum	Class	Arginine	Creatine
Protozoa		−	−
Porifera		−	−
Coelenterata	Scyphozoa	+	−
	Actinozoa	+	−
	Ctenophora	+	−
Platyhelminthes		+	−
Nemertea		+	−
Mollusca	Amphineura	+	−
	Lamellibranchiata	+	−
	Gastropoda	+	−
	Cephalopoda	+	−
Annelida	Polychaeta	−	−
Gephyrea		−	−
Phoronidea		+	−
Arthropoda	Crustacea	+	−
	Insecta	+	−
	Arachnida	+	−
Echinodermata	Crinoidea	+	−
	Asteroidea	+	−
	Ophiuroidea	−	+
	Holothuroidea	+	−
	Echinoidea	+	+
Protochordata	Tunicata	+	−
	Enteropneusta	+	+
	Cephalochorda	−	+
Vertebrata	Pisces	−	+
	Amphibia	−	+
	Reptilia	−	+
	Aves	−	+
	Mammalia	−	+

discovered. It was Metschnikow who, some time later, showed that the *Tornaria* larva, far from being an echinoderm larva as was previously believed, gives rise in the adult form to *Balanoglossus*, an enteropneust.

From the phylogenetic standpoint the natural distribution of these two bases, arginine and creatine, is clearly of considerable interest. The chemical evidence available favours Bateson's views on the origin of vertebrates by pointing to the echinoderms and the enteropneusts as links between the invertebrates on the one hand and the vertebrates on the other. Other theories of vertebrate descent have been put forward by morphologists in the past, but for none of them has any substantial chemical support yet been found.

Passing reference may here be made to the annelids and gephyreans. The latter contain a new phosphagen which resembles but is not identical with the arginine compound. The same substance is present also in numerous marine polychaetes, sometimes alone and sometimes in company with another compound which superficially resembles creatine phosphate. In other species again this second new phosphagen occurs alone. Neither of these new phosphagens has yet been isolated nor have their basic components been identified.

$$AGMATINE, \quad HN{=}C\begin{cases} NH_2 \\ NH \\ | \\ (CH_2)_3 \\ | \\ CH_2NH_2 \end{cases}$$

is a strong base which can be prepared chemically by the decarboxylation of arginine. It has been isolated from a few invertebrate sources, notably from the sponge, *Geodia gigas*, and from several cephalopods. Its mode of formation is not known: perhaps it is formed by the action of an arginine decarboxylase, but there is no evidence as yet for the occurrence of such an enzyme in animal tissues, although bacterial arginine decarboxylases are known.

METHYLAGMATINE

A methylagmatine of undetermined constitution has been reported as present in *Octopus* muscle, but the worker concerned was unable to detect either arginine or octopine, both of which have been repeatedly obtained by other investigators, and it seems reasonable to assume that this methylagmatine does not exist or, if it does, is probably an artefact. Its discovery has not so far been confirmed.

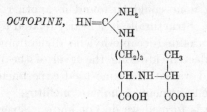

This interesting substance was first isolated from the muscles of *Octopus*, but has since been obtained from several other cephalopod species and a few lamellibranchs. It is not present in perfectly fresh muscle but arises as a post-mortem product, arginine disappearing as octopine is formed. Its constitution has been established by synthesis, which can be accomplished by the reductive condensation of arginine with pyruvic acid (p. 138). It is possible that octopine arises in this manner in *Octopus* muscle, for it has been known for some time that this, unlike most muscular tissues, contains very little lactic acid in fatigue or at death. Lactic acid is formed as a general rule by the reduction of pyruvic acid, but in the case of *Octopus* it seems possible that pyruvic acid may condense with arginine to yield an intermediate complex, which then undergoes reduction in place of pyruvic acid itself. Alternatively, octopine might arise directly by the condensation of arginine with lactic acid, but present evidence is insufficient to allow a definite decision on this point.

The discovery of octopine has been of particular interest because of its structural relationship to the hypothetical intermediary involved in transamination and transdeamination (p. 138).

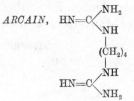

(tetramethylene diguanidine), has been isolated only from *Arca noae*. It was again isolated from a second batch of the same organism, but none could be found in another lamellibranch, *Mytilus edulis*. Structurally it is nearly related to the synthetic substance synthalin (decamethylene diguanidine), which has a profound effect in lowering the level of the blood sugar in mammals, and was at one time used experimentally for that purpose in the treatment of diabetes mellitus.

How arcain is formed we do not know. Several suggestions have been made, but there is no evidence to favour one rather than another. Probably it must arise in some way from arginine.

$$ASTERUBIN, \quad HN=C \underset{NH}{\overset{N(CH_3)_2}{<}}$$
$$CH_2$$
$$CH_2SO_3H$$

is not, as its name might suggest, a pigment, but a sulphur-containing guanidine derivative which, up to the present, has been obtained only from two species of star-fishes. Its mode of synthesis is unknown. It may be considered as being derived from an amidinated taurine, taurine itself being widely distributed in nature. Asterubin, like taurine itself, belongs to the class of sulphonic acids, a somewhat rare group in nature.

DISTRIBUTION OF IMINAZOLE BASES

In addition to the amino-acid histidine, in which the iminazole ring is present, several other iminazole compounds have been found in animal tissues. Of these the most widely distributed are carnosine and anserine, which appear to be peculiar to the muscular tissues of vertebrates, for neither has ever been found among the extractives of invertebrate materials.

$$CARNOSINE, \quad \underset{N \quad NH}{=\!\!=} CH_2CH \overset{NH-OC.CH_2CH_2NH_2}{\underset{COOH}{<}}$$

(β-alanylhistidine), is something of a biological curiosity, being derived from the rare β-amino-acid, β-alanine. It is, therefore, not a typical dipeptide, since all such are derived wholly from α-amino-acids. Carnosine has been known since 1900, when it was isolated from Liebig's meat extract, and since that time it has been obtained from the muscles of representatives of all classes of vertebrate animals.

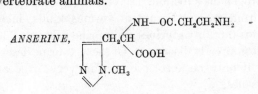

ANSERINE,

a methylated carnosine, is also a derivative of β-alanine. It was first isolated from the muscle of the goose, *Anser*, from which it received its name. It was thought for a time that carnosine and anserine mutually replace each other, but in more recent times it has become evident that the two not uncommonly occur side by side in one and the same tissue.

The function of these peculiar bases is very obscure. Attempts have been made to show that the amount of these iminazole bases is correlated with the activity of the muscle, but without success. Indeed, the only hint we have about their possible function is the fact that both are strong buffers.

How carnosine and anserine are formed in animal tissues is still unknown. Anserine can arise by the transmethylation of carnosine. Carnosine itself can replace the essential amino-acid histidine in the diet of rats, from which we may conclude that carnosine can be hydrolysed in the tissues, and a specific carnosinase is in fact known to occur in the rat (p. 94). It is possible, therefore, that it may arise by condensation between β-alanine, or some forerunner of β-alanine, and histidine. If this is so, the origin of β-alanine remains to be accounted for. Certain bacteria can produce it by the α-decarboxylation of aspartic acid, and it may be that a similar process can take place in plants:

$$HOOC.CH_2CH(NH_2).COOH \longrightarrow HOOC.CH_2CH_2NH_2 + CO_2.$$

There is no indication at present that this reaction takes place in animal tissues, but, if it occurs in plants, β-alanine is presumably available to animals in their food.

DISTRIBUTION OF OTHER NITROGENOUS COMPOUNDS

Many nitrogenous substances have been isolated at one time or another from animal tissues of various kinds, including free amino-acids (notably glycine) and purine bases (p. 359), in addition to those already discussed. Of these, taurine deserves special mention, if only because it occurs in very large amounts in certain tissues.

$$TAURINE, \quad \begin{array}{c} CH_2SO_3H \\ | \\ CH_2NH_2 \end{array}$$

has long been known as a constituent of the bile of vertebrates, in which it is present in conjugation with cholic and other bile acids (p. 249). Its metabolic relationships with cysteine have already been discussed (p. 286).

That free taurine often occurs in very notable quantities among invertebrates has been known for many years. Thus the adductor muscle of the edible mussel, *Mytilus edulis*, contains 4–5 %, while the muscles of an annelid worm, *Audouinia spirabranchus*, contain 3 % of taurine. Muscles of vertebrate organisms also contain free taurine, though in much smaller amounts. Its function in muscle, however, is unknown: conceivably it plays an important part in regulating the osmotic pressure of the contents of those cells in which it is present in high concentrations.

CHAPTER XIV

METABOLISM OF PURINE DERIVATIVES

NUCLEOPROTEINS

IN this chapter we have to deal with a group of natural compounds called nucleoproteins and with certain products arising by their breakdown. Nucleoproteins contribute only a small proportion of the total nitrogen of any average diet and account for only a small fraction of the total nitrogen of most cells and tissues but, as their name implies, they occur especially in cell nuclei, and are very important substances. Any cell that contains a high proportion of nuclear material will form a good source of nucleoproteins, and glandular materials such as pancreas and thymus have been used extensively for their preparation. The richest source of all seems to be the heads of ripe spermatozoa: indeed, it has been estimated that the nucleoprotein content of fresh spermatozoa is from 50–80 % of the total solid matter. Ripe fish milt (soft roes) therefore provides a valuable source of nucleoproteins and their derivatives.

It is only during the last few years that the nucleoproteins have attracted very much interest. The early preparations were rather crude, insoluble substances unattractive to the pure chemist, and the present phase of interest began when it was discovered that certain plant viruses can be isolated in crystalline form and are, in fact, nucleoproteins. Unlike the products formerly obtained, these virus proteins give beautiful, water-soluble crystals. A number of plant viruses have now been shown to consist of crystallizable nucleoproteins, and among animal viruses there are many, including vaccinia, the virus of cowpox, which contain, even if they do not consist entirely of, nucleoprotein material.

It had hitherto been supposed that viruses are living organisms, small enough to pass through the pores of bacterial filters and to be invisible under the microscope. Yet virus diseases can be transmitted to healthy plants either by inoculation with sap from an infected plant or with the crystalline virus protein. If healthy plants are infected by means of a pure virus nucleoprotein and allowed to develop the disease, the virus protein can later be isolated in quantities very much in excess of those used for the original inoculation. These discoveries produced some shocks among biologists who, as a whole, had always supposed that there exists some sharp line of demarcation between things that are living and things that are not. Yet, in these virus proteins, we have something which can be crystallized and can at the same time transmit disease from a sick to a healthy plant and, moreover, reduplicates or 'reproduces' as the disease develops.

More recently still it has been shown that chromosomes too consist largely of nucleoprotein material, so that we must look on the nucleoproteins not only as the causative agents of a large number of infectious diseases, but also as the vehicles whereby hereditary characteristics are transmitted from parents to offspring. Virus proteins and chromosomes have several important features in common. Both exist as long, fibrous or filamentous structures, and both, given the interior of the right kind of cell as environment, can reduplicate. Further, both show the phenomenon of mutation, either in the course of nature or under the artificial influence of X-rays or γ-radiation. Just as new strains of organisms can suddenly appear as a result of genetic mutations, so, too, new virus strains can suddenly appear as a result of mutations in the old. This process of mutation among viruses is quite probably the reason for the hitherto inexplicable variability in the virulence of many virus-borne diseases, e.g. influenza.

It will be clear to the reader that the nucleoproteins are at present a subject of manifold interest. A full knowledge of their chemical constitution must necessarily await further developments in protein chemistry as far as their protein components are concerned, but, in the meantime, considerable strides are being made in the chemistry of their non-protein, prosthetic components, the nucleic acids.

NUCLEIC ACIDS

Nucleoproteins are conjugated proteins, formed by the essentially salt-like union of a nucleic acid with a basic protein such as a protamine or a histone. If thymus gland material is macerated with large volumes of water the thymus nucleoprotein is extracted, and the protein component, in this case a histone, can be precipitated by saturation of the extract with sodium chloride. On the further addition of ethyl alcohol, nucleic acid is precipitated as a fibrous mass.

Two chief types of nucleic acids have so far been recognized, one of which can be obtained from thymus gland and the other from yeast. These acids are built up from smaller units known as nucleotides, which yield on hydrolysis one molecule each of a nitrogenous base, a pentose sugar and phosphoric acid. These nucleotides are, in fact, phosphate esters of the N-glycosides of certain nitrogenous bases. According to the older work, four of these nucleotide units go to make up one molecule of nucleic acid, but recent determinations of the particle weight, carried out by the method of ultracentrifugation, give values ranging from about 200,000 to several millions. Physical studies show that the particles are long, rod-like or thread-like objects, each of which appears to consist of aggregates of smaller units. These aggregates can be made to depolymerize in various ways, and the smallest units so far obtained by disaggregation have particle weights of the order of 15,000. If, as seems possible, these are really molecular units, it follows that each molecule of nucleic acid must contain many more than the four nucleotide radicals formerly postulated. At present the tendency is to think of nucleic acids as being built up by the union of large numbers of nucleotide units, much in the way that proteins are built up by the union of large numbers of amino-acid units. The possible number of nucleic acids, like that of proteins, is exceedingly large.

The most striking differences between nucleic acids of the yeast and thymus types lie in the nature of the sugar radicals involved in the nucleotide units. Nucleic acid prepared from yeast contains β-D-ribofuranose, while that from the thymus gland of animals contains β-D-2-desoxyribofuranose:

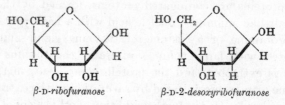

β-D-*ribofuranose*   β-D-2-*desoxyribofuranose*

It was at one time believed that plant and animal cells always and only contain ribonucleic and desoxyribonucleic acids respectively. This view has turned out to be entirely erroneous. Probably all cells contain nucleic acids of both types, the desoxyribose compounds preponderating in the nucleus and the ribose compounds in the cytoplasm generally.

Both types of nucleic acids contain phosphate radicals, and both contain bases belonging to the purine and pyrimidine groups, i.e. bases containing the following ring systems:

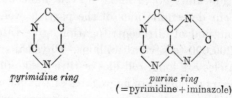

pyrimidine ring   *purine ring*
           (= pyrimidine + iminazole)

Hydrolysis of the nucleic acids by means of dilute acids or the appropriate enzymes yields the following recognized products:

	CYTOPLASM	NUCLEUS
	RIBONUCLEIC ACID ('*yeast nucleic acid*')	DESOXYRIBONUCLEIC ACID ('*thymonucleic acid*')
Pentose:	D-ribose	D-desoxyribose
Pyrimidines:	cytosine; uracil	cytosine; thymine
Purines:	adenine; guanine	adenine; guanine

The chief differences lie, therefore, in the nature of the pentose radicals, and in the presence of thymine and of uracil in desoxyribonucleic ('DNA') and ribonucleic acids ('RNA') respectively. Since at least these four different bases are found in whichever nucleic acid is taken, it follows that at least four nucleotide radicals enter into the composition of the nucleic acid concerned;

but, as has been pointed out already, there is reason to believe that many more than four nucleotides, perhaps some fairly high multiple of four, are present.

DIGESTION OF NUCLEOPROTEINS

The salt-like union between the nucleic acid and the basic protein component of a typical nucleoprotein is disrupted by the acidic contents of the stomach, the protein fragment being digested along with the other food proteins. Nucleic acids are further split by enzymes contributed by the pancreatic and intestinal juices. Our knowledge of these enzymes is somewhat fragmentary at present, but they appear to comprise (i) *nucleases*, which liberate the component nucleotides (p. 109), (ii) *nucleotidases*, which catalyse the dephosphorylation of the nucleotides, yielding nucleosides, which are N-glycosides of the nitrogenous bases (p. 109), and (iii) *nucleosidases*, which hydrolyse the nucleosides to liberate the basic and glycosidic components.

Relatively little is known about the fates of the pyrimidine bases and we shall not consider them here. Their structures, together with that of pyrimidine itself, are appended as a matter of interest, and in passing it should be noticed that a large and important group of drugs, the barbiturates, are structurally related to the pyrimidine group, and that vitamin B_1 also is a pyrimidine derivative:

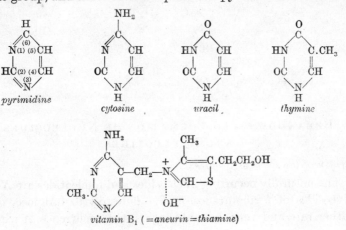

pyrimidine   *cytosine*   *uracil*   *thymine*

vitamin B_1 (=*aneurin* =*thiamine*)

Similarly, it may be pointed out, caffein and a number of other important drugs are methylated purines.

Considerably more is known about the fates and functions of the purine bases. The parent of this group of compounds is purine, with the following structure:

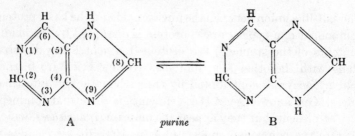

The iminazole portion of the ring system is tautomeric, and it should be noticed that while form A is the one usually figured in text-books, B is probably the more biologically important for, when the purines enter into glycoside formation with ribose, the union takes place at position (9) according to all available evidence, including the brilliant synthetic work achieved in this field, particularly by A. R. Todd.

The most important of the purine bases is probably *adenine*, 6-aminopurine:

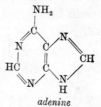

adenine

BREAKDOWN AND FORMATION OF NUCLEOSIDES AND NUCLEOTIDES

Origin of the Pentose Sugars

The naturally occurring nucleosides and nucleotides are N-β-glycosides of D-ribofuranose and D-2-desoxyribofuranose, two rather rare and very unstable sugars, the occurrence of which appears to be restricted to this particular group of compounds and their derivatives. The origin of the desoxy-compound is still unknown, but D-ribose is now known to arise from 6-phosphogluconic acid formed by the action of hexosemonophosphate dehydrogenase and Co II upon glucose-6-phosphate (p. 197). The reactions involved may be summarized as follows:

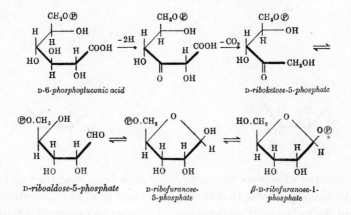

The first reaction in this sequence destroys the assymetry at carbon 3 of the hexose and carbon 1 is then removed by decarboxylation, yielding the 5-phosphate ester of the ketose form of ribose. The conversion of this into the isomeric aldehyde is asymmetrically catalysed by an enzyme, phosphoriboisomerase, which catalyses an aldose-ketose isomerization (p. 145). The cyclized form of the aldose, ribofuranose-5-phosphate, an ester, is finally brought into equilibrium with the 1-phosphate, a riboside: the enzyme concerned has been named phosphoribomutase, since its action is analogous to that of phosphoglucomutase (p. 146).

Formation of Nucleosides

It has been known for several years that certain nucleosides can be reversibly broken down by phosphorolysis to yield β-ribose-1-phosphate together with the purine, pyrimidine or other nitrogenous base. The reaction is therefore one of transglycosidation. The first reaction of this kind to be discovered was the phosphorolysis of inosine (hypoxanthine-9-N-β-D-riboside) catalysed by a specific inosine phosphorylase:

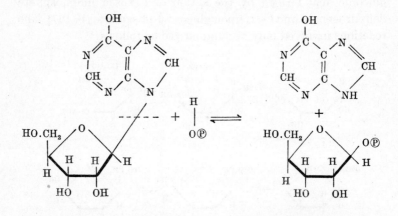

A number of similar reactions have since been described and it now seems probable that this reaction is typical of the synthesis and degradation of nucleosides. It applies to nucleosides fairly generally, and applies as well to ribo- and to desoxy-ribonucleosides, but nucleotides are not affected. The following are some examples:

hypoxanthine-N-riboside + HO.℗ ⇌ hypoxanthine + ribose-1-phosphate,
nicotinic amide-N-riboside + HO.℗ ⇌ nicotinic amide + ribose-1-phosphate,
hypoxanthine-N-desoxyriboside + HO.℗ ⇌
                                  hypoxanthine + desoxyribose-1-phosphate,
guanine-N-desoxyriboside + HO.℗ ⇌ guanine + desoxyribose-1-phosphate,
thymine-N-desoxyriboside + HO.℗ ⇌ thymine + desoxyribose-1-phosphate.

Little is known about the specificities of the transribosidases concerned in these reactions, but always the nitrogenous and phosphatic aglycones seem to be freely interchangeable.

Phosphorylation: Formation of Nucleotides

Several examples of the formation of nucleotides from nucleosides have been demonstrated. In each case the source of the

phosphate radical lies in ATP and the phosphorylation is catalysed by an appropriate phosphokinase. For example:

adenine-*N*-riboside + ATP → adenosine-5′-phosphate + ADP,
riboflavine + ATP → riboflavin-5′-phosphate + ADP.

In this manner adenylic acid and flavinmononucleotide are
formed.

It would appear, then, that we are well on the way to a proper
understanding of the problem of nucleotide formation and
further advances are to be anxiously awaited, not only because
of the outstanding interest and importance of nucleic acids and
nucleoproteins at the present time, but also because of the
enormous importance of certain mono- and dinucleotides in
intermediary metabolism (see Table 30).

TABLE 30. NUCLEOTIDES AND DERIVATIVES
OF CATALYTIC IMPORTANCE

Compound	Abbreviation	Coenzyme or prosthetic group of
Adenosine diphosphate	ADP	phosphokinases
Adenosine triphosphate	ATP	phosphokinases
Adenine nicotinic amide dinucleotide	Co I (DPN)	dehydrogenases
Adenine nicotinic amide dinucleotide-2′-phosphate	Co II (TPN)	dehydrogenases
Adenine flavin dinucleotide	AFDN	oxidases, diaphorases
Flavin mononucleotide	FMN	cytochrome reductase
Adenine mononucleotide-pantothenic acid complex	Co A	transacetylases

Note that adenosine monophosphate, adenylic acid and adenine mononucleotide
are synonymous.

FUNCTIONS OF NUCLEOSIDES AND NUCLEOTIDES

Adenosine (adenine-9-β-D-ribofuranoside) is perhaps the most
important member of the family of nucleosides, since by phosphorylation in position 5′ of the ribose radical it gives rise to
the nucleotide, adenylic acid.

Adenylic acid, also known as *adenosine monophosphate*
(AMP) and *adenine mononucleotide*, can be formed from adenosine by an enzyme-catalysed reaction with ATP (above),

and has the following structural formula, according to all the available evidence:

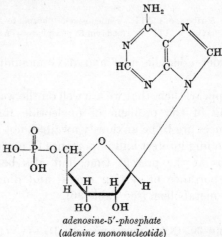

adenosine-5'-phosphate
(adenine mononucleotide)

The nucleic acid of yeast yields another form of adenylic acid, however; this is phosphorylated in position 3' of the pentose ring.

Further phosphate radicals can be attached to that of adenosine monophosphate to yield *adenosine diphosphate* (ADP) and *adenosine triphosphate* (ATP). These substances play a fundamental part in the energetics of living systems and have been discussed in the chapter on biological energetics (Chap. III). In ATP itself the three phosphate radicals are believed to be attached end to end, so that, if we represent adenosine by A and the energy-rich bonds by the symbol ∼, the structure of ATP can be represented as follows:

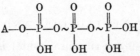

The special importance of ATP arises from the fact that, under the influence of the appropriate enzymes, the phosphokinases, its terminal phosphate radical, *together with the energy of the terminal energy-rich bond*, can be transferred intact to other substances, so that energy is, as it were, forced into the phosphate receptor. This appears to be a fundamental operation in the synthesis of complex biological compounds from simpler starting-materials, and as far as we know at the present time, synthetic operations of this kind can only be accomplished at the expense of the terminal energy-rich bond of adenosine triphosphate. ATP itself can be reformed from ADP at the expense of the free energy of the numerous katabolic processes that lead to the generation of new energy-rich bonds, but the transmission of these new bonds to other substances can only be accomplished through the intermediation of the ADP⇌ATP system.

As we shall see, ATP can also react with certain mono-nucleotides, transferring adenine mononucleotide, to yield dinucleotides and free, inorganic pyrophosphate (pp. 358–9).

Adenine compounds also play a fundamental part in metabolic processes leading to the generation of new energy-rich bonds, quite apart from their function as carriers of these bonds. These reactions, for the most part, are oxidative in nature, and involve the participation of Co I, Co II and adenine-flavin dinucleotide. Adenylic acid enters into the composition of all three of these important compounds, in which it is present in combination with other nucleotides or near-nucleotides. These are, respectively, nicotinic amide mononucleotide and the so-called flavin mono-nucleotide. Adenylic acid also occurs in Co A.

Nicotinic amide mononucleotide is a true nucleotide, the base present being nicotinic amide and the pentose sugar D-ribo-furanose:

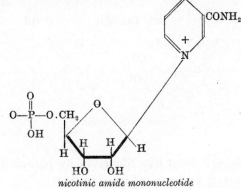

nicotinic amide mononucleotide

Coenzyme I (cozymase) consists of a molecule of adenylic acid (adenine mononucleotide) and one of nicotinic amide mononucleotide, the union between them being formed by condensation between their respective phosphate radicals. It can be formed directly by an enzyme-catalysed reaction between nicotinic amide mononucleotide and ATP, which is the pyrophosphate of adenine mononucleotide:

Nicotinic amide mononucleotide + ATP $\longrightarrow$ Co I + pyrophosphate.

By phosphate transfer from a further molecule of ATP, Co I can be converted into *coenzyme* II,

Co I + ATP $\longrightarrow$ Co II + ADP.

The third phosphate radical present in Co II is probably attached at position 2′ of the ribose ring of Co I. These two coenzymes are often loosely referred to as 'diphospho-' and 'triphosphopyridine' nucleotides respectively (DPN and TPN).

Flavin mononucleotide is not a true nucleotide, although it is usually accorded that title. A nitrogenous base is present in the form of 6:7-dimethyl-*iso*-alloxazine, but the place of the pentose sugar is taken by the corresponding sugar-alcohol, D-ribitol:

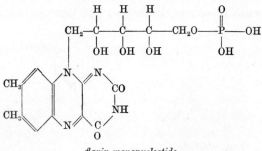

flavin mononucleotide

It can be formed from free riboflavin by phosphate transfer from ATP, catalysed by flavokinase (p. 355).

Adenineflavin dinucleotide consists of a molecule of adenine mononucleotide and one of flavin mononucleotide, and again the dinucleotide can be formed from flavin mononucleotide by an enzyme-catalysed reaction with ATP, which again donates adenine mononucleotide:

flavin mononucleotide + ATP $\longrightarrow$ adenineflavin dinucleotide + pyrophosphate.

This dinucleotide is known to occur, as indeed is the mono-nucleotide itself, as the prosthetic group of certain oxidizing enzymes which we have already considered (pp. 201–6).

METABOLISM OF PURINE BASES

Adenine (6-aminopurine) occurs in small amounts in the free state and has been isolated from many vertebrate and in-vertebrate tissues. It also arises by the breakdown of nucleic acid. On the synthetic side it undergoes conversion into adenosine, adenylic acid, etc., and is degraded by hydrolytic deamination to yield *hypoxanthine* (6-hydroxypurine) under the influence of a purine deaminase called adenase. Adenase appears to be widely but somewhat erratically distributed and has been detected in the tissues of numerous animal species.

Guanine (2-amino-6-hydroxypurine), like adenine, occurs in nucleic acid, but there is no reason to think that it plays as important a part in cellular metabolism as does adenine. It is an exceedingly insoluble substance and is deposited in crystal-line form in special cells, known as iridocytes, in many animals, where it is responsible for the beautiful iridescence of many fishes, for example. Guanine has a special and apparently unique function among spiders, where it is said to replace uric acid as the predominant product in nitrogenous excretion (p. 329).

Like adenine, guanine is degraded by hydrolytic deamination to yield *xanthine* (2:6-dihydroxypurine). Hypoxanthine and xanthine then undergo serial oxidation under the influence of xanthine oxidase to give *uric acid*. These metabolic relationships may be summarized as follows:

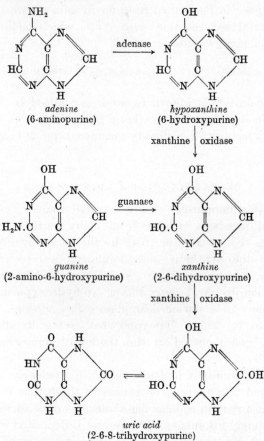

In passing, it should be noticed that all the hydroxypurines (often known as 'oxypurines') are tautomeric substances which readily undergo transformation at the

$$-N=C(OH)- \rightleftharpoons -NH-CO-$$

groupings. In the scheme above, only the *enol* forms are given for the sake of clarity, except in the case of uric acid, in which the keto form is believed to predominate.

The distribution of adenase, guanase and xanthine oxidase among animal tissues is very erratic. It is said, for example, that man and the rat possess no adenase, though the enzyme is common elsewhere, while the tissues of the embryonic pig are stated to contain guanase, in contradistinction to those of the adult, which do not. Again, xanthine oxidase is present in the liver of most birds, e.g. goose and domestic fowl, but is absent from that of the pigeon (p. 327).

METABOLISM OF URIC ACID

Uric acid may arise from purine bases in animals of any kind, whether they are ammonotelic, ureotelic or uricotelic, but very little is known about the biosynthesis of the purine ring system as such (p. 327). Uricotelic animals, as we have seen, convert the bulk of their waste nitrogen into uric acid, but the amounts of uric acid that arise from purine metabolism are relatively very small, accounting perhaps for about 5 % of all the nitrogen excreted.

Uric acid is excreted without further chemical manipulation by uricotelic animals, but in most other forms it is more or less extensively degraded before being excreted (see Table 31). The first stage in the process of uricolysis consists in the oxidation of uric acid itself to the more soluble substance allantoin, under the influence of urico-oxidase. This takes place in all mammals apart from man and the higher apes (Primates), while the Dalmatian coach-hound is peculiar among dogs in that it excretes only a small part of its total purines in the form of allantoin (see p. 162). In other mammals, however, allantoin is excreted in place of uric acid, but uricolysis stops at this stage. In most other non-uricotelic animals, allantoin is further degraded to yield allantoic acid, thence to urea, and finally even to ammonia, though in some animal groups the complete set of uricolytic enzymes is lacking. The stages involved in the complete process are summarized in Table 31, together with the names of the enzymes concerned and some indications of their distribution.

It is worthy of note that, like adenase, guanase and xanthine oxidase, the uricolytic enzymes are very erratically distributed among animals. In particular, it is interesting to notice that, with the evolution of more complex forms of life, the tendency, as far as purine metabolism is concerned, has been to lose old enzymes rather than to acquire new ones, a fact which is amply illustrated by Table 31.

TABLE 31. END-PRODUCTS OF PURINE METABOLISM

(*After* Florkin and Duchâteau)

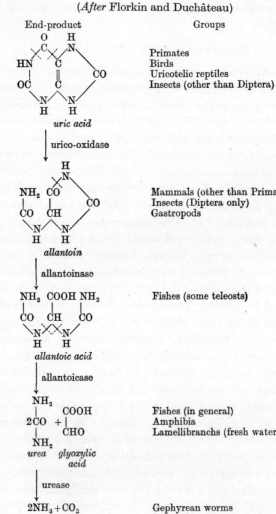

End-product	Groups
uric acid	Primates Birds Uricotelic reptiles Insects (other than Diptera)
allantoin	Mammals (other than Primates) Insects (Diptera only) Gastropods
allantoic acid	Fishes (some teleosts)
urea glyoxylic acid	Fishes (in general) Amphibia Lamellibranchs (fresh water)
$2NH_3 + CO_2$	Gephyrean worms Lamellibranchs (marine) Crustacea

CHAPTER XV

ANAEROBIC METABOLISM OF CARBOHYDRATES: ALCOHOLIC FERMENTATION

INTRODUCTION

RELATIVELY little has been learned about the aerobic breakdown of carbohydrates until recent years, though a great deal was known about their anaerobic metabolism in yeast and in muscle. It may strike the reader as curious that these two kinds of cells, so different in their organization and function, should have been selected for examination rather than any others. Yeast, however, has long been a matter of great commercial importance for the production of alcoholic beverages and for the manufacture of industrial alcohol. Furthermore, various important by-products of fermentation, such as the components of fusel oil, find many important applications in chemical technology. No wonder, then, that alcoholic fermentation has been extensively studied. In the case of muscle, interest has been aroused by more academic considerations. Muscle does mechanical work. Many muscles can be isolated and made to contract outside the body, and in these, beyond all other tissues, we have an opportunity of measuring the amount of work done by a biological system and attempting to correlate it with the amount of chemical change simultaneously taking place. It was rather late in the history of the subject before it was realized that, in spite of their many apparent differences, yeast and muscle both derive the energy they expend through very similar chemical manipulations of their carbohydrate starting-materials.

The enzymes concerned in the anaerobic degradation of carbohydrates can readily be obtained in particle-free cell extracts, whereas those concerned with their oxidative metabolism are intimately bound up with the structural elements of the cell, especially with the mitochondria. Anaerobic metabolism can

therefore proceed and can be studied independently by the use
of simple aqueous extracts of cells and tissues after the solid
matter has been removed by filtration or centrifugation. We
know now that the aerobic metabolism of starch, glycogen and
glucose is, so to speak, a continuation of their anaerobic metabolism and, moreover, that it is much more complicated. Here,
therefore, we shall deal first with anaerobic and later with
aerobic metabolism. Starch, glycogen and glucose provide major
sources of energy for plants and animals, to make no mention
of the innumerable micro-organisms which likewise derive energy
and employment from the breakdown of these substances. Their
breakdown is attended by the liberation of some at least of the
intrinsic energy of the carbohydrate molecule, but how much of
the free, or available, energy becomes *biologically* available to
any given organism depends upon the nature of the chemical
changes the organism is able to accomplish.

When glucose is burned in a bomb calorimeter the heat set
free $(-\Delta H)$ amounts to about 674,000 cal. per g.mol. The change
of entropy $(T.\Delta S)$ corresponds to some 12,000 cal., so that the
loss of free energy $(-\Delta F)$ associated with the complete combustion of 1 g.mol. of glucose is approximately 686,000 cal. The
synthesis of 1 g.mol. of glucose, in a green plant for example,
therefore requires the provision of about 686,000 cal. of energy.
When an animal oxidizes 1 g.mol. of glucose to carbon dioxide
and water, 686,000 cal. of energy become free and available.

The *biological efficiency* of an organism can be measured in
terms of the extent to which these 686,000 cal. can be harnessed
by the organism and put to service for biological purposes. In
considering biological efficiency, however, it is necessary to distinguish between the *efficiency of energy capture*, i.e. the efficiency
with which the free energy of the substrates of metabolism can be
captured in the form of ATP, and the efficiency with which
energy so captured can be utilized in the performance of
mechanical or some other kind of biological work. We may
therefore distinguish between the energy-capture efficiency and
the overall efficiency of a cell, tissue or organism. Generally
speaking, living cells can achieve an energy-capture efficiency

of 50–75 %, but their overall efficiency is not much greater than that of the majority of man-made machines.

Now glucose can be broken down in other ways than by complete oxidation. Muscle cells, working under anaerobic conditions, can convert glucose into lactic acid, a process known as glycolysis:

$$C_6H_{12}O_6 = 2CH_3CH(OH)COOH.$$

Yeast, again, can carry out an anaerobic fermentation of glucose, yielding ethyl alcohol and carbon dioxide:

$$C_6H_{12}O_6 = 2C_2H_5OH + 2CO_2.$$

In neither of these transformations is the change of free energy as large as it is in complete combustion, for a large proportion of the total free energy of the starting material remains in the products, and access to this can only be gained by further degradation of these substances.

The change of free energy associated with complete oxidation of lactic acid amounts to about 325,000 cal. per g.mol., or 650,000 cal. for the 2 g.mol. formed from 1 g.mol. of glucose. Consequently, the loss of free energy associated with glycolysis is less than that associated with complete combustion of glucose by approximately 650,000 cal. per g.mol. of glucose transformed. The loss of free energy in glycolysis therefore amounts to only $(686,000 - 650,000) = 36,000$ cal. per g.mol. of glucose approximately. Anaerobically, therefore, muscle gains access to only 36,000 cal. as contrasted with the 686,000 cal. which become available when the same amount of glucose is completely oxidized under aerobic conditions. To gain access to the same amount of energy, therefore, a muscle will require to glycolyse nearly 20 times as much glucose as it will if it oxidizes glucose to carbon dioxide and water completely. Aerobic metabolism, in fact, is far more efficient than anaerobic. But in neither case does it necessarily follow that the cell or tissue can actually harness and utilize *all* the energy to which it gains access by oxidizing, glycolysing or fermenting its food materials. How this energy is trapped, and how much of it can be trapped, we shall see in ensuing chapters, but at the present time we are only at the beginning of a knowledge of biochemical energetics.

It is convenient to classify organisms as aerobic or anaerobic as the case may be. Relatively few living organisms are strictly anaerobic. Indeed, as far as we know, strict anaerobiosis is practically restricted to a few groups of bacteria, and these are not merely unable to utilize oxygen but are actually poisoned by it. The vast majority of micro-organisms are facultative anaerobes, i.e. they can utilize oxygen when it is available and oxidize their foodstuffs completely, but can still survive under anaerobic conditions by catalysing a partial or 'fermentative' breakdown of the same food materials. Animals for the most part might almost be classified as 'strict aerobes', since few of them can live for long in complete absence of oxygen. But certain processes can go on in animal tissues under anaerobic conditions, provided that the 'oxygen debt' thus incurred can sufficiently soon be repaid.

Alcoholic Fermentation

Alcoholic fermentation has been familiar to the human species since prehistoric times, yet it was not until after 1857 that its cause was discovered. In that year Louis Pasteur was studying the lactic fermentation of milk and trying to discover its cause. The views held at that time look very strange by modern standards, for the great Liebig himself considered that the nitrogenous constituents of the fermenting mixture reacted with air, setting up 'unstabilizing vibrations' as they did so, and these vibrations were believed to rupture the fermenting molecules. The fact that a new fermentation could be initiated by inoculating the medium with a trace of an already fermenting fluid was attributed to the transference of vibrating material to the new medium.

Pasteur began his experiments with media containing very simple substances such as sugars, ammonium tartrate and mineral phosphates, none of which could reasonably be expected to develop 'unstabilizing vibrations'. His results were simple and clear-cut. Fermentation took place only in the presence of certain microscopic organisms, the lactic acid-producing bacteria of the present day. When precautions were taken to exclude these organisms, no fermentation occurred. Extending his studies to alcoholic fermentation in 1860, Pasteur showed that whenever it took place the appropriate micro-organism, in this case yeast, grew and multiplied. He therefore concluded that fermentation is a physiological process, intimately bound up with the life of the yeast cell. In 1875, having shown that fermentation can take place in complete absence of oxygen, Pasteur defined fermentation as 'Life without oxygen'.

More than 20 years elapsed before the next major step forward, but in 1897 Hans and Eduard Buchner made a key discovery which opened the door not only to the investigation of the mechanisms of fermentation but to the whole of modern enzyme chemistry. Like many other great discoveries, that of the Buchners had in it an element of chance. They were primarily interested in making cell-free extracts of yeast for therapeutic purposes, and this they accomplished by grinding yeast with sand, mixing it with kieselguhr, and squeezing out the juice with a hydraulic press. There then arose the problem of preserving their product. Since it was to be used for experiments on animals the ordinary antiseptics could not be used, so they tried the method usual in kitchen-chemistry of adding large amounts of sucrose. This led to the momentous discovery that sucrose is rapidly fermented by yeast juice. Here, for the first time, fermentation was observed in the complete absence of living cells, and at last it was possible to study the processes of alcoholic fermentation independently of all the other processes—growth, multiplication and excretion—which accompany fermentation in the living yeast cell.

The Buchners' work was soon followed by intensive studies of the properties of yeast juice. It was found capable of fermenting glucose, fructose, mannose, sucrose and maltose, all of which are fermented by living yeast. The disaccharides, sucrose and maltose, are broken down in some way to yield their constituent monosaccharides before being fermented. Glucose itself is almost quantitatively converted into ethyl alcohol and carbon dioxide according to the equation

$$C_6H_{12}O_6 = 2CO_2 + 2CH_3CH_2OH.$$

Traces of glycerol are always found among the products.

Fresh yeast juice is much less active than living yeast. The rate of fermentation can be followed by measurements of the rate of evolution of carbon dioxide, and experiments carried out in this way show that living yeast works 10–20 times as fast as an equivalent quantity of yeast juice. Moreover, the fermentative power of the yeast juice falls off rapidly with time. The juice is not inactivated by drying at 30–35° C. or by the addition of chloroform, but loses its activity if heated to 50° C., suggesting that enzymes must be involved.

The first important step towards analysing the mode of action of yeast juice was made by Harden and Young in 1905. If fresh yeast juice is added to a solution of glucose at pH 5–6, fermentation begins almost at once. The rate of carbon dioxide production presently falls off, but can be restored by the addition of inorganic phosphate. The recovery is only temporary, however; the added phosphate disappears, and the rate of fermentation falls off as the concentration of free phosphate declines. The addition of more phosphate produces another burst of fermentation and so on.

The disappearance of added inorganic phosphate from fermenting mixtures suggested that organic phosphate esters must probably be formed and, as Harden and Young showed, this is indeed the case, for they were able to isolate such an ester in the form of fructofuranose-1:6-diphosphate ('hexose diphosphate'). This substance, like glucose, is fermented if added to an actively fermenting system, and must probably be an intermediate in the process of fermentation. Later Robison isolated another sugar phosphate, this time a monophosphate which, on detailed examination, proved to consist of an equilibrium mixture of glucopyranose-6-phosphate and fructofuranose-6-phosphate. Like hexose diphosphate these esters are fermentable. It seemed clear that these substances must arise by the coupling of inorganic phosphate with glucose, the respective esters probably arising in the following order:

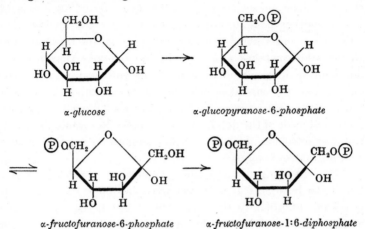

How these esters are formed, and in what way the fructose diphosphate is eventually converted into alcohol and carbon dioxide, are questions which were only answered over a period of decades and by the efforts of many workers in many different countries. Certain stages were first elucidated by studies of muscle extracts, for it became clear in time that the fermentation of glucose by yeast juice runs closely parallel to the glycolysis of glycogen by suitable muscle extracts. Among the names that stand out in connexion with the further analysis of fermentation and glycolysis are those of Embden, Neuberg, Meyerhof, Parnas, D. M. Needham and the Coris, but these are only a few of the many who have contributed.

The next fundamental step forward was also made by Harden and Young when they discovered that yeast juice loses its activity if dialysed. Activity could be restored to dialysed juice, either by adding the dialysate, or by means of small quantities of boiled juice. This showed that, in addition to enzymes, yeast juice contains dialysable, thermostable substances which function as coenzymes. Yeast juice thus came to be regarded as consisting of 'zymase', a non-dialysable, thermolabile enzyme, plus 'cozymase', a dialysable, thermostable fraction. We know now, of course, that zymase is in reality a complex mixture of enzymes and that cozymase consists not of one substance only but of several.

It is neither possible nor desirable here to give an historical account of subsequent work on the problem of fermentation. There were mistakes and gaps in the schemes that replaced one another in quick succession during the ensuing years, but one by one the mistakes were rectified and the gaps filled in until, at the present time, we have what we believe to be a clear picture of most of the details of the process. Before we can study this picture it is necessary to know something more about the composition of cozymase.

Cozymase comprises a number of factors. *Co-carboxylase*, now known to be identical with the pyrophosphate of vitamin B_1 (aneurin, thiamine), is the coenzyme of carboxylase, an enzyme which catalyses the 'straight' decarboxylation of pyruvic acid to form acetaldehyde and carbon dioxide. *Co I* (also known as cozymase, or sometimes as cozymase I) is identical with the adenine-nicotinic amide dinucleotide which we have discussed already. In fermentation, as in respiration, this substance functions in collaboration with certain dehydrogenases as a hydrogen acceptor, donator and carrier. *Adenosine triphosphate*, which we have discussed, acts as a phosphate carrier: as will be remembered, the terminal phosphate radical is bound to the rest of the molecule by an energy-rich bond, the energy associated with which can be transferred, along with the phosphate radical itself, to other substances. *Magnesium ions*, too, are involved. They function as activators for many enzymes concerned with phosphate metabolism and, in particular, for enolase, an adding enzyme. In addition to these 'classical' coenzymes, dialysis removes other substances, including the ions of *inorganic phosphate, calcium* and *potassium*, and evidence is accumulating to show that, for certain reactions at least, even these substances are of great importance and may strictly be classified as coenzymes of fermentation.

Since all of these co-substances are essential components of the fermenting systems of yeast juice, it follows that the breakdown brought about by dialysis is due, not to the abolition of some one particular reaction, but of many. Dialysed juice, with and without the addition of one or more of the known coenzymes, has therefore played a large part in unravelling the intricate reaction sequence that underlies fermentation. Much further information has been gained by taking advantage of the fact that certain substances have empirically been found to slow down or stop particular reactions. The addition of these selective inhibitors leads to the accumulation of intermediate products which can be isolated and identified. The reagents most widely used for this purpose have been *sodium bisulphite, sodium fluoride* and *sodium iodoacetate.*

For purposes of discussion the reaction sequence of fermentation can be arbitrarily divided into several stages, each of which involves one or more individual chemical operations, but because we can dissect the whole process into stages and steps in this way, it is not to be supposed that fermentation as such is a step-by-step process, catalysed by a mere mixture of enzymes. The living cell is something more than a mere bag full of enzymes; fermentation is a highly organized procession of chemical events, the overall result of which is the decomposition of glucose, with production of alcohol and carbon dioxide, together with the provision and capture of free energy which enables the cells to carry out the synthesis of the new tissue materials required for their maintenance, growth and reproduction.

(i) *Formation of Phosphorylated Sugars.* We have already seen that several sugar phosphates can be isolated from fermenting systems to which glucose and inorganic phosphate have been added. If glucose and inorganic phosphate are added to a dialysed juice, however, there is no fermentation and no sugar esters are formed, showing that one or another of the coenzymes must play a part in their synthesis. If ATP is added to the dialysed juice, however, phosphorylation of the sugar begins again, and fructofuranose-1:6-diphosphate, fructofuranose-6-phosphate and glucopyranose-6-phosphate can be isolated from the system. Work with highly purified enzymes has resolved this stage into three separate reactions. First of all one phosphate radical is transferred from ATP to glucose, yielding glucopyranose-6-phosphate and ADP, a process which is catalysed by *hexokinase* (reaction 1). Next the glucose ester is reversibly converted into fructofuranose-6-phosphate (reaction 2), the catalyst being *oxoisomerase*. A phosphate radical is then transferred from a second molecule of ATP to the fructose mono-ester, yielding fructofuranose-1:6-diphosphate. This reaction (reaction 3) is catalysed by *phosphohexokinase*. This group of reactions may be summarized as follows, writing only the forward reactions for the sake of clarity:

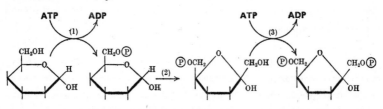

(ii) *Splitting of the Hexose Chain.* If glucose or one of the intermediate esters is added to yeast juice in the presence of iodoacetate, small amounts of 'triose phosphate' can be isolated, showing that hexose diphosphate is split into two 3-carbon fragments which, on isolation, prove to consist of an equilibrium mixture of 3-phosphoglyceraldehyde and phosphodihydroxyacetone. The enzyme concerned, *aldolase*, has been isolated, and the reaction it catalyses (4) shown to be reversible:

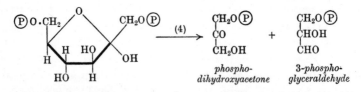

phospho-dihydroxyacetone   *3-phospho-glyceraldehyde*

Of the two components of triose phosphate the 3-phosphoglyceraldehyde is the more important from our point of view, since its derivatives appear lower down in the reaction chain, whereas no direct derivatives of phosphodihydroxyacetone are found except under special conditions. But dihydroxyacetone phosphate is not lost to the system, which contains a powerful *phosphotriose isomerase.* This enzyme catalyses the interconversion of the two triose phosphates (reaction 5):

$$
\begin{array}{ccc}
\text{CH}_2\text{O}\textcircled{P} & & \text{CH}_2\text{O}\textcircled{P} \\
| & (5) & | \\
\text{CO} & \rightleftharpoons & \text{CHOH} \\
| & & | \\
\text{CH}_2\text{OH} & & \text{CHO} \\
(4\,\%) & & (96\,\%)
\end{array}
$$

The original hexose has now been phosphorylated and quantitatively split into phosphorylated triose.

(iii) *Oxidation of Phosphoglyceraldehyde.* If hexose diphosphate or 'triose phosphate' is added to yeast juice in the presence of fluoride, two further phosphorylated derivatives of glycerol accumulate, viz. phosphoglycerol and phosphoglyceric acid in equimolecular proportions. On isolation and examination the acid proves to be an equilibrium mixture of 3- and 2-phosphoglyceric acids. Of these the primary product must presumably be the 3-compound since it is formed from 3-phosphoglyceraldehyde. These products arise by the oxidation of a molecule of phosphoglyceraldehyde at the expense of the reduction of a molecule of phosphodihydroxyacetone.

Yeast juice contains a powerful *triosephosphate dehydrogenase,* an enzyme which requires Co I, which is also present. But the amount of coenzyme is very small, and the whole would soon become reduced by acting as hydrogen acceptor for the oxidation of phosphoglyceraldehyde (reacting in its hydrated form):

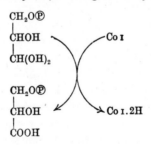

Once all the available coenzyme had been reduced in this way, fermentation would come to an end. But yeast juice contains also a *soluble α-glycerophosphate dehydrogenase* (see p. 193). This dehydrogenase also co-operates with Co I and, like dehydrogenases generally, can act reversibly. The reduced coenzyme can therefore become reoxidized by passing on its 2H to a molecule of phosphodihydroxyacetone, which is thereby reduced to phosphoglycerol:

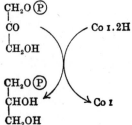

As a result of this operation the reduced coenzyme becomes reoxidized and available, therefore, for the oxidation of another batch of phosphoglyceraldehyde molecules.

It may be pointed out in passing that the reduction of the ketone to phosphoglycerol is not normally a large-scale process, but one that only takes place under unusual circumstances such, for instance, as when the system is poisoned with fluoride, and the reasons for this we shall discover presently.

In recent years it has been found that the oxidation of phosphoglyceraldehyde is a considerably more complex process than was formerly supposed. It was observed by Meyerhof and by D. M. Needham, independently and at the same time, that when phosphoglyceraldehyde is oxidized to phosphoglyceric acid in muscle extracts, one molecule of ATP is synthesized for every molecule of phosphoglyceric acid formed. A similar phenomenon could also be observed in yeast-juice fermentation, and attempts were made to discover its cause, using highly purified (crystalline) triosephosphate dehydrogenase. It was then found that no oxidation of phosphoglyceraldehyde takes place except in the presence of inorganic phosphate. When the latter was added, however, a brisk oxidation took place, one molecule of phosphate disappearing for every molecule of phosphoglyceraldehyde oxidized. The product of oxidation now proved to be, not 3-phosphoglyceric acid, but a new compound, 1:3-diphosphoglyceric acid.

To account for the disappearance of inorganic phosphate in a yeast-juice fermentation it may therefore be supposed that an intermediate 1:3-diphosphoglyceraldehyde is first formed (reaction 6) and then undergoes dehydrogenation (7) under the influence of *triosephosphate dehydrogenase*, yielding 1:3-diphosphoglyceric acid. Reaction 7 is inhibited by iodoacetic acid, which blocks the —SH groups of the dehydrogenase. The next stage consists in the transference of the phosphate radical at position 1 to a molecule of ADP, so that 3-phosphoglyceric acid and ATP are formed (reaction 8), the process being catalysed by *phosphoglyceric phosphokinase*. The 3-phosphate is then converted into the 2-ester (reaction 9) through the agency of *phosphoglyceromutase*. The reactions, all of which are reversible, may be written in the following manner:

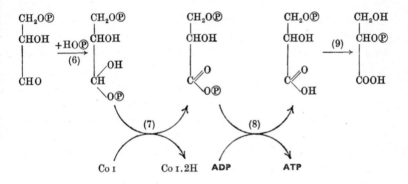

(iv) *Dephosphorylation of Glyceric Acid.* If one or both of the phosphoglyceric acids is added to whole yeast juice it undergoes fermentation. If, however, a dialysed juice is used there is no fermentation, but a new intermediate accumulates, viz. phospho-*enol*-pyruvic acid. This arises by the dehydration of 2-phosphoglyceric acid (reaction 10) at the hands of *enolase*. It is at this point that fluoride inhibits fermentation; it does so because enolase requires magnesium ions for activity and is, apparently, a magnesium protein. Fluoride forms a complex magnesium fluorophosphate in the presence of inorganic phosphate. Dialysis, as ordinarily performed, does not stop enolase activity; it does, however, remove the coenzyme required for the next reaction, viz. the decomposition of phosphopyruvic acid.

If ADP is added to a dialysed juice containing phosphopyruvic acid, the latter begins to break down, and pyruvic acid appears. This reaction (11) is catalysed by *pyruvic phosphokinase*, and the phosphate radical is transferred to ADP, yielding ATP once again:

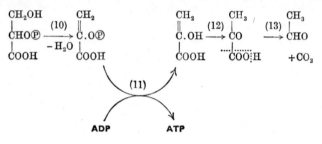

The *enol*-pyruvic acid liberated in reaction 11 may pass over into the more stable *keto*-form (reaction 12); it may be, however, that the less stable and therefore more reactive *enol*-form enters the next reaction as fast as it is produced.

Pyruvic acid accumulates in a dialysed extract provided with ADP and phosphopyruvic acid. It does so because the next reaction, in which the pyruvic acid is decarboxylated, requires the presence of *co-carboxylase*, together with the enzyme *carboxylase*. The products of this reaction (13) are carbon dioxide and acetaldehyde, and the formation of the latter can be demonstrated by adding sodium bisulphite to a fermenting mixture, when the addition compound, acetaldehyde-sodium bisulphite, $CH_3CH(OH)SO_3Na$, is formed and can be isolated. The splitting of pyruvic acid is probably the only irreversible process in the whole fermentation sequence, apart from the initial phosphorylations (reactions 1, 3).

(v) *Production of Alcohol*. The final stage of the process consists in the reduction of acetaldehyde to ethyl alcohol, and the mechanism of this reaction requires special consideration.

It will be remembered that in the presence of fluoride, phosphoglyceric acid and phosphoglycerol are produced. Phosphoglyceric acid is formed from phosphoglyceraldehyde by reactions which involve the reduction of Co I. The reduced coenzyme passes on its 2H to a molecule of phosphodihydroxyacetone and, without this, the whole of the available coenzyme would soon become and remain reduced. As no more phosphoglyceric acid could then be formed, fermentation would speedily come to an end.

In a normal as opposed to a fluoride fermentation, phosphodihydroxyacetone is not required at this point, for there is available an alternative hydrogen acceptor in the form of acetaldehyde. Under the influence of *alcohol dehydrogenase*, working 'in reverse', the 2H of the reduced coenzyme are transferred instead to acetaldehyde, alcohol is formed, and the oxidized form of Co I is regenerated and can be used over again (reaction 14). This final operation can be written as follows:

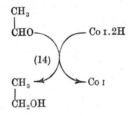

Reaction 14, like 7, is inhibited by iodoacetate, which blocks the —SH groups of alcohol dehydrogenase.

The overall results of this reaction sequence, which is summarized in Fig. 26, are, first, that *for each molecule of glucose fermented, two molecules of alcohol and two of carbon dioxide are formed*. Secondly, for each molecule of phosphoglyceraldehyde oxidized, one molecule of Co I is reduced, and later reoxidized at the expense of the molecule of acetaldehyde formed from the phosphoglyceraldehyde, so that *the coenzyme finishes in the oxidized condition in which it began*. Thirdly, two molecules of ATP are dephosphorylated in the phosphorylation of each molecule of glucose. Each molecule of the phosphorylated product, fructose-1:6-diphosphate, yields two molecules of 3-phosphoglyceraldehyde, and each of these takes up a molecule of inorganic phosphate before being oxidized. After oxidation has taken place, the phosphate radicals, two for each molecule of glucose

entering the system, are returned in the form of ATP in reaction 8, so that, at this stage in fermentation, the yeast has just
recovered the amount of ATP used in the first stages. Presently,
however, two more molecules of ADP are taken in and, from
these, two fresh molecules of ATP are formed in reaction 11.
Thus, as far as the ADP/ATP system is concerned, *two new
molecules of ATP are gained for each molecule of glucose fermented.*

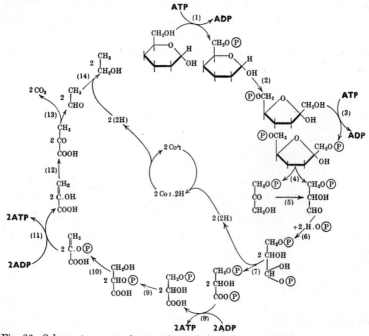

Fig. 26. Scheme to summarize reactions of alcoholic fermentation of glucose by
yeast juice. The reactions are numbered to correspond to the description given
in the text. For names of enzymes, coenzymes and inhibitors, see Table 32.

ENERGETICS OF FERMENTATION

Now let us recall the overall equation of alcoholic fermentation:

$$C_6H_{12}O_6 = 2CO_2 + 2CH_3CH_2OH.$$

The loss of free energy in this reaction is roughly 50,000 cal.
per g.mol. glucose fermented. Two new energy-rich bonds are

formed at the cost of one molecule of glucose. Now each of these energy-rich bonds represents some 11,500 cal. of *immediately available free energy.* It follows that of the 50,000 cal. or thereabouts which become available when a gram-molecule of glucose is fermented, 23,000 cal. are transferred from their source, glucose, to the energy-rich bonds of adenosine triphosphate, *the only known source of energy that can be directly utilized by living organisms.* About 46 % of the total free energy lost when glucose

TABLE 32. ALCOHOLIC FERMENTATION: ENZYMES, COENZYMES AND INHIBITORS

(see also Fig. 26)

Reaction	Enzyme	Coenzyme	Inhibited by
1	Hexokinase	ATP	Dialysis
2	Oxoisomerase	.	.
3	Phosphohexokinase	ATP	Dialysis
4	Aldolase	.	.
5	Phosphotrioseisomerase	.	.
6	? Spontaneous	$-PO_3H_2$	Dialysis
7	Triosephosphate dehydrogenase	Co I	Dialysis; $CH_2I.COOH$
8	Phosphoglyceric phosphokinase	ADP	Dialysis
9	Phosphoglyceromutase	2:3-diphosphoglyceric acid	.
10	Enolase	Mg ions	NaF
11	Pyruvic phosphokinase	ADP	Dialysis
12	? Spontaneous	.	.
13	Carboxylase	Cocarboxylase	Dialysis
14	Alcohol dehydrogenase	Co I	Dialysis; $NaHSO_3$; $CH_2I.COOH$

undergoes fermentation is thus rendered immediately accessible to the cell. That part of the energy which is not transferred from glucose to ATP is degraded in the form of heat, in part at any rate, and this, probably, is why the temperature of a fermenting liquor is always rather higher than that of its surroundings. This, however, is not altogether disadvantageous, since, within limits, fermentation, growth and multiplication all proceed more rapidly at higher temperatures.

The question is often asked, why is it that yeast does not break up glucose into alcohol and carbon dioxide directly, instead of in this rather complicated manner? The *total* free-energy yield of the process would be the same, no matter how the sugar was fermented, but, by working in the way it does, the yeast is able, step-by-step, to transfer a large proportion of the total free energy of the process to the directly utilizable energy-rich bonds of ATP. If the glucose were *directly* split, even if enzymes existed that could catalyse this process, the chances are that the vast bulk of the free energy that fermentation renders available would be degraded as heat, and thus lost to the system.

Let us now see how this important transference of chemical energy from one place to another is achieved. Living cells seem never to have discovered enzymes capable of catalysing a complete breakdown of the 6-carbon chain of unmodified glucose. The preliminary phosphorylation reactions seem, therefore, to be devices for getting glucose into a metabolizable form. To accomplish this, chemical work has to be done, and is carried out at the expense of the terminal energy-rich phosphate bonds of two molecules of ATP (reactions 1, 3). Then, and only then apparently, the 6-carbon chain can be ruptured. In the subsequent metabolism of the products, the energy originally put in is recovered (reaction 8) and the energetic *status quo* is reestablished. Later, still more energy becomes available (reaction 11), and may be used to start off the fermentation of fresh molecules of glucose, for example, or for the synthesis of new and complex tissue materials, so that the cells may grow and, in due time, divide.

The resynthesis of ATP from ADP requires the provision of some 11,500 cal. of free energy per gram-molecule. This is provided by the generation of new energy-rich bonds in the partial-breakdown products of glucose. The first new bond appears when the presumptive 1:3-diphosphoglyceraldehyde is oxidized to the corresponding acid (reaction 7). This, it will be remembered, is a process of dehydrogenation, and the removal of 2H from the aldehydic molecule results in structural changes within the molecule. These are attended by a redistribution of the intrinsic energy of the system, leading to a concentration of energy in the bond which links the phosphate radical in position 1; in other words, to the generation of a new energy-rich bond. The process can be represented in the following manner:

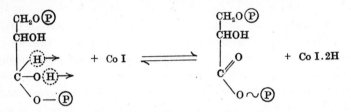

The free energy of this new bond has been estimated at about 16,250 cal., i.e. rather more than is required to forge a new ATP bond, so that in the subsequent transfer reaction,

$$R\sim\textcircled{P} + A—\textcircled{P}\sim\textcircled{P} \rightleftharpoons RH + A—\textcircled{P}\sim\textcircled{P}\sim\textcircled{P},$$

the reaction swings far over towards the right-hand side.

Further energy-rich bonds are generated later when 2-phospho-glyceric acid loses water to yield phospho-*enol*-pyruvic acid (reaction 10):

$$\begin{array}{ccc} CH_2OH & & CH_2 \\ | & & \| \\ CHO—\textcircled{P} & \rightleftharpoons & C.O\sim\textcircled{P} + H_2O. \\ | & & | \\ COOH & & COOH \end{array}$$

Here, as before, a chemical change, this time a dehydration, leads to redistribution of the internal energy of the molecule; another new energy-rich bond is generated, and this, like the former, is transferred almost intact to a molecule of ADP, yielding ATP once again.

Fermentation by Living Yeast

Yeast-juice fermentation differs from fermentation by live yeast cells in several noteworthy respects. In the first place, the juice is far less active than intact cells. This is probably because the enzymes and coenzymes are not arranged at random in the cell, as presumably they must be in the extract, but in some definite, orderly manner. It is probably safe to assume that, in the yeast cell, as in a factory, the machinery is arranged in a manner calculated to yield the greatest possible degree of efficiency, and it may not be going too far to suggest that the organization is such that the substance produced by one enzyme in the series is passed immediately on to the next. We know relatively little about the submicroscopic internal organization of this or of any other kind of cell, but that an organization of a high order of complexity exists can hardly be doubted.

A second important difference between yeast and yeast juice lies in the effect of inorganic phosphate upon fermentation in the two cases. As Harden and Young first showed, yeast juice can only ferment sugar so long as there is free inorganic phosphate in the medium. The reason for this is clear from what we now know about the mechanisms involved, for inorganic phosphate is required for the conversion of phosphoglyceraldehyde into the diphosphoglyceraldehyde which is the true substrate of the so-called triosephosphate dehydrogenase. The important oxidation process (reaction 7) therefore ceases when inorganic phosphate is not available. Any free phosphate that is present is taken up (reaction 6) and transferred by way of the diphosphates of glyceraldehyde and the corresponding acid to ADP (reactions 7, 8), and the ATP so formed is used to esterify more glucose (reactions 1, 3). If inorganic phosphate is added to a juice fermentation, therefore, it disappears and is replaced by the organically bound phosphate of the sugar esters. But the addition of inorganic phosphate has no effect on the rate of fermentation of sugar by intact yeast cells. Once again the notion of intracellular organization has to be invoked: one must suppose that the interior of the cell is so arranged that inorganic phosphate is always available in the cell at the right place and at the right time.

In the intact cell, we must believe, ATP synthesized by the cell's fermentative activities is utilized for the performance of work of various kinds, especially for the synthesis of new tissue materials for growth and reproduction, so that the terminal phosphate units of ATP are set free again in one way or another. This inorganic phosphate is caught up by the fermentation machine, recharged, so to speak, and again returned to ATP, and so on; a continual cycle of phosphate is built up and used to transfer energy obtained by fermentation to the places at which it is required and, presently, is actually put to employment.

Related to the effect of phosphate there is an interesting phenomenon known as the arsenate effect. If arsenate is added to a juice fermentation that has stopped through lack of phosphate, a long-continuing but very slow fermentation begins. This is because arsenate is able to replace phosphate in reaction 6, so that an arseno-phosphoglyceraldehyde is formed and is then oxidized in reaction 7. The product fails, however, to react with ADP in reaction 8, but 1-arseno-3-phosphoglyceric acid is rather unstable and breaks down slowly, liberating arsenate, so that 3-phosphoglycerate is slowly produced. This re-enters the re-action sequence at reaction 9 so that a slow fermentation takes place. An important feature of this arsenate effect is that re-action 8 is by-passed, so that the energy-rich bonds normally generated at this stage are no longer available to the system.

The final products of fermentation, by yeast cells or by juice, always include small quantities of *glycerol* and other substances. The formation of glycerol can readily be accounted for. At the very beginning of fermentation, glucose is phosphorylated and split to yield phosphoglyceraldehyde and phosphodihydroxy-acetone. If fermentation is to proceed, the phosphoglyceralde-hyde must be oxidized to form phosphoglyceric acid, a process in which Co I is reduced. As yet, no acetaldehyde has been formed by the reduction of which reduced Co I can be reoxidized and so put back into commission. But, as we have learned from experiments on fluoride inhibition, phosphodihydroxyacetone can be used instead of acetaldehyde, and this does in fact take place until some acetaldehyde has been produced. Even when acetaldehyde is being formed, however, small amounts of phos-phodihydroxyacetone continue to be reduced, for the system contains a soluble α-glycerophosphate dehydrogenase. The acetaldehyde/alcohol dehydrogenase system gets the lion's share of the reduced coenzyme, partly because acetaldehyde is more readily reduced than is phosphodihydroxyacetone, and partly because the alcohol dehydrogenase is more abundant than the glycerophosphate enzyme. A small proportion of the reduced coenzyme nevertheless reacts with phosphodihydroxyacetone so that a little phosphoglycerol is formed. This is the D-isomer, which proves that it is formed from the optically inactive phosphodihydroxyacetone (see p. 193) and not, as was formerly supposed, from phosphoglyceraldehyde. The latter arises from hexose diphosphate in the L-form (p. 117) and yields L-phosphoglycerol on reduction (p. 190).

Finally the phosphoglycerol is hydrolysed by a phosphatase that occurs in yeast, and glycerol itself is set free.

Fermentative Manufacture of Glycerol

Glycerol is a very important article of commerce, especially in time of war when large amounts are used in the manufacture of explosives. In ordinary times, the glycerol of commerce is a by-product from the manufacture of soaps by the saponification of fats, and fats are always in short supply in war-time. During the war of 1914–18 the British blockade led to a serious fat shortage in Germany, and the resultant shortage of glycerol meant a shortage also of explosives. The problem was met by making use of the ability of yeast to form glycerol.

High yields of glycerol can be obtained from sugar by modifying the course of normal fermentation in either of two ways. The two modified forms are known as Neuberg's 'second' and 'third' forms of fermentation respectively, the 'first' form being normal alcoholic fermentation. In Neuberg's second form, sodium bisulphite is introduced into the fermenting liquors. This gives an addition-compound with acetaldehyde, thus depriving the cells of their normal hydrogen acceptor for the reoxidation of reduced Co I. Its place is taken by phosphodihydroxyacetone, and one molecule of phosphoglycerol is accordingly formed for each molecule of phosphoglyceric acid. The phosphoglycerol is hydrolysed by the yeast phosphatase, while the phosphoglyceric acid continues along its usual path until acetaldehyde is formed and reacts with bisulphite. Each molecule of glucose therefore yields one molecule of glycerol and one each of carbon dioxide and the aldehyde-bisulphite addition compound. The process is sketched out in Fig. 27 b, which may be compared with Fig. 27 a, which represents normal fermentation in similar terms.

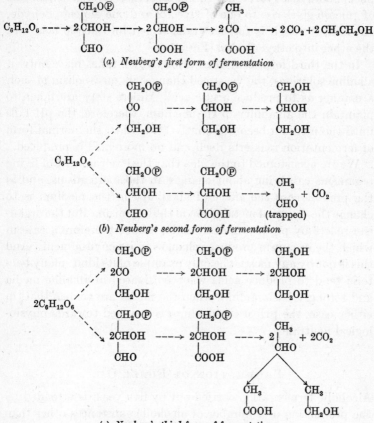

(a) *Neuberg's first form of fermentation*

(b) *Neuberg's second form of fermentation*

(c) *Neuberg's third form of fermentation*

Fig. 27. Neuberg's three 'forms' of fermentation.

The third form of fermentation sets in if the fermenting liquors are made and kept alkaline. Under alkaline conditions, acetaldehyde is no longer reduced to alcohol in the normal manner, but instead undergoes dismutation. One molecule is oxidized to acetic acid and a second simultaneously reduced to alcohol, and this takes place quite independently of the normal reactions. Again acetaldehyde is no longer available for the reoxidation of reduced Co I, and its place in that reaction is again taken by phosphodihydroxyacetone. In this case, therefore, each molecule of glucose gives rise to one of glycerol and one of acetaldehyde, one-half of which is further transformed into acetic acid and the other into ethyl alcohol (Fig. 27c).

In the third form of fermentation, which takes place only in alkaline solutions, the yeast cell changes its metabolism in such a manner as to produce acetic acid. Unless steps are taken to maintain the alkalinity of the medium, therefore, the pH falls until the medium becomes faintly acid, when the normal form of fermentation reasserts itself and no more acid is produced.

We are accustomed to the idea that the environment of living organisms can bring about changes in those organisms, and in the present case the effect of alkalinity in the medium is to change the course of metabolism in the organism. But the organism reacts by producing acid, and we have therefore a case in which the organism produces changes in its environment. And this is not by any means the only example of its kind: many bacteria tend to produce acids when cultivated in alkaline media and strongly basic amines when the media are acid so that, in either case, the pH of the medium is changed towards physiological neutrality.

PRODUCTION OF FUSEL OIL

Alcoholic fermentation carried out by live yeast is attended by the production of a number of alcoholic substances other than ethyl alcohol and glycerol, and to these the collective name of 'fusel oil' is applied. These substances usually account for less than 1 % of the total alcohols, but are of considerable industrial importance. They are interesting, too, because they are largely responsible for the characteristic flavours and bouquets of alcoholic beverages. Heavy wines, such as port, contain considerable amounts of higher alcohols and their esters, especially *iso*-amyl alcohol, and these are responsible not only for the taste of the wine but also, in large measure, for the unpleasant effects of over-indulgence, since the higher alcohols are powerful narcotics. Another interesting product of the same kind is the bitter principle of beer: this again is an alcohol, in this case tyrosol.

These alcohols arise from amino-acids. The crude liquor contains amino-acids arising from grapes, hops and the like, and more are contributed by the autolysis of dead yeast cells. They are deaminated, apparently to furnish ammonia for the synthesis of the new yeast proteins which are required as the cells grow and multiply, for if ammonium salts are added to the fermenting liquor there is a marked fall in the yields of fusel oil.

Yeast deaminates amino-acids in a peculiar manner that is perhaps unique, the process consisting in an apparently simultaneous decarboxylation and hydrolytic deamination:

$$R.CH(NH_2)COOH + H_2O = R.CH_2OH + NH_3 + CO_2.$$

In this way the leucines, for example, give rise to the corresponding amyl alcohols, while valine yields *iso*-butyl alcohol, e.g.

$$\begin{array}{c} CH_3 \\ > CH.CH_2CH(NH_2)COOH + H_2O = \\ CH_3 \end{array} \begin{array}{c} CH_3 \\ > CH.CH_2CH_2OH + NH_3 + CO_2. \\ CH_3 \end{array}$$

leucine   iso-*amyl alcohol*

Tyrosol arises in the same way from tyrosine.

CHAPTER XVI

ANAEROBIC METABOLISM OF CARBO-HYDRATES: MUSCLE AND LIVER

INTRODUCTION

MODERN muscle biochemistry was founded at the beginning of the present century. Before that time, muscular contraction or any other kind of cellular activity was thought to depend upon the sudden decomposition of large, unstable molecules of a hypothetical stuff called 'inogen'. In the case of muscle, this 'inogen' was supposed to give rise to carbon dioxide and L-(+)-lactic acid, furnishing the energy expended by the muscle. It was already well known that muscles produce carbon dioxide when they contract, and that lactic acid is produced in greater or smaller amounts at the same time.

'The justification for considering muscle tissue especially, out of all the active tissues of the organism, lies in the fact that only in muscle can we come near to comparing the chemical changes going on with the simultaneous work done or the energy set free as heat. It is difficult to assess the work performed by a secreting gland, and the metabolism of such an organ can only be studied in elaborate perfusion experiments; great advances have been made in the study of nerve tissue, but here the changes going on are so small as to make their detection only lately possible by modern methods. But certain muscles, and a variety of them, can be removed from the body with absolutely no injury, and can be kept functional for days' (D. M. Needham).

Many different methods have been used to elucidate the problems of muscular contraction. Histology, physiology, biochemistry, X-radiography and electron microscopy have all played a part. From the point of view of the histologist we can distinguish between three main types of muscle. These are: (1) the striped or striated voluntary muscle of the skeletal system, (2) the plain, unstriated or involuntary muscle of the visceral system, and (3) cardiac muscle. Most of the chemical work has been done on skeletal muscle, but there seem to be few differences between the different types from the point of view of the chemistry of their contractile processes.

The structural unit of striated muscle is the *myofibril*, a spindle-shaped little cell. Several of these go to make up a muscle fibre, and many fibres to make up a whole muscle. Under the microscope the muscle fibre shows alternating light and dark bands, or transverse striations. The differences between the appearances of the two kinds of bands are due to differences in their optical properties. The dark-looking striations or *anisotropic bands* show strong double refraction, and when the muscle contracts it can be seen that only these anisotropic regions undergo shortening. The light-looking *isotropic bands*, which are not doubly refracting, do not.

Chemically speaking, muscle consists chiefly of the muscle protein *actomyosin*, apparently in the form of a gel which accounts for 75–80 % of the whole muscle substance. Now actomyosin is a protein of which the molecule is a thread-like or 'fibrous' particle and is a complex formed by the association of two proteins, *actin* and *myosin*. A solution of actomyosin is singly refracting when at rest, when the molecules have a purely random distribution. But if the solution is made to flow along a glass tube, the thread-like particles all become orientated in the same direction, pointing in the direction of flow, and the solution becomes doubly refracting. It is therefore probable that the anisotropic regions of the muscle fibre are doubly refracting because all the actomyosin molecules point in the same direction, while in the singly refracting, isotropic regions they lie perhaps entirely at random. There is now abundant evidence to show that the molecule of actomyosin, like that of keratin, possesses contractile properties, and we know too that only the anisotropic regions shorten when a muscle contracts. It therefore seems likely that the contraction of the muscle as a whole is in reality due to summation of the individual molecular contractions of all the actomyosin particles which, lying parallel to one another, account for the double refraction of the anisotropic, contractile bands.

This is a rough picture of what is generally regarded as the contractile machinery. We now have two main problems to consider. First, what is the chemical source of the energy which is expended when the muscle machine does its work and, secondly, how is this energy transformed into the mechanical energy of contraction? At the present time we have a considerable amount of information on the first of these problems, but only a few intriguing hints and a considerable number of rival hypotheses about the second.

The first really significant experiments on the chemistry of muscular contraction were carried out by Fletcher and Hopkins and published in 1907. Working on frog muscles, they showed that larger or smaller amounts of lactic acid are formed when muscle contracts. The general plan of the experiments was as follows. The sartorius or gastrocnemius muscles were removed from the hind legs of a frog and kept under identical conditions. One of the pair was made to do work by being stimulated, and this, the experimental muscle, and the unstimulated control were then dropped into ice-cold alcohol and finely ground with sand. These workers realized that a muscle is capable of doing a very large amount of work in a very short period of time, and that to injure a muscle amounts to stimulating it. By using small muscles, chilling and extracting them very quickly with ice-cold alcohol it was possible to inactivate the muscle enzymes very rapidly indeed, and so to prevent the large-scale chemical changes which would otherwise result from injuries inflicted in the process of grinding. The chemical changes corresponding to the work done by the experimental muscle could then be found by analysing and comparing the extracts with those of control muscles. Other workers had done similar experiments already, but no precautions were then taken to cool the muscle before grinding, with the result that little difference could as a rule be detected between the experimental and control muscles, so grievous is the injury inflicted by grinding.

Fletcher and Hopkins, with their new technique, confirmed and extended the older observations that lactic acid is formed when muscle contracts, and their results demonstrated with beautiful clarity the following points. (i) Muscle can contract in a perfectly normal manner in complete absence of oxygen. (ii) Lactic acid is produced during anaerobic contraction, and piles up with continued stimulation until, in the end, the muscle becomes fatigued. (iii) If the fatigued muscle is then put into oxygen it recovers its ability to contract, and lactic acid simultaneously disappears. (iv) Less lactic acid is formed in a muscle that is allowed access to oxygen than in one which works anaerobically.

Shortly afterwards it was shown by Meyerhof that the lactic acid is formed from glycogen and that, under anaerobic conditions, the amount of lactic acid formed is chemically equivalent to the quantity of glycogen broken down. A mass of later work made it clear that there is strict proportionality between the amount of work done, the heat produced, the tension developed in a muscle, and the quantity of lactic acid formed; and by 1927 it had become evident that the energy expended in muscular contraction comes from the conversion of glycogen to lactic acid.

A good deal of interest centred round the phosphate compounds present in muscle, for it was already clear that phosphates play an important part in muscle glycolysis, just as they do in fermentation. The method in general use for extracting phosphates from muscle tissue consisted in chilling the material thoroughly and extracting it by grinding with ice-cold trichloracetic acid or some other protein precipitant. Ice-cold conditions were used here, as in the original work on lactic acid formation, in order to inactivate the muscle enzymes as rapidly as possible. Once the extract had been prepared it was allowed to warm up, and estimations of the phosphate content were subsequently made.

In 1927, however, it was discovered that the ice-cold filtrates from trichloracetic precipitation contain a hitherto undetected phosphate compound. This substance is exceedingly rapidly hydrolysed in acid solution and had not previously been noticed for that reason. In order to detect and estimate it, the trichloracetic filtrate must be kept ice-cold until it has been neutralized to a pH of about 8, at which the new compound is fairly stable. In due course the new substance was isolated and shown to be *phosphocreatine*, to which the name of *phosphagen* and the following formula have been assigned:

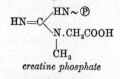

creatine phosphate

Later investigations showed that this compound is present in the striated, smooth and cardiac muscles of all classes of vertebrates, but absent from those of invertebrates (see p. 339 et seq.). In its place, invertebrate muscles usually contain an analogous derivative of arginine, *phosphoarginine*, with the following structure:

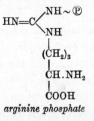

arginine phosphate

In passing it should be noticed that both phosphagens contain an energy-rich phosphate bond, a feature which turns out to be of great physiological significance. In what follows we shall discuss mainly the creatine compound, but it may be assumed that what goes for this substance is also true of the arginine analogue.

A wave of interest in the new compound soon developed, and within a few years it became known that it plays an important part in the chemistry of muscular contraction. Phosphagen, it was shown, breaks down during activity and is resynthesized during rest, aerobically and anaerobically alike, and, moreover, it breaks down far more rapidly than does glycogen. It was suspected by some that, since the breakdown of phosphagen precedes that of glycogen, it must be the immediate source of contraction energy, the more slowly acting process of glycolysis being used to resynthesize the phosphagen, rather as the lever of an air-gun is used to reset the spring after the trigger has been pulled. But this idea did not find much favour; muscle chemists were still too much wedded to the older lactic acid hypothesis.

In 1930, however, new evidence appeared. Lundsgaard, who was studying the pharmacological properties of iodoacetic acid, observed that in animals dying from iodoacetate poisoning the muscles went into rigor, but that, instead of becoming markedly acid as was to be expected, they actually became faintly alkaline. Closer examination showed that no lactic acid whatever had been produced. This discovery caused a good deal of surprise, since it demonstrated conclusively that muscle can contract *without producing any lactic acid at all*. Further work on iodo-acetate-poisoned muscles showed that phosphagen breaks down when work is done, the amount split being strictly proportional to the amount of energy expended. Further, phosphagen was not resynthesized if an iodoacetate-poisoned muscle was allowed to rest, and, with repeated stimulation, the muscle went into rigor as soon as its stock of phosphagen was exhausted.

By this time it had begun to appear that muscle resembles yeast rather closely in its carbohydrate metabolism. Compounds such as the hexose phosphates could be detected as well in the one as in the other, while that all-important compound adenosine triphosphate was also detected in both. Most of the work so far described had been done on intact, isolated muscles, mostly of frogs, kept under anaerobic conditions, but in 1925 Meyerhof published a method for the preparation from muscle of extracts analogous to the yeast juice that had been so valuable in the study of fermentation. The method employed is roughly as follows.

The animal is anaesthetized and cooled to 0° C. The muscles are carefully cut away with the least possible injury, and care is taken to keep them cold. The tissue is put through an ice-cold mincer and allowed to stand for 30–60 min. with ice-water or isotonic KCl. After straining and centrifuging, a rather viscous liquid is obtained and stored in the refrigerator until required.

Extracts prepared in this way contain all the enzymes and coenzymes required for the production of lactic acid from added glycogen, and will also break down creatine phosphate and ATP if these are added. Most of the recent progress in muscle chemistry has been achieved with the aid of extracts of this kind. Dialysis removes the coenzymes, just as it does in the case of yeast juice, and many experiments have been carried out with extracts previously dialysed or treated with fluoride or iodoacetate. One point that should be noticed is that, although they can convert glycogen into lactic acid, these extracts do not respire, so that it is possible to work on extracts in the presence of air instead of having to take elaborate precautions to ensure anaerobiosis, as is necessary when isolated muscles are employed. Whereas the enzymes concerned in glycolysis are present in the cytoplasm and come out into the extract, cytochrome oxidase and certain other enzymes essential for respiration are not soluble but remain attached to the insoluble cell debris, especially the mitochondria. Another important feature of these extracts is that, unlike intact muscle, they have no action upon glucose. Intact muscle cells can convert glucose into glycogen with the aid of an enzyme closely resembling the hexokinase of yeast, but this enzyme is insoluble and consequently absent from muscle extracts.

FORMATION OF LACTIC ACID

The reactions involved in glycolysis are very similar to those involved in alcoholic fermentation. The first step in muscle extract consists in the phosphorolysis of glycogen, i.e. splitting of the glycogen molecule by the elements of phosphoric acid. The reaction, which is reversible, is catalysed by *muscle phosphorylase* and yields α-glucose-1-phosphate:

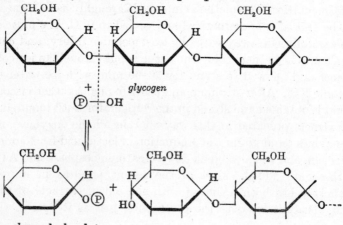

α-*glucose*-1-*phosphate*

The product is then converted into glucose-6-phosphate by *phosphoglucomutase*:

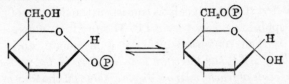

From this point glycolysis and fermentation follow a common path until pyruvic acid is formed. Here the pathways diverge again, for muscle, unlike yeast, does not contain carboxylase. Co-carboxylase is present, but, like Co I and Co II, it collaborates with more enzymes than one, and its presence in muscle is in no way an indication that carboxylase itself is present. In yeast, it will be remembered, pyruvic acid is split into carbon dioxide and acetaldehyde, the latter then functioning as a hydrogen acceptor in the reoxidation of reduced Co I. In muscle extract, however, no carboxylase being present, pyruvic acid itself discharges this function and is reduced asymmetrically to L-(+)-lactic acid, under the influence of *lactic dehydrogenase*:

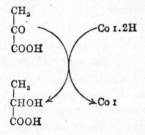

The overall effect of this reaction sequence is that, on the carbohydrate side, *one 6-carbon unit of glycogen yields two molecules of lactic acid*. Co I is alternately reduced and reoxidized just as it is in fermentation, but there are differences as far as the ATP/ADP system is concerned. In yeast juice and in muscle extract alike the sequence as a whole leads to the generation of four new energy-rich phosphate bonds for each 6-carbon unit metabolized. In fermentation, two of these new bonds are used to compensate for those used in the preliminary phosphorylation of the glucose molecule, so that in this case there is a net gain of two molecules of ATP for each glucose molecule fermented. Muscle extract, however, starts from glycogen, not from glucose, and the first stage in glycolysis consists in the splitting of glycogen by phosphoric acid, not by ATP. The product, glucose-1-phosphate, is then converted into the 6-phosphate, and *only one molecule of ATP has therefore to be used up in the production of each molecule of fructofuranose diphosphate.* Of the four molecules of ATP subsequently produced, only one is required to restore the status quo, so that *in muscle glycolysis there is a net gain of three molecules of ATP for each 6-carbon unit of glycogen metabolized*, as compared with a gain of two molecules for each 6-carbon *glucose unit* metabolized in the case of fermentation.

Calculations show that the conversion of glycogen into lactic acid, under biological conditions, is accompanied by a loss of free energy equivalent to approximately 57,000 cal. for each 6-carbon unit glycolysed. Three new energy-rich phosphate bonds are formed at the same time, so that the amount of energy 'captured' in the form of energy-rich bonds is about 34,500 cal., which corresponds to approximately 60 % of the total free energy exchange. This, of course, is in muscle extract, and there are reasons for believing that an even higher proportion of the energy may be 'captured' in the intact muscle cell. This is really a remarkable performance when it is realized that the efficiency of even the most modern superheated steam turbines barely reaches 50 % or thereabouts. If glycolysis began with glucose instead of glycogen the free-energy change would be about 36,000 cal. per g.mol. and in this case there would be a net gain of only two energy-rich bonds, as in alcoholic fermentation, corresponding to an energy-capture of 23,000 cal. per g.mol., or 64 %. Thus the convenience of having a localized store of readily available carbohydrate in the muscle costs very little in terms of efficiency.

Parts played by ATP and Phosphagen

The reactions of glycolysis involve breakdown and resynthesis of ATP, just as do those of fermentation, and the resemblances between the two processes are very striking indeed. There is, however, one very important difference between yeast and muscle, for whereas the latter contains phosphagen, yeast does not.

If an intact, isolated muscle is allowed to contract under anaerobic conditions there is a decrease in the amount of phosphagen present, together with corresponding increases in the amounts of free creatine and free inorganic phosphate. This suggests that muscle must contain an enzyme catalysing the hydrolysis of creatine phosphate. This possibility was investigated by Lohmann. If creatine phosphate is added to a preparation of muscle extract it is rapidly split into creatine and inorganic phosphate. But, Lohmann found, there is no hydrolysis of phosphagen added to a dialysed extract, indicating that some dialysable factor is involved. This factor was identified with ADP, and it was then discovered that phosphagen is not hydrolysed, as had formerly been supposed, but that *it reacts with ADP*, a phosphate radical being transferred, yielding free creatine together with ATP. ATP is split by a powerful adenosine triphosphatase that is present in the extract, ADP is formed and phosphorylated at the expense of the phosphagen and so on, until no more phosphagen remains:

$$\text{ATP} + \text{H}_2\text{O} \rightarrow \text{ADP} + \text{HO}\circled{P},$$
$$\text{ADP} + \text{C}\circled{P} \rightarrow \text{ATP} + \text{C},$$

Overall :
$$\text{C}\circled{P} + \text{H}_2\text{O} \rightarrow \text{C} + \text{HO}.\circled{P}.$$

Lohmann further discovered that adenosine triphosphatase can be inactivated by prolonged dialysis at $0°$ C. and, when the enzyme had thus been inactivated, he was able to show that the reaction between creatine phosphate and ADP is freely reversible:

$$\text{ADP} + \text{C}\circled{P} \rightleftharpoons \text{ATP} + \text{C}.$$

Very little energy change is involved and no inorganic phosphate is set free in this, which is known as the Lohmann reaction. From the existence of this equilibrium system we can make certain deductions concerning the part played by phosphagen in the economy of the muscle. Anything that tends to decompose ATP will force the reaction over towards the right and phosphagen will be broken down. If, on the other hand, glycolysis is in progress so that new energy-rich bonds are being generated, fresh ATP will be formed, the reaction will swing towards the left and phosphagen will be resynthesized.

Perhaps the most important feature of Lohmann's work was his discovery that, until some ATP has been broken down to provide ADP, no decomposition of phosphagen can take place: in other words, *the breakdown of ATP must take place even earlier than that of phosphagen*. The breakdown of ATP, in fact, is the *earliest* reaction we have so far been able to detect and hence is the *most immediate known source of contraction energy*. This suggests that ATP must play some part in contraction, over and above the part it plays in glycolysis.

The probable nature of this additional function was first revealed by the work of Engelhart & Lubimova, who found that the adenosine triphosphatase activity of muscle is inseparable from and apparently identical with 'myosin'. This was before the discovery of actin and actomyosin, and there is not much doubt that their 'myosin' consisted in reality of a mixture of actomyosin and myosin proper. Thus actomyosin, the actual contractile protein of muscle, appears to be identical with the enzyme that catalyses the decomposition of ATP and leads to the liberation of the free energy of its terminal energy-rich bond. Experiments by D. M. Needham, J. Needham and others have given results which are completely in harmony with the supposition that, when actomyosin and ATP come into contact, a sudden shortening of the molecules takes place, followed by decomposition of the ATP and a return of the protein molecules to their former length. These results were obtained by measurements of the viscosity and refractive indices of solutions of 'myosin'. Threads prepared from actomyosin similarly contract if treated with ATP, and again, it is possible, by treating muscle with the collagenase of *Clostridium welchii*, to obtain isolated myofibrils which similarly contract on addition of ATP.

The ability to contract in response to ATP is evidently a built-in property of the muscle proteins *in situ* for, if a few fibres are stripped from the *psoas* muscle of a rabbit, they contract when treated with ATP, and the same results are obtained even when the excised tissue has been preserved in 50 % glycerol for many months in the cold. Exactly what happens in the process of shortening we still do not know, but the problem is being studied intensively. The shortening of actomyosin and preparations containing it in an orientated form appears to be due to an ATP-induced dissociation or disaggregation of actomyosin into actin plus myosin.

If we accept these results at their face value it follows that the first reaction known to take place when a muscle is stimulated consists in the decomposition of ATP, a process which is attended by a sudden shortening of the actomyosin molecules and, in some manner which is quite obscure at the present time, by the conversion of the free energy of its terminal energy-rich phosphate bond into the mechanical energy of contraction. This field is being very actively studied and there is no lack of hypotheses, but the nature of the contractile process itself is still unknown. There can be no doubt, however, that very intimate relationships exist between the source of contraction energy (ATP), the enzyme that catalyses the liberation of that energy (ATP-ase) and the contractile material itself (actomyosin).

It is difficult, in view of the evidence, to escape the conclusion that ATP plays a most intimate part in muscle contraction, but as yet it has not been possible to demonstrate any direct decomposition of ATP in a stimulated muscle until the muscle has reached a very advanced stage of fatigue and is on the very threshold of rigor. This we interpret as due to the extreme rapidity with which ADP, formed, as we believe it to be formed, in contraction, is rephosphorylated by phosphagen through the Lohmann reaction, but until such a breakdown of ATP can actually be demonstrated in normal contraction there will still be some who will regard the ATP theory with suspicion if not with actual scorn. This vitally important demonstration might be forthcoming from studies of some kind of slow-acting muscle, such as that of the tortoise or toad, especially at low temperatures as A. V. Hill has suggested, or by the discovery of some selective inhibitor of the Lohmann reaction. In the meantime we have a widely accepted working hypothesis.

If we accept this hypothesis the function of phosphagen becomes clear. The muscle contains relatively small amounts of ATP, and these would soon be exhausted but for the fact that the ADP formed by its decomposition can be rapidly rephosphorylated at the expense of phosphagen, through the Lohmann reaction. This means that the muscle can go on acting several times longer than it could if no phosphagen was present, for the amount of phosphagen present in a typical striated muscle is several times greater than that of ATP. These facts are illustrated in Table 33.

TABLE 33. PHOSPHORUS PARTITION IN STRIATED MUSCLE

(mg. P per 100 g.)

Animal	Inorganic-P	Phosphagen-P	Pyro-P	Ratio (Inorg. + Phosphagen)-P / Available pyro-P
Frog	30	50	30	5·3
Rat	35	80	40	5·7
Rabbit	26	62	40	4·4

Notes. (1) The 'available' pyrophosphate-P is 50% of the total pyrophosphate-P of the ATP present, since only the terminal energy-rich bond is directly available through the activity of adenosine triphosphatase.

(2) The inorganic phosphate found in trichloracetic extracts of muscle is mainly formed by the breakdown of some of the phosphagen during the extraction. The sum, (inorganic + phosphagen)-P may therefore be taken as an approximation to the true phosphagen-P of the resting muscle.

Phosphagen, then, may be regarded as a reserve of phosphate-bond energy. The free energy of its energy-rich bonds is not *immediately* available to the muscle machine but can rapidly be made available by transference to ADP through the Lohmann reaction. In creatine phosphate the free-energy value of the phosphate bond has been estimated at about 13,000 cal. per g.mol., and that of arginine phosphate at about 12,000 cal. per g.mol.

In all, three ways are known in which ATP can be synthesized anaerobically from ADP in muscle. The first of these, the Lohmann reaction, is used at the onset of contraction and enables the muscle to keep up a high level of immediately available energy in the form of ATP by drawing upon the stored bond-energy of phosphagen. The second source of supply consists in the new energy-rich bonds generated in the course of glycolysis and this is the main ultimate source of energy when activity is prolonged. Glycolysis gets under way relatively slowly, however, and phosphagen is used to tide the muscle over the interval between the onset of activity and the establishment of the glycolytic reaction sequence. But there is yet a third possible source of ATP, though this is probably only used when the muscle is *in extremis*. In all the processes mentioned so far, only the terminal energy-rich bond of ATP is involved. After this has been utilized there remains another such bond in each ADP molecule, but this is not directly accessible. Muscle, however, contains myokinase and this enzyme, acting upon two molecules of ADP, can catalyse the transfer of a phosphate radical from one molecule to a second, yielding a molecule of ATP, together with adenylic acid (see p. 122). As has been suggested, this way of producing ATP is probably only used as a last resort. The free adenylic acid produced is highly toxic and, once formed, rapidly undergoes deamination at the hands of the adenylic deaminase of muscle to yield inosinic acid, and the muscle goes into rigor. Inosinic acid cannot replace adenylic acid as a carrier of phosphate, nor does the action of the adenylic acid deaminase appear to be reversible.

CHEMICAL EVENTS IN NORMAL CONTRACTION

We are now in a position to make some sort of picture of the course of events in normal muscular contraction. It will be convenient first to consider what takes place during contraction in a muscle previously poisoned with iodoacetate. This drug, it will be recalled, abolishes the activity of triosephosphate dehydrogenase and therefore puts a stop to glycolysis and therefore to the oxidative breakdown of its products, so that only two anaerobic sources of ATP are now available to the cells.

On the arrival of a nerve impulse, ATP is broken down, giving rise, by way of unknown intermediary processes probably involving actomyosin or its components, to ADP and inorganic phosphate, and furnishing at the same time the contraction energy. The ADP is promptly converted again into ATP at the expense of phosphagen and no change in the ATP content of the muscle can be detected; some phosphagen disappears, however, and is replaced by free creatine and free inorganic phosphate. If repeated stimuli are applied to the muscle, these processes continue until, eventually, no phosphagen remains. As a last resort the myokinase of the muscle is called into play and the last traces of ATP are decomposed, giving, in the end, adenylic acid, which is deaminated. The muscle goes into rigor, and the ammonia produced by the deaminase can be detected in the cells.

In the case of a normal, unpoisoned muscle working anaerobically, glycolysis also comes into the picture. The following phenomena can be observed during *the period of anaerobic activity*:

> ATP remains unchanged.
> Phosphagen disappears.
> Free creatine appears.
> Free inorganic phosphate appears.
> Glycogen disappears.
> Lactic acid is formed.

These changes continue as long as the muscle is active. There then follows a short *period of anaerobic recovery* and during this interval, which amounts to about 30 sec., the following further changes take place:

> ATP remains unchanged.
> Phosphagen is resynthesized.
> Free creatine disappears.
> Free inorganic phosphate disappears.
> Glycogen disappears.
> Lactic acid is formed.

Thus glycolysis continues for a short time even after the cessation of muscular activity, and this 'glycolysis of recovery' is attended by resynthesis of phosphagen and a return to the *status quo* of the resting muscle apart, of course, from the conversion of some glycogen into lactic acid.

All these phenomena can be accounted for in terms of the reactions we have considered. While activity lasts, ATP is broken down to provide the energy expended by the muscle. Phosphagen is used up to maintain the level of ATP and corresponding amounts of creatine and inorganic phosphate are set free. The free phosphate is taken up, for the phosphorolysis of glycogen in the first instance, and later for the conversion of 3-phosphoglyceraldehyde into the 1:3-diphosphate. This is followed by the generation of new energy-rich bonds in the usual way, the new bonds being transferred to ADP and fresh ATP synthesized. This relieves the drain on the phosphagen stores of the muscle and, indeed, once glycolysis is well established, new energy-rich bonds are usually generated more rapidly than they are expended in the breakdown of ATP. The surplus energy-rich bonds are transferred through ATP to free creatine accordingly, and phosphagen begins to be resynthesized even while activity is still in progress, and it has been shown that during a short period of moderate activity there is at first a steep fall in the phosphagen content of the muscle, followed by a rise to a new, steady level.

During the period of anaerobic recovery, glycolysis continues as long as free inorganic phosphate is available, glycogen accordingly disappearing and lactic acid being formed. ATP is synthesized as long as glycolysis is in progress and, since it is no longer being broken down for energy production, tends to accumulate. The Lohmann reaction therefore goes in reverse and the remaining free creatine is esterified.

GLYCOLYSIS IN TISSUES OTHER THAN MUSCLE

That two types of cells so different in morphology and function as yeast and muscle should make use of practically the same reactions for the breakdown of carbohydrate could hardly have been anticipated. The discovery that such close parallels exist between the two seems to be a hint that the reactions we have been considering may perhaps form a part of the fundamental metabolic equipment of living cells in general, and this does in fact seem highly probable. There is now evidence that tissues other than muscle, tissues such as liver, kidney, brain and so on, make use of reactions which are essentially the same as those

employed in muscle. It seems certain that many bacteria and
even plants also contain many or most of the enzymes involved
in fermentation and in muscle glycolysis, and that ATP is an
almost universal go-between which gathers up available energy
from carbohydrate sources and stores it up in an immediately
accessible form.

TABLE 34. CONCENTRATION OF PHOSPHAGEN
IN VARIOUS TISSUES

(mg. P per 100 g.)

Organ and animal	Creatine phosphate	Arginine phosphate	Inorganic phosphate	Total phosphagen + inorganic-P
Striated muscle:				
Rabbit	62	.	26	88
Guinea-pig	22	.	58	80
Frog	50	.	30	80
Sea-urchin	11	18	9	38
Scallop	0	42	25	67
Electric tissue:				
Electric ray	37	.	25	62
Cardiac muscle:				
Rat	5	0	31	36
Unstriated muscle:				
Rat (stomach)	3	0	13	16
Sea-cucumber (body wall)	.	28	5	33
Nerve:				
Dog (brain)	12	.	.	12
Rabbit (sciatic)	6	.	9	15
Frog (sciatic)	7	.	10	17
Testis:				
Rabbit	1·4	.	11·6	13
Jensen sarcoma	1·2	.	22	23·2

The principal differences between different animal tissues from
the point of view of their glycolytic mechanisms lie in the
amounts of phosphagen they contain (Table 34). The larger and
more powerful skeletal muscles usually seem to contain larger
amounts of phosphagen, while the slow-acting, smooth muscle
of the gastro-intestinal canal, for example, contains only a fraction, amounting to perhaps one-fifth, of the amount present in
the average striated muscle. Cardiac muscle also contains rela-

tively little. The only tissues known to contain phosphagen in concentrations comparable with those of striated muscle are the electric organs of certain fishes, e.g. *Torpedo*. Like striated muscle, these organs are capable of going into activity almost instantaneously and of dissipating very large amounts of energy in very short periods of time. There can be little doubt that the phosphagen mechanism is an energy-storing device which makes it possible for an organ to go rapidly into action and to do a large amount of work in a short time. Our knowledge of the part it plays in muscle certainly confirms this idea.

Phosphagen is also present in spermatozoa in appreciable amounts, and there is evidence that these cells draw the energy for their locomotion from typical glycolytic processes involving ATP and phosphagen. Traces of phosphagen are found in nerve, brain and various glandular structures, and it has been suggested that it plays a part in their activity also. Tissues of this kind are usually richly vascularized, however, and it may be that the phosphagen present is chiefly associated with the muscle cells that enter into the make-up of the blood vessels.

The phosphagen system apart, glycolysis seems to be an almost universal feature of the make-up of living cells, at any rate under anaerobic conditions, and it seems tolerably certain that ATP likewise occurs almost universally. In view of the evidently great importance of these processes, therefore, the reaction-sequence of glycolysis is summarized for reference in Fig. 28, though the part played by phosphagen has been omitted from the scheme for the sake of simplicity. The enzymes and their coenzymes and inhibitors are tabulated in Table 35 for reference.

Emphasis must now be placed upon one feature of the glycolytic reaction sequence that hitherto has been but little mentioned, namely that, as far as the carbohydrate side is concerned, *all the reactions involved are reversible*. It was formerly believed that the phosphate-transfer reaction between phospho-*enol*-pyruvic acid and ADP is irreversible, but it has now been shown that ATP can phosphorylate pyruvic acid, given certain conditions, viz. (*a*) a high concentration of ATP and (*b*) the presence of potassium ions. One stage in the reverse sequence requires special comment, viz. the dephosphorylation of fructofuranose-1:6-diphosphate to yield the 6-monophosphate. This does not proceed by reaction with ADP, since the sugar ester contains no energy-rich bond such as is required for the phosphorylation of

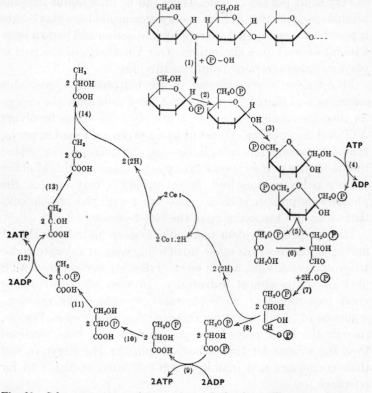

Fig. 28. Scheme to summarize reactions of glycolysis. The part played by phosphagen (where present) is omitted. For names of enzymes, coenzymes and inhibitors, see Table 35. (See also Fig. 26, p. 378.)

ADP. This dephosphorylation is thought to be carried out hydrolytically with the aid of a phosphatase, and phosphatases are present in most cells and tissues. Hence, as far as the carbohydrate side of glycolysis is concerned it is true to say that *glycolysis is a reversible operation.*

According to the work of Meyerhof on frog muscle, some 80 % of the lactic acid formed during anaerobic activity is reconverted into glycogen in the muscle when the latter is allowed to rest in oxygen. The remaining 20 % is oxidized to furnish the energy required for the resynthesis. While we may take Meyerhof's authority for the belief that this happens in frog muscle, there is little reason to think that it normally takes place in mammalian muscle. As Cori & Cori have shown, any lactic acid formed in

TABLE 35. GLYCOLYSIS: ENZYMES, COENZYMES AND INHIBITORS

(see also Table 32, p. 379)

Reaction	Enzyme	Coenzyme	Inhibited by
1	Phosphorylase	$-PO_3H_2$	Dialysis
2	Phosphoglucomutase	Glucose-1:6-diphosphate	.
3	Oxoisomerase	.	.
4	Phosphohexokinase	ATP	Dialysis
5	Aldolase	.	.
6	Phosphotriose isomerase	.	
7	? Spontaneous	$-PO_3H_2$	Dialysis
8	Triosephosphate dehydrogenase	Co I	Dialysis; $CH_2I.COOH$
9	Phosphoglyceric phosphokinase	ADP	Dialysis
10	Phosphoglyceromutase	2:3-diphosphoglyceric acid	.
11	Enolase	Mg ions	NaF
12	Pyruvic phosphokinase	ADP	Dialysis
13	? Spontaneous	.	.
14	Lactic dehydrogenase	Co I	Dialysis

the mammalian muscle *in situ* diffuses out and is carried, by way of the blood stream, to the liver. Here it is oxidized to pyruvic acid with the aid of lactic dehydrogenase and Co I, the product being phosphorylated, presumably at the expense of ATP, and built up into liver glycogen by reversal of the glycolytic reaction sequence.

Since it is from the stored glycogen of the liver that muscle glycogen is drawn in the first place, it is to the carbohydrate metabolism of the liver that we must now turn our attention.

THE LIVER: GLYCOGENESIS, GLYCOGENOLYSIS AND GLYCONEOGENESIS

The carbohydrate metabolism of animals centres round the processes of glycogenesis and glycogenolysis, i.e. the production and breakdown of glycogen. These processes take place mainly in the liver. Glycogen can be formed from carbohydrate materials, in which case we speak of *glycogenesis* but, as we have already seen, it can also be formed by the liver from non-carbohydrate sources such, for example, as certain amino-acids, glycerol, lactic, pyruvic and propionic acids and many other simple substances. In this case, therefore, we speak of *glyconeogenesis.* The term *glycogenolysis* is used to refer to the breakdown of glycogen to glucose, as opposed to the more extensive process of disintegration which we call *glycolysis*.

As far as is known, the carbohydrates of the food do not contribute any materials that are 'essential' in the sense that certain of the amino-acids are essential. Their function is pre-eminently that of furnishing a readily metabolized source of energy. The principal monosaccharide formed by the digestion of an average meal is glucose; other sugars play a relatively small part as a rule; but in the infant mammal, whose sole food carbohydrate is lactose, one-half of the lactose molecule gives rise to galactose on hydrolysis. Other monosaccharides that arise from food include fructose, formed from sucrose and to some extent from fructofuranosans.

Pentoses, if injected, are not utilized, but appear largely unchanged in the urine, while disaccharides similarly undergo excretion if injected into the blood stream. Glucose, together with fructose, galactose and the rarer sugar mannose, all lead to the deposition of glycogen in the liver. Glucose itself is phosphorylated by hexokinase at the expense of ATP and the product, glucose-6-monophosphate, is transformed by phosphoglucomutase into glucose-1-phosphate, the raw material for the direct synthesis of glycogen by liver phosphorylase and the branching factor. Fructose also can be phosphorylated at the expense of ATP under the influence of fructohexokinase to yield fructofuranose-6-monophosphate which, in turn, is convertible into glucose-6-phosphate by oxoisomerase and hence, by way of glucose-1-phosphate, gives rise to glycogen. Mannose too can be phosphorylated by a specific phosphokinase, yielding mannose-6-phosphate which, in the presence of phosphomannose isomerase and oxoisomerase, gives an equilibrium mixture of the 6-phosphates of glucose and fructose, from which α-glucose-1-phosphate

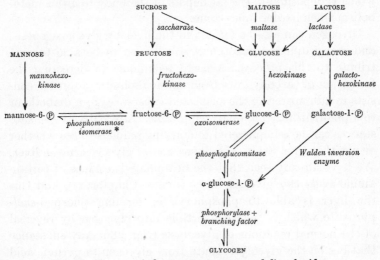

Fig. 29. Glycogenesis from common mono- and disaccharides.
* Ssee p. 145.

can be formed in the usual way. Galactose, apparently, can be phosphorylated at the expense of ATP by a specific galactokinase to yield galactose-1-phosphate and the latter, under the influence of a second enzyme ('Walden inversion enzyme'), which requires a thermostable complement (coenzyme; p. 147), gives rise to α-glucose-1-phosphate directly. No matter which of the utilizable monosaccharides is administered, the polysaccharide formed in the liver is always glycogen and the routes of conversion are summarized in Fig. 29 for convenience of reference. Different methods of administration can produce glycogens which differ somewhat in average chain-length and molecular weight but otherwise are indistinguishable.

From the standpoint of general metabolism it is important to realize that, even under strictly normal conditions, the liver's capacity to form and store glycogen is by no means unlimited. Rabbits, for example, can be literally crammed with foods rich in carbohydrate, but a glycogen content of more than 18–20 % in the liver is seldom or never realized. Carbohydrate, if administered in excess of the storage capacity of the liver, gives rise to fat, which is deposited in the fat depots of the body to await metabolism when harder times come.

Glycogen can also be formed in the liver by glyconeogenesis, and many different substances are known to be able to contribute to this process. A usual technique for detecting the formation of carbohydrate from non-carbohydrate sources consists in administering the suspected substances to a diabetic or to a phlorrhizinized animal (see p. 224). Alternatively the substances can be administered to starving animals to see whether or not they give rise to the deposition of glycogen in the liver. We have already seen that the deaminated residues of certain amino-acids can give rise to pyruvate (Chapter XI), and this the liver is able to phosphorylate, forming phospho-*enol*-pyruvate which is then convertible into glycogen by reversal of the normal reactions of glycolysis (Fig. 28). Any substance that lies on the glycolytic route from glycogen to pyruvic acid or which gives rise to any substance lying on this route, can be converted into glycogen, and we can account for most of the reactions involved in the conversions of such substances. Thus glycerol, a well-known glucose-former, can in all probability be phosphorylated through the agency of one or other of the tissue phosphokinases to yield glycerol-α-phosphate, which can then be oxidized to triosephosphate by the α-glycerophosphate dehydrogenases which are present in animal tissues generally. Triosephosphate lies directly on the route leading back to glycogen and we can therefore give a reasonable account of the processes which underlie the formation of glycogen from glycerol. Propionic acid, again, is capable of giving rise to glycogen, and does so by way of acrylic, lactic and pyruvic acids (p. 273). Propionic acid is of considerable importance, for it is one of the predominant short-chain fatty acids produced from cellulose when the latter is attacked by the symbiotic micro-organisms of the rumen-contents of the sheep. Similar processes probably go on in other herbivores, and it is likely that the bulk of the carbohydrate produced and laid down in such animals arises, not directly from the carbo-hydrates of the food, but by glyconeogenesis by way of propionic acid.

Glucose does not lie directly on the pathway of glycolysis and its free interconvertibility with glycogen has therefore to be specially considered. There is now abundant evidence that *glucose must be phosphorylated before it can be stored as glycogen or can enter into the glycolytic reaction sequence.* This indispensable preliminary phosphorylation is catalysed by hexokinase. Most animal tissues, including muscle, contain enzymes analogous to the hexokinase of yeast, which catalyses the phosphorylation of free glucose at the expense of ATP, yielding glucose-6-mono-phosphate and hence the 1-phosphate, from which glycogen is synthesized by the tissue phosphorylases. (Muscle *extracts* do not contain hexokinase and cannot, therefore, act upon free glucose. Presumably the enzyme is either destroyed, inactivated by dilution, or else is insoluble and remains on the tissue debris.)

Apart from the liver, which is the central storehouse for glycogen, the muscles contain considerable quantities of this polysaccharide. Other tissues contain only small quantities. These peripheral stores of glycogen are built up mainly and perhaps entirely at the expense of the liver glycogen, by way of the circulating glucose of the blood. The interconnexions are illustrated in Fig. 30. Liver glycogen undergoes phosphorolysis to yield α-glucose-1-phosphate and hence the 6-phosphate, which is readily dephosphorylated by liver phosphatase to give free glucose. It is generally believed that the blood glucose arises mainly in this way, since glucose-1-phosphate, which is a glyco-side and not an ester, is relatively slowly attacked by liver phosphatase. The free glucose passes into the blood stream. Other tissues such, for instance, as the muscles, take up this free glucose and phosphorylate it at the expense of ATP by means of their hexokinase. The product, glucose-6-phosphate, is transformed into glucose-1-phosphate by phosphoglucomutase in the usual way and hence, with the aid of the tissue phosphorylases and branching factors, into glycogen. The latter is then held in readiness for use when the need arises. Essentially similar reactions are involved in the synthesis and breakdown of starch in plant tissues.

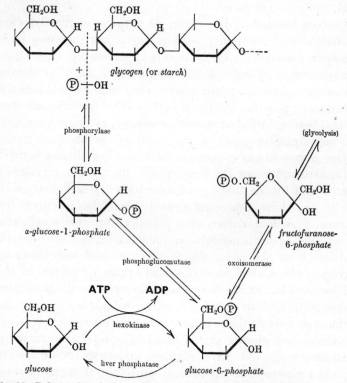

Fig. 30. Relationships between glycogenesis, glycogenolysis and glycolysis. Note the irreversibility of the reaction between glucose and ATP. Free glucose is regenerated from the 6-phosphate by liver phosphatase.

The concentration of free glucose in mammalian blood is very finely adjusted at a level of about 100 mg. per 100 ml., the precise concentration varying somewhat from species to species. Any rise in the blood-sugar level is compensated by the deposition of glycogen in the tissues, mainly in the liver, and any fall by the mobilization of more liver glycogen. Precisely how the blood concentration is controlled is still highly uncertain however, but it is perhaps significant that the liver phosphorylase, which is intimately involved in the process, is powerfully inhibited by free glucose.

The maintenance of the normal level of the blood sugar and the normal storage of glycogen in the liver are profoundly influenced by a number of hormones. Insulin, the internal secretion of the islets of Langerhans in the pancreas, encourages the deposition of glycogen in the liver at the expense of the blood sugar. The 'diabetogenic hormone' of the anterior pituitary body, on the other hand, encourages the mobilization of glycogen and tends therefore to raise the level of the blood sugar. Clinical diabetes, a condition which is characterized by intense hyperglycaemia and low glycogen storage on the part of the liver, can be due either to insufficiency of insulin secretion or to excessive production of the 'diabetogenic hormone'. It has been discovered that certain extracts of the anterior pituitary have a powerful inhibitory action upon hexokinase, an effect that is antagonized by insulin. This discovery goes a long way towards explaining the chemical features of some types of diabetes. If glucose is to be stored and metabolized in the normal manner it must first of all be phosphorylated. A relative preponderance of the hexokinase-inhibitory factor over insulin will lead to suppression of hexokinase activity and this, in turn, to subnormal storage and subnormal metabolism of glucose. The other characteristic features of diabetes (ketosis and ketonuria) are metabolic consequences of the suppression of carbohydrate metabolism (Chapter XVIII). Although the 'diabetogenic hormone' and the hexokinase-inhibitory factor are both present in some extracts of the anterior pituitary there is, as yet, no evidence that the two substances are identical.

Apparently the pituitary produces more than one 'diabetogenic hormone'. The growth hormone has pronounced diabetogenic and anti-insulin properties, while the adrenocorticotropic hormone (ACTH) leads to a transient glucosuria in normal rats and intensifies the glucosuria of diabetic animals. Repeated injections of either of these hormones reduce the tolerance towards carbohydrate and susceptibility to insulin, leading to total diabetes if administration is sufficiently prolonged, apparently by exhaustion of the pancreatic islet tissue. ACTH is believed to act by stimulating the secretion of cortical hormones, but certain of these promote the deposition of glycogen in liver slices while inhibiting it in diaphragm muscle. Clearly much remains to be done before the phenomena of the diabetic state can be fully explained in purely biochemical terms, but at least a promising start in this direction has been made.

Other hormones also, notably adrenaline, influence the level of the blood sugar, but their effects are usually short-lived and not to be compared with the long-term control exercised by insulin and the 'diabetogenic hormone'. It would profit us little at this stage to go further into the relationships that exist between liver glycogen, blood glucose, and the secretions of the various endocrine organs that have influence upon them, and for further discussion of these problems the reader is referred to the standard physiological text-books and to the monographs that have been devoted to them.

CHAPTER XVII

AEROBIC METABOLISM OF CARBOHYDRATES

INTRODUCTION

THE bulk of our knowledge of the mechanisms of muscle glycolysis was gained by studies of muscle extracts, which function anaerobically, or else of intact, isolated muscles kept under anaerobic conditions. Now a typical muscle *in situ* enjoys an excellent blood supply, and there is physiological evidence that this blood supply is actually increased when the muscle goes into activity. Analysis of the blood entering and leaving a perfused muscle shows that activity is attended by the utilization of large amounts of oxygen and the formation of correspondingly large quantities of carbon dioxide. Moreover, many muscles contain a special intracellular store of oxygen in the form of muscle oxyhaemoglobin (myoglobin), upon which they can draw for additional oxygen during the interval between the onset of activity and the physiological augmentation of the normal blood supply. For these reasons we must enquire whether we have perhaps been led astray by studying muscle metabolism only under anaerobic conditions, and whether anaerobic contraction has any real biological significance at all.

It is characteristic of the anaerobic metabolism of muscle that glycogen is broken down and lactic acid formed. Lactic acid arises by the reduction of pyruvic acid, and its formation provides a mechanism for the reoxidation of reduced Co I. Unless the reduced coenzyme were in some way reoxidized, no further production of phosphoglyceric acid could take place and the generation of new energy-rich bonds for the resynthesis of ATP would come to an end. Under aerobic conditions, however, the reduced coenzyme is rapidly reoxidized through the diaphorase/cytochrome/cytochrome oxidase reaction chain, and no lactic acid need be produced at all; instead, it might be anticipated, pyruvic acid would accumulate in the muscle. But there is no evidence that pyruvic acid does so accumulate in normal muscle, nor is there evidence that much pyruvic acid escapes from the muscle into the blood. We are left, therefore, with the conclusion that if pyruvic acid is formed under aerobic conditions, it must be oxidized, and that it is the source of much or all of the carbon dioxide produced by an active muscle. We know that the amount of energy that becomes accessible to an organ or cell that oxidizes its metabolites completely is greatly in excess of that obtained by partial, anaerobic breakdown and, since the muscle is evidently capable of using oxygen and is provided with elaborate devices for supplying it with oxygen, it becomes more than ever doubtful whether anaerobic contraction has any biological function, and whether lactic acid is ever formed *in vivo*.

Careful estimations show that small quantities of lactic acid are normally present in the blood even at rest, and that the amount is somewhat increased as a result of moderate exercise. After very violent exertion, however, there is a sharp rise in the blood lactic acid, but the level soon begins to fall again as the lactic acid is taken up by the liver and converted into glycogen. A typical curve is shown in Fig. 31, for moderate (*a*) and for strenuous work (*b*). If now we consider the conditions prevailing in an intact muscle *in vivo*, these phenomena can be accounted for. In mild or moderate exercise, oxygen is brought into the cells fast enough to reoxidize the reduced coenzyme as rapidly as it is formed, so that little or no lactic acid is produced, and pyruvic acid, instead of being reduced, is completely oxidized. If now the degree of exertion is increased, glycogen will be more rapidly broken down and Co I proportionately more rapidly reduced. Eventually, with increasing severity of exercise, a point will be reached at which the oxygen supplied by the circulatory apparatus can only just keep pace with the reduction of the coenzyme. But the muscle can work still harder by (*a*) utilizing oxygen as fast as it is made available by the circulatory system, *and* (*b*) reoxidizing any coenzyme that still remains in the reduced condition by using the anaerobic device of lactic acid formation. In the case of an antelope running for its life from a pursuing lion, the ability to use its muscles anaerobically, above and beyond the limits set by the efficiency of its circulatory apparatus, may allow of the extra turn of speed that saves the antelope's life: but the lion, unfortunately, can make use of the same trick!

As has been pointed out already, when lactic acid is formed a good deal of potentially available free energy remains in the lactic acid molecules, so that anaerobic metabolism is very unproductive from the point of view of the muscle. But this residual

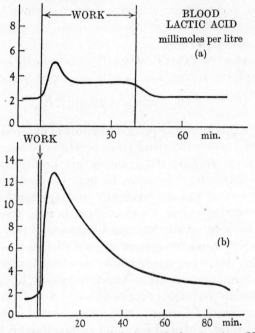

Fig. 31. Changes of blood lactic acid during and after exercise. (Modified after Lipmann, from data by Bang.) (a) moderate work, (b) strenuous work.

energy is not lost to the organism, for any lactic acid formed rapidly escapes from the muscles into the blood and is transported to that maid-of-all-work, the liver, which proceeds to transform it again into glycogen.

These considerations raise a host of new problems. We must enquire into the mechanisms whereby pyruvic acid is oxidized and into the origin of the respiratory carbon dioxide which is so characteristic an end-product of aerobic, as opposed to anaerobic, metabolism.

ORIGIN OF RESPIRATORY CARBON DIOXIDE

Carbon dioxide can be formed anaerobically as well as aerobically; indeed, it is one of the two chief products of alcoholic fermentation. It is formed in this case by the action of carboxylase and co-carboxylase upon pyruvic acid. Animal tissues, however, contain no carboxylase, although co-carboxylase is present among them, and we must therefore look for other possible sources of carbon dioxide.

Certain amino-acids are decarboxylated in animal tissues with formation of the corresponding amines, together with carbon dioxide:

$$R.CH(NH_2)\overset{.......}{COO}H = R.CH_2NH_2 + CO_2.$$

Reactions of this kind take place commonly in bacteria, but they are rare and probably small-scale processes among animals. Histidine and tyrosine, for example, are decarboxylated by specific decarboxylases in animals, but the products are immensely powerful pharmacologically and are formed only in traces, so that the yields of carbon dioxide from these sources are comparatively trivial. Not many enzymes of this kind have been detected: those at present known include the histidine and tyrosine decarboxylases already mentioned, together with specific glutamic and cysteic acid decarboxylases, but we cannot look to these for the origin of the large volumes of carbon dioxide produced by animal tissues.

One important potential source of carbon dioxide lies in the dicarboxylic acids, succinic, fumaric, malic and oxaloacetic. These compounds are mutually interconvertible through succinic and malic dehydrogenases together with fumarase, a group of enzymes which appear to be universally distributed:

$$
\begin{array}{cccc}
\text{COOH} & \text{COOH} & \text{COOH} & \text{COOH} \\
| & | & | & | \\
\text{CH}_2 \xrightleftharpoons{\pm 2\text{H}} & \text{CH} \xrightleftharpoons{\pm \text{H}_2\text{O}} & \text{CH}_2 \xrightleftharpoons{\pm 2\text{H}} & \text{CH}_2 \\
| & || & | & | \\
\text{CH}_2 & \text{CH} & \text{CHOH} & \text{CO} \\
| & | & | & | \\
\text{COOH} & \text{COOH} & \text{COOH} & \text{COOH} \\
\textit{succinic} & \textit{fumaric} & \textit{malic} & \textit{oxaloacetic} \\
\textit{acid} & \textit{acid} & \textit{acid} & \textit{acid}
\end{array}
$$

Malic acid undergoes a curious reaction under the influence of an enzyme which is particularly abundant in pigeon liver and requires Co II and Mn^{++} for activity. This *malic decarboxylase* catalyses a simultaneous oxidation and decarboxylation of its substrate, and the reaction is reversible:

$$
\begin{array}{cc}
\text{COO|H} & \\
| & \\
\text{CH}_2 & \text{CH}_3 \\
| & | \\
\text{CHOH} + \text{Co II} \rightleftharpoons & \text{CO} \quad + \text{CO}_2 + \text{Co II}.2\text{H} \\
| & | \\
\text{COOH} & \text{COOH}
\end{array}
$$

Oxaloacetic acid is an unstable substance which, even *in vitro*, undergoes slow spontaneous decarboxylation in the β-position to give pyruvic acid:

$$
\begin{array}{cc}
\text{COO|H} & \\
| & \\
\text{CH}_2 & \text{CH}_3 \\
| & | \\
\text{CO} \rightleftharpoons & \text{CO} \quad + \text{CO}_2 \\
| & | \\
\text{COOH} & \text{COOH}
\end{array}
$$

This reaction, which is reversible, is catalysed in liver, though not apparently in other tissues, by a specific enzyme known as *oxaloacetic decarboxylase* (or β-carboxylase).

Another important decarboxylating enzyme is *oxalosuccinic decarboxylase*, which is very widely distributed:

$$
\begin{array}{cc}
\text{COOH} & \text{COOH} \\
| & | \\
\text{CH}_2 & \text{CH}_2 \\
| & | \\
\text{CH|COO|H} \rightleftharpoons & \text{CH}_2 \quad + \text{CO}_2 \\
| & | \\
\text{CO} & \text{CO} \\
| & | \\
\text{COOH} & \text{COOH}
\end{array}
$$

The two last are interesting but atypical processes: the usual fate of α-keto-acids is that they undergo *oxidative decarboxylation* at the α-carbon atom according to the following overall equation:

$$
\text{R.CO|COO|H} + \tfrac{1}{2}\text{O}_2 = \text{R.COOH} + \text{CO}_2.
$$

This reaction appears to be irreversible in animal tissues and is strongly inhibited by arsenite. Two points may be emphasized in connexion with this, which is an important source of respiratory carbon dioxide. First, it is essentially an oxidative process and therefore differs sharply from the 'straight' decarboxylations catalysed by carboxylase and by the amino-acid decarboxylases. The second important feature is that this reaction, though general for α-keto-acids, does not extend to β-keto-acids.

OXIDATIVE METABOLISM OF PYRUVATE

Although oxidative decarboxylation differs in most respects from the 'straight' decarboxylation catalysed by carboxylase, it resembles it closely in one important particular, namely that it requires the participation of co-carboxylase. This substance is identical with the pyro-phosphate of vitamin B_1 and is usually referred to as diphosphothiamine or aneurin diphosphate. The relationship between the oxidation of pyruvic acid and diphosphothiamine was brought out very clearly indeed by the work of Peters on the brain tissue of B_1-deficient pigeons. Normal brain tissue metabolizes little but carbohydrate, which it oxidizes completely. Peters found, however, that the brain tissue of pigeons deprived of thiamine carries the breakdown of glucose as far as pyruvic acid, but can go no further. If a little thiamine is added it rapidly undergoes phosphorylation in the tissue, yielding co-carboxylase, and pyruvic acid begins to disappear. Under aerobic conditions it is largely oxidized but gives rise in part to acetic acid. Under anaerobic conditions one molecule of pyruvate can be oxidatively decarboxylated, yielding acetic acid and CO_2, while a second molecule is reduced to lactate:

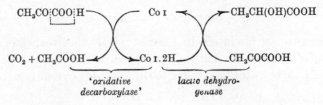

Several important deductions can be made from these observations. They show in the first place that diphosphothiamine is indispensable for oxidative decarboxylation, and it may be mentioned in passing that the presence of pyruvic acid in the blood and its excretion in the urine are regular features of advanced vitamin B_1 deficiency in animals. Peters's observation that the oxidative decarboxylation of pyruvate is associated with the formation of small amounts of lactate probably indicates that Co I must be involved, since the lactic dehydrogenase that catalyses the reduction requires the collaboration of Co I, and it is known that such a system can only couple with one requiring the same coenzyme (p. 210). Finally, since the reaction still takes place in an oxidative manner, even under anaerobic conditions, Peters's work serves to emphasize the essentially *oxidative* nature of this particular type of decarboxylation. Oxidative decarboxylation is not only important in the metabolism of pyruvate and carbohydrate but also in protein metabolism, since the oxidative deamination of amino-acids leads invariably to the formation of the corresponding α-keto acids.

THE MECHANISMS OF OXIDATIVE DECARBOXYLATION

The first detailed study of the oxidative decarboxylation of pyruvic acid we owe to Lipmann, who examined the process with the aid of enzymes prepared from a micro-organism, *B. delbrückii*. Lipmann observed that, in crude extracts of this organism, the oxidative decarboxylation of pyruvate was attended by the disappearance of inorganic phosphate from the mixture and by a simultaneous synthesis of ATP. Suspecting therefore that a phosphorylated intermediate of some kind must be involved he went further and was able to analyse the process into two distinct stages which may be represented as follows:

(i) $CH_3CO \cdot COO \cdot H + HO\textcircled{P} + \tfrac{1}{2}O_2 = CH_3COO \sim \textcircled{P} + CO_2 + H_2O,$

(ii) $CH_3COO \sim \textcircled{P} + ADP = CH_3COOH + ATP.$

The intermediate body, variously known as phosphoacetic acid or acetyl phosphate, can be isolated in the form of its silver salt. Further work with partially purified enzyme preparations showed that the process as a whole requires the presence of a considerable group of small-molecular materials including *diphosphothiamine, Co* I, *ADP, inorganic phosphate* and *magnesium ions*. The last of these requirements might perhaps have been predicted, since Mg^{++} is necessary whenever diphosphothiamine is required: indeed, magnesium-deficiency leads to symptoms similar to those of vitamin B_1 deficiency in experimental animals. We do not yet know the precise details of the intermediate reactions but, bearing in mind the close parallel between the conditions required for oxidative decarboxylation on the one hand and for the oxidation of 3-phosphoglyceraldehyde to 3-phosphoglyceric acid on the other (p. 196) the following reactions might be suggested:

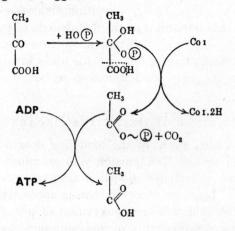

This scheme accounts for the observed disappearance of inorganic phosphate, for the intermediate formation of acetyl phosphate and for the synthesis of ATP. It accounts also for the fact that ADP and Co I are required, but gives no account of the participation of diphosphothiamine. Since the latter is also required in the 'straight' decarboxylation catalysed by carboxylase, it is perhaps reasonable to suppose that it is specifically concerned with the removal of carbon dioxide from some intermediate reaction complex.

The production of acetyl phosphate in bacteria seems to have no parallel in animal tissues although, as we have seen, acetate can be formed by the oxidative decarboxylation of pyruvate by enzymes of animal origin. Now acetate formed in this way is very reactive indeed in biological systems, so much so, indeed, that it is commonly referred to as '*active acetate*'. The chemical nature of 'active acetate' has been an outstanding biochemical problem for several years. It was thought at first that 'active acetate' might be identical with acetyl phosphate, especially since the latter contains an energy-rich phosphate bond and might therefore be expected to be highly reactive. It had, moreover, been isolated from *B. delbrückii* as an intermediate in the oxidative decarboxylation of pyruvate. But many experiments with synthetic acetyl phosphate have gone to show that this compound is relatively inert in biological systems and has few, if any, of the characteristic properties of 'active acetate' itself.

Recent work has thrown new light upon the identity of this elusive compound. 'Active acetate' generated from pyruvate can bring about the acetylation of a considerable number of substances in the presence of transacetylases extracted from liver: free acetate cannot. Now biological acetylation is by no means a rare phenomenon. Many substances such as sulphanilamide and aniline undergo acetylation when given by mouth and appear in acetylated form in the urine, e.g.:

$$CH_3CO.HN\!\!\diagdown\diagup\!\!SO_2NH_2 \qquad CH_3CO.HN\!\!\diagdown\diagup$$

N-*acetylsulphanilamide*   *acetyl aniline* (*acetanilide*)

Acetylation is also involved in the elaboration of the mercapturic acids (p. 287) and in the formation of acetylcholine from choline, and we may also refer to the acetylation of acetate itself to yield acetoacetate. The acetylation of sulphanilamide and choline takes place readily in tissue preparations, e.g. in tissue slices, but is dependent upon concomitant respiration, which provides the free energy necessary for these endergonic processes. Free energy can also be effectively provided by the addition of ATP, when acetylation proceeds anaerobically, but in neither case will acetyl phosphate replace free acetate plus ATP.

The study by Lipmann of biological acetylation in homogenates and cell-free tissue extracts has shown that, even in the presence of ATP and free acetate, a thermostable factor is required as coenzyme. This, the coenzyme of acetylation, or *coenzyme* A, seems always to be involved in biological acetylations, and is very generally present in cells and tissues. Its chemical structure is not yet fully known. It is, however, derived from the virtually omnipresent pantothenic acid, and the best preparations so far obtained also contain adenylic acid and either cysteine or its decarboxylated product, β-mercaptoethylamine. The —SH group plays a very important part in the activity of Co A, for the latter is inactivated by exposure to mild oxidizing conditions, reactivated by cysteine or by the reduced form of glutathione, and irreversibly inactivated by iodoacetate.

The recent work of Lynen on yeast has led to the isolation of an acetylated form of Co A. The acetyl group appears to be attached to the —SH group because, while acetyl-Co A is capable of acetylating sulphanilamide in liver extracts and is not affected by iodoacetate, the latter inactivates the free coenzyme completely. Tentatively, therefore, if we represent Co A itself by A—SH, this new acetyl compound may be formulated as A—S ~ OC.CH₃ for reasons that will shortly appear.

Now the acetylation of sulphanilamide by free acetate requires the presence of Co A and ATP, but *acetyl-Co A can replace all three*, suggesting that *acetyl-Co A is identical with 'active acetate' itself*. In addition, acetyl-Co A will react with oxaloacetate in the presence of a so-called 'condensing enzyme' to form citrate—another characteristic property of 'active acetate' itself. Here again, free acetate fails to react except in the presence of ATP and Co A. But in neither of these cases can acetyl phosphate replace acetate plus ATP plus Co A, nor can it replace acetyl-Co A. It seems probable, then, that acetyl-Co A can arise either from pyruvate through reactions which we still have to consider, or from free acetate through reactions involving both ATP and Co A but not acetyl phosphate, perhaps as follows:

(i) $A—SH + ATP \rightleftharpoons A—S \sim ℗ + ADP$,

(ii) $A—S \sim ℗ + HOOC.CH_3 \rightleftharpoons A—S \sim OC.CH_3 + HO.℗$.

Acetyl phosphate is not formed in animal tissues. These are probably preliminary steps in the *utilization of free acetate*: free acetate itself, when formed as product of metabolism, might arise by the decomposition of acetyl-Co A, either by reversal of reaction (ii) or, perhaps, by hydrolysis.

Since it is known that the evidently energy-rich acetyl-Co A can acetylate sulphanilamide or react with oxaloacetate without the participation of ATP, it is clear that this compound qualifies for identification with 'active acetate'. At the present time we know of no other 'active' form of acetate and, since Co A itself is very widely distributed indeed it seems very probable that 'active acetate' is always of this form. One important point should be noted before we proceed further. The acetyl radical of acetyl-Co A can react either through its carboxyl or through its methyl group, as is clear from the following equations:

Carboxyl:

$$CH_3CO \sim S—A + H_2N\langle\ \rangle SO_2NH_2 \longrightarrow CH_3CO . HN\langle\ \rangle SO_2NH_2 + HS—A$$

sulphanilamide

Methyl:

$$\begin{array}{l} COOH \\ | \\ CH \\ \| \\ C(OH)COOH \\ + \\ CH_3 \\ | \\ CO \sim S—A \end{array} + H_2O \longrightarrow \begin{array}{l} COOH \\ | \\ CH_2 \\ | \\ C(OH)COOH + HS—A \\ | \\ CH_2 \\ | \\ COOH \end{array}$$

citrate

Apparently, therefore, the oxidative decarboxylation of pyruvate in animal tissues gives rise to acetate by way of an 'active' acetate in the form of acetyl-Co A. There is circumstantial evidence in favour of this notion, for the oxidative metabolism of pyruvate is subnormal in the tissues of pantothenic acid deficient ducks. But there is now reason to think that acetyl-Co A is an intermediate in the oxidative decarboxylation of pyruvate by bacteria as well as by animal tissues. This information has come out of careful studies of the oxidative decarboxylation of pyruvate by cell-free extracts of *Escherichia coli*, another micro-organism which, like *B. delbrückii*, forms acetyl phosphate. These extracts will carry out the following coupled oxido-reduction:

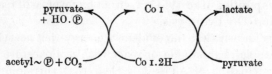

$$\text{pyruvate} + \text{HO.}\textcircled{P} \quad\longrightarrow\quad \text{Co I} \quad\longleftarrow\quad \text{lactate}$$

$$\text{acetyl}\sim\textcircled{P} + CO_2 \quad\longleftarrow\quad \text{Co I.2H} \quad\longrightarrow\quad \text{pyruvate}$$

The reductive reaction only requires the presence of lactic dehydrogenase and Co I for its accomplishment, but the oxidative process is much more complicated. It requires at least three enzymes, one of which is a transacetylase, together with Co A and magnesium ions, Co I and free phosphate: none of these can be omitted. The requirement for Co A suggests that acetyl-Co A must be involved in some way. Proof that 'active acetate' is formed as an intermediary comes from observations that (*a*) no acetyl phosphate is formed if inorganic phosphate is omitted from the reaction system, but that (*b*), if oxaloacetate and the 'condensing enzyme' are added instead, citrate is formed:

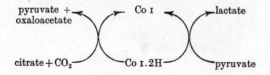

$$\text{pyruvate} + \text{oxaloacetate} \quad\longrightarrow\quad \text{Co I} \quad\longleftarrow\quad \text{lactate}$$

$$\text{citrate} + CO_2 \quad\longleftarrow\quad \text{Co I.2H} \quad\longrightarrow\quad \text{pyruvate}$$

The details of the partial reactions making up oxidative decarboxylation are not certainly known, but the following may be proposed as the first steps in the sequence:

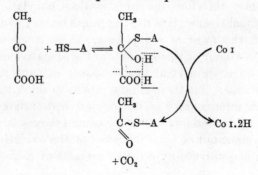

Very probably the formation of acetyl-Co A from pyruvate in animal tissues follows the same general plan.

If the oxidative reaction is to continue, however, it is necessary for free Co A to be regenerated. This happens if the newly formed acetyl-Co A enters into an acetylation reaction, or reacts with oxaloacetate to form citrate (p. 425), but it can also react, at any rate in bacteria, to give acetyl phosphate by *transacetylation*:

$$\text{(i)} \quad CH_3CO{\sim}S{-}A + HO.\textcircled{P} \rightleftharpoons CH_3COO{\sim}\textcircled{P} + HS{-}A.$$

In animals, apparently, acetyl phosphate is not produced and reaction (i) is replaced by other reactions:

$$\text{(ii)} \quad CH_3CO{\sim}S{-}A + HO.\textcircled{P} \rightleftharpoons CH_3COOH + \textcircled{P}{\sim}S{-}A,$$
$$\text{(iii)} \quad \textcircled{P}{\sim}S{-}A + ADP \rightleftharpoons HS{-}A + ATP.$$

In this way not only can the coenzyme be regenerated but the energy-rich bond could be conserved by the formation of a new molecule of ATP.

If we add the reactions suggested for the oxidative split of pyruvate to reaction (i) we get:

$$CH_3CO.COOH + HS.A + Co\ I \longrightarrow CH_3CO{\sim}S.A + CO_2 + Co\ I.2H,$$
$$\text{(i)} \qquad CH_3CO{\sim}S.A + HO.\textcircled{P} \longrightarrow CH_3COO{\sim}\textcircled{P} + HS.A$$

$$\overline{CH_3CO.COOH + Co\ I + HO.\textcircled{P} \longrightarrow CH_3COO{\sim}\textcircled{P} + CO_2 + Co\ I.2H}$$

which is precisely what we observe in extracts of *B. delbrückii* and *Esch. coli*. If instead we add the reactions of the oxidative split to (ii) and (iii) we obtain:

$$CH_3CO.COOH + HS.A + Co\ I \longrightarrow CH_3CO{\sim}S.A + CO_2 + Co\ I.2H$$
$$\text{(ii)} \qquad CH_3CO{\sim}S.A + HO.\textcircled{P} \longrightarrow CH_3COOH + \textcircled{P}{\sim}S.A$$
$$\text{(iii)} \qquad \textcircled{P}{\sim}S.A + ADP \longrightarrow HS.A + ATP$$

$$\overline{CH_3CO.COOH + Co\ I + HO.\textcircled{P} + ADP \longrightarrow CH_3COOH + CO_2 + Co\ I.2H + ATP}$$

and this is the overall reaction that we observe in animal tissues.

But in both cases an 'active acetate' in the form of acetyl-Co A is produced as an intermediary product and may enter into other processes, including biological acetylation and the synthesis of citrate. The latter, as we shall see later, is a reaction of fundamental importance in aerobic metabolism generally.

GENERAL METABOLISM OF PYRUVIC ACID

It will be clear from what has gone before that pyruvic acid occupies a central position in the metabolism of carbohydrates. It can be formed either from glucose (after phosphorylation) or

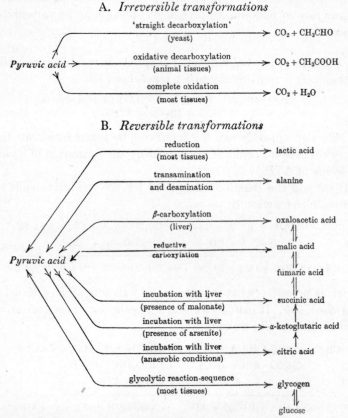

A. *Irreversible transformations*

Pyruvic acid →

'straight decarboxylation' (yeast) ——→ $CO_2 + CH_3CHO$

oxidative decarboxylation (animal tissues) ——→ $CO_2 + CH_3COOH$

complete oxidation (most tissues) ——→ $CO_2 + H_2O$

B. *Reversible transformations*

reduction (most tissues) ——→ lactic acid

transamination and deamination ——→ alanine

β-carboxylation (liver) ——→ oxaloacetic acid

reductive carboxylation ⇄ malic acid

fumaric acid

incubation with liver (presence of malonate) ——→ succinic acid

incubation with liver (presence of arsenite) ——→ α-ketoglutaric acid

incubation with liver (anaerobic conditions) ——→ citric acid

glycolytic reaction-sequence (most tissues) ——→ glycogen

glucose

Fig. 32. Formation and fate of pyruvic acid. Note that the synthesis and breakdown, e.g. of succinic acid, do not necessarily follow the same route.

from glycogen (after phosphorolysis) by the normal reactions of glycolysis. By reversal of these processes it can contribute to the synthetic formation of carbohydrate. It constitutes, moreover, a link between the metabolism of carbohydrates and that of proteins, for it arises more or less directly from the products of deamination of a number of amino-acids. These are only a few of the processes into which pyruvic acid enters, and a summary of some of the more important of its known origins and fates is presented in Fig. 32.

Under anaerobic conditions pyruvic acid can be broken down by 'straight' decarboxylation, as it is in yeast, or it may undergo reduction to lactic acid, as it does in muscle. If aerobic conditions prevail it can be completely oxidized, as in muscle, kidney, brain and other tissues, or it may be oxidatively decarboxylated to yield 'active acetate' and hence free acetate. Since acetate is a potential source of fat, pyruvic acid may be regarded as a link between the metabolism of carbohydrates and that of fat, as well as that of proteins.

We can already give a tolerably satisfactory account of some of the processes listed in Fig. 32. But pyruvic acid can give rise, when incubated with liver tissue under suitable conditions, to citric, α-ketoglutaric, succinic, fumaric and oxaloacetic acids among other compounds, and there is evidence that carbon dioxide is 'fixed' when these synthetic reactions take place. Radioactive samples of citrate and α-ketoglutarate, for example, have been obtained by the incubation of liver tissue with pyruvate in the presence of radioactive carbon dioxide. This is due in the first instance to the β-carboxylation of pyruvic acid, a reaction which is catalysed by the oxaloacetic decarboxylase of liver:

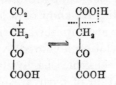

The responsible enzyme was first detected in bacteria, from which it has since been isolated, and there is now good evidence for its occurrence in mammalian liver. It appears, however, to be absent from tissues other than the liver.

Oxaloacetic acid itself is a very reactive compound under biological conditions, and attempts to demonstrate the production of its isotopic form in liver provided with pyruvate and isotopic carbon dioxide have not so far proved fruitful. Other substances to which oxaloacetic acid itself gives rise (α-keto-glutarate, citrate) have, however, been isolated and shown to contain the isotopic carbon.

AEROBIC METABOLISM OF CARBOHYDRATES

We know of no oxidizing enzyme or enzymes capable of cata-lysing directly the complete oxidation of glucose or glycogen on the large scale. The liver contains a glucose dehydrogenase (p. 194) which catalyses the oxidation of glucose to the corresponding gluconic acid, while there occurs in the red blood cells and else-where a hexosemonophosphate dehydrogenase (p. 197) which catalyses the oxidation of glucose-6-monophosphate to 6-phos-phogluconic acid. We know of the existence of further enzymes that can remove one carbon atom from 6-phosphogluconic acid to give ribose-5-phosphate (p. 353), a very unstable product.

Other oxidised sugar derivatives, e.g. the uronic acids, also occur biologically. In particular, glucuronic acid is used by mammals in the detoxication of phenolic and other substances, but there is no evidence that it arises from glucose: indeed, such evidence as we have suggests that it does not.

There is, then, little reason to believe that the 6-carbon units of glucose undergo direct oxidation in the body, and it must therefore be supposed that they are broken into smaller frag-ments prior to oxidation. We know of at least one way in which such a splitting can be accomplished on the large scale, viz. by preliminary phosphorylation, followed by the action of aldolase and other soluble tissue enzymes, i.e. by glycolysis. This leads, in the end, to the formation of pyruvate, which is known to be completely oxidizable by most tissues when conditions are fully aerobic. We may therefore visualize the complete oxidation of glucose and glycogen as proceeding by way of the usual glycolytic reactions, yielding pyruvic acid in the first instance, followed by the total oxidation of pyruvic acid in the presence of the insoluble tissue enzymes.

The muscles are the biggest consumers of carbohydrate and it is natural therefore that most of the early work on the aerobic metabolism of carbohydrates should have been done with muscle tissue. Muscle extracts cannot be used for this purpose because, as will be remembered, they contain only the soluble enzymes of the tissues and do not respire. This fortunate circumstance made it possible to obtain a clear picture of anaerobic glycolysis before the more complex operations of aerobic glycolysis plus oxidation were investigated.

The foundations of our present knowledge of aerobic metabolism were laid by Szent-Györgyi, using suspensions of minced pigeon-breast muscle as his material. This is a very active muscle and one which contains a good deal of muscle haemoglobin so that, in the minced form, it can keep itself well supplied with oxygen. Indeed, Szent-Györgyi found, minced pigeon-breast muscle respires very actively and produces little or no lactic acid. He studied the rate of respiration of his preparations under a variety of experimental conditions and made the following fundamental observations: (a) The rate of respiration is very high at first but falls off slowly with time. (b) The fall in the rate of respiration is paralleled by the rate at which succinate disappears from the mince, and (c) the respiratory rate of a failing preparation can be restored to its original high level by the addition of catalytic amounts of succinate or fumarate. (d) For each volume of oxygen consumed by the tissue an equal volume of carbon dioxide is formed, indicating that the material undergoing oxidation is a carbohydrate of some kind:

$$(CH_2O)_n + nO_2 = nCO_2 + nH_2O.$$

(The ratio carbon dioxide produced/oxygen consumed is called the respiratory quotient and, in theory, is characteristic of the kind of fuel being oxidized: for carbohydrate oxidation R.Q. = 1, while for fat and protein the values are about 0·7 and 0·8 respectively.)

From these observations Szent-Györgyi concluded that the oxidation of carbohydrate is in some way catalysed by succinate and fumarate and, since it was already well known that these two acids are interconvertible through the activity of succinic dehydrogenase, he concluded that this enzyme must be intimately concerned in the oxidation of carbohydrate materials. This led to another important discovery. It had already been established that malonate is a powerful, competitive inhibitor of succinic dehydrogenase, and Szent-Györgyi was able to show that malonate prevents the catalytic effect of succinate and fumarate in failing preparations and, moreover, has a powerfully depressant action upon the respiration of the fresh mince.

To account for these observations, Szent-Györgyi brought forward the suggestion that succinate and fumarate act together as a carrier system for hydrogen removed from carbohydrate materials of some kind. If we represent these unknown substances by AH_2, his hypothesis can be schematically represented as follows:

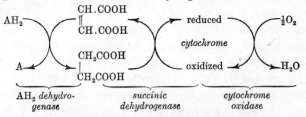

In this system, succinic dehydrogenase would have to work 'backwards' instead of 'forwards' but, as was already known, dehydrogenases in general are capable of acting reversibly, and in this, as well as in its general aspects, the scheme was consistent with the contemporary knowledge of biological oxidations. Moreover, in this system, everything depends upon succinic dehydrogenase, so that the dire effects of malonate on respiring muscle tissue are readily explained. In the absence of any positive clue to the identity of 'AH_2', Szent-Györgyi suggested that this might be triosephosphate or, perhaps, pyruvate.

These results stimulated other investigators to study other materials and it soon became clear that Szent-Györgi's malonate-sensitive system must be as widely distributed in living tissues as are cytochrome and cytochrome oxidase, for cells and tissues of many kinds were found to behave in the same manner towards succinate, fumarate and the inhibitory substance malonate. Presently it was discovered by Szent-Györgyi himself that two other C_4-dicarboxylic acids act in the same way as succinate and fumarate, viz. malate and oxaloacetate, and he sought to explain these observations by the interpolation of another cyclical carrier stage in his original reaction sequence:

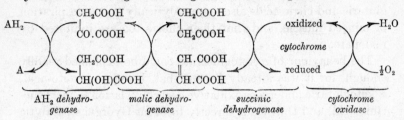

$$AH_2 \quad CH_2COOH \mid CO.COOH \qquad CH_2COOH \mid CH_2COOH \qquad oxidized \qquad H_2O$$

cytochrome

$$A \quad CH_2COOH \mid CH(OH)COOH \qquad CH.COOH \parallel CH.COOH \qquad reduced \qquad \tfrac{1}{2}O_2$$

| AH_2 dehydrogenase | malic dehydrogenase | succinic dehydrogenase | cytochrome oxidase |

In this way the catalytic action of malate and oxaloacetate could readily be explained, together with the fact that their action, like that of succinate and fumarate, is abolished by malonate.

This revised scheme was less fortunate than its predecessor for, when the system was reconstructed from purified components by Green and his collaborators, it was found that the succinic system, which requires no coenzyme, fails to couple with the malic system, which requires Co I for activity. Szent-Györgyi was therefore thrown back upon his original hypothesis, the effects of malate and oxaloacetate being explained by the fact that malate and fumarate are interconvertible through the action of fumarase. Oxaloacetate and malate are themselves interconvertible through malic dehydrogenase and could thus 'feed' the catalytic cycle with fumarate:

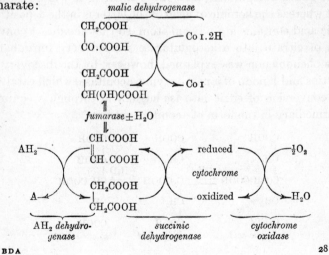

malic dehydrogenase

$$CH_2COOH \mid CO.COOH \qquad Co\ I.2H$$

$$CH_2COOH \mid CH(OH)COOH \qquad Co\ I$$

$$\Updownarrow$$
fumarase $\pm H_2O$

$$CH.COOH \parallel CH.COOH$$

$$AH_2 \qquad reduced \qquad \tfrac{1}{2}O_2$$

cytochrome

$$A \qquad CH_2COOH \mid CH_2COOH \qquad oxidized \qquad H_2O$$

| AH_2 dehydrogenase | succinic dehydrogenase | cytochrome oxidase |

Shortly afterwards Krebs announced the discovery that, in addition to succinate, fumarate, malate and oxaloacetate, α-keto-glutaric and citric acids also act catalytically on the respiration of minced muscle, and that their effects too are inhibited by malonate.

The behaviour of α-ketoglutarate could be explained readily enough, for it was already known that, being an α-keto-acid, α-ketoglutaric undergoes oxidative decarboxylation to yield succinic acid, and thus leads directly to Szent-Györgyi's catalytic cycle:

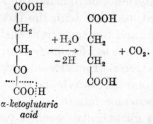

α-ketoglutaric acid

The behaviour of citric acid too was explicable in terms of the widely distributed citric dehydrogenase, for this enzyme was believed to convert citric into α-ketoglutaric acid, from which succinic acid can then be formed. If, however, the formulae of citric and α-ketoglutaric acids are compared, it will be noticed that whereas the ketonic oxygen of the latter is in the α-position, citric acid contains a β-oxygen atom, so that the direct conversion of citrate into α-ketoglutarate seemed very improbable. This phenomenon was explained, however, by the discovery by Martius and Knoop of a new enzyme, aconitase, which catalyses the conversion of citric into iso-citric acid through a common intermediary in the form of aconitic acid:

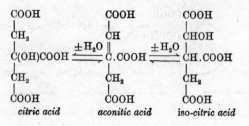

citric acid   aconitic acid   iso-citric acid

Reinvestigation of the old citric dehydrogenase now showed that it is specific for *iso*-citric acid, and has no action upon citric acid itself except in the presence of aconitase, with which the early preparations were invariably contaminated.

iso-Citric dehydrogenase, which collaborates with Co II, catalyses the dehydrogenation of *iso*-citric acid to yield oxalosuccinic (α-keto-β-carboxyglutaric) acid. This compound then, under the influence of a specific oxalosuccinic decarboxylase, loses carbon dioxide and gives rise to α-ketoglutaric acid. *iso*-Citric dehydrogenase and oxaloacetic decarboxylase are closely associated and have not so far been separated, but the reactions they catalyse can be studied separately because the decarboxylase but not the dehydrogenase requires the presence of manganese ions for its activity:

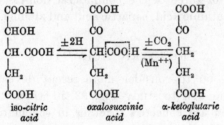

The product can then be oxidatively decarboxylated to yield succinic acid, and thus leads to one of the primary catalysts of the Szent-Györgyi system.

It became possible, therefore, to trace out metabolic connexions between all the substances known to act catalytically on the oxidation of carbohydrates by minced pigeon-breast muscle and by many other kinds of cells and tissues. Their action could be explained by their convertibility into succinate and fumarate, the two primary catalysts which, according to Szent-Györgyi, function as a hydrogen-carrying system. The effect of malonate was explained because malonate specifically inhibits the succinic dehydrogenase, upon which the carrier activity of the succinate-fumarate system depends. Thus all the phenomena observed in Szent-Györgyi's original experiments, together with a number of later observations, could be accounted for, apart only from the slow decline that takes place in the respiration of minced pigeon-breast muscle. Even this last phenomenon can be accounted for, however, by the slow, spontaneous β-decarboxylation of oxaloacetate which takes place under physiological conditions, yielding pyruvate, which does not act catalytically. Oxalo-acetate and the other catalytic substances therefore drain slowly away and, as their concentrations decline, the rate of respiration of the preparation falls off.

In passing it should be noticed that the reaction chain leading from α-ketoglutaric, through succinic, fumaric, malic and oxalo-acetic acids to pyruvic acid is an important link between carbo-hydrate metabolism and that of proteins, for α-ketoglutaric, oxaloacetic and pyruvic acids respectively are formed by the deamination of three of the commonest non-essential amino-acids, viz. glutamic acid, aspartic acid and alanine.

The Citric Acid Cycle

Before going on to consider more recent developments the reader will do well to study Fig. 33, in which the reactions just discussed are collected together in schematic form and the compounds shown in relation to some other metabolic products.

The whole picture took on an entirely new aspect with the suggestion by Krebs that pyruvic and oxaloacetic acids might react together to form a 7-carbon compound, from which citrate (6C), α-ketoglutarate (5C), and the 4-C dicarboxylic acids were then re-formed. What had formerly been considered simply as a chain or series of reactions was now visualized as a cycle. In its simplest form this hypothetical scheme can be written as in Fig. 34. Pyruvic acid, with its three carbon atoms, enters this cycle by reacting with oxaloacetic acid. With each turn of the wheel one pyruvate molecule enters, three molecules of carbon dioxide are produced, and oxaloacetate is regenerated to take up a further molecule of pyruvate. Since a single molecule of oxaloacetate can be used over and over again in the oxidation of a (theoretically) unlimited number of molecules of pyruvate, it follows that oxaloacetate, or any substance lying on the cycle, can act catalytically in the oxidation of pyruvate to carbon dioxide. The mechanisms postulated involve succinate, fumarate, malate, oxaloacetate, α-ketoglutarate and citrate, all of which

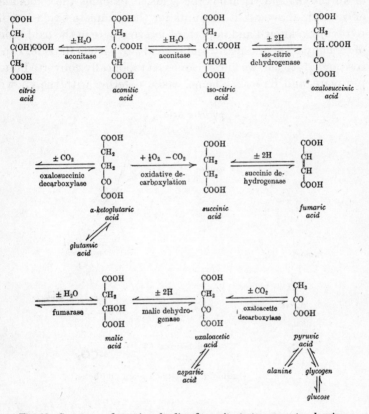

Fig. 33. Summary of reactions leading from citrate to pyruvate, showing some metabolic interrelationships.

are known to act catalytically on the oxidative breakdown of carbohydrate. Succinic dehydrogenase is directly involved in the cycle in the oxidation of succinate to fumarate, so that the effect of malonate on the oxidation of carbohydrate is readily explained, while the slow failure of respiration in minced muscle preparations can again be explained in terms of a slow, spontaneous breakdown of oxaloacetate to pyruvate.

Krebs's hypothesis therefore goes much further than that of Szent-Györgyi. It accounts at once for the catalytic activity of all the di- and tricarboxylic acids, it explains the malonate effect and, above all, it accounts for the complete oxidation of pyruvate, a known and important intermediate in the oxidation of carbohydrate and many amino-acids, to carbon dioxide. Glucose and glycogen, we know, can be metabolically converted into pyruvate, and Krebs's scheme, taken together with the known

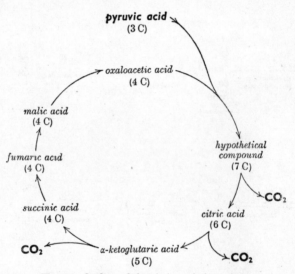

Fig. 34. Outline of the citric cycle hypothesis.

reactions of glycolysis, can account therefore for the complete oxidation of glucose and glycogen. Szent-Györgyi's scheme, by contrast, could only account for the dehydrogenation of the unidentified carbohydrate intermediate which we have described here as 'AH$_2$'.

Krebs himself supplied the first evidence in favour of his 'citric acid cycle'. Pyruvate and oxaloacetate were incubated together with minced muscle under strictly anaerobic conditions.

By working anaerobically it was expected that, as the cycle is essentially an aerobic system, some product might accumulate instead of being oxidized if, in fact, pyruvate and oxaloacetate do react together. After incubation, Krebs was able to demonstrate the formation of substantial amounts of citric acid. Other workers have since repeated and confirmed Krebs's observations on a variety of tissues, and there cannot be much doubt that some reaction between pyruvate and oxaloacetate does indeed take place.

Other significant experiments have been carried out on liver tissue. If pyruvate is incubated with liver tissue it is possible to demonstrate the formation of considerable yields of succinic acid, together with smaller quantities of α-ketoglutaric acid. This had been known to take place some years earlier, and the synthesis had formerly been explained on the supposition that two molecules of pyruvate react together to give a di-α-keto-acid. This, after oxidative decarboxylation at one end of the chain, would yield α-ketoglutaric acid and, after a second oxidative decarboxylation, succinic acid would be formed:

$$
\begin{array}{ccccccc}
\text{COOH} & & \text{COO}\vdots\text{H} & +\,CO_2 & & & \\
| & & \overset{\cdots|\cdots}{|} & & & & \\
\text{CO} & & \text{CO} & & \text{COOH} & & \text{COOH} \\
| & & | & & | & & | \\
\text{CH}_3 & \xrightarrow{\ -2H\ } & \text{CH}_2 & \rightarrow & \text{CH}_2 & \rightarrow & \text{CH}_2 \\
+ & & | & & | & & | \\
\text{CH}_3 & & \text{CH}_2 & & \text{CH}_2 & & \text{CH}_2 \\
| & & | & & | & & | \\
\text{CO} & & \text{CO} & & \text{CO} & & \text{COOH} \\
| & & | & & \overset{\cdots|\cdots}{} & & \\
\text{COOH} & & \text{COOH} & & \text{COO}\vdots\text{H} & +\,CO_2 &
\end{array}
$$

No experimental evidence has ever been found for the initial oxidative reaction, however, though the remaining stages are likely enough. The discovery of the oxaloacetic decarboxylase of liver suggested another possible route for the synthesis of succinate from pyruvate, since the latter, by β-carboxylation, yields oxaloacetic acid, from which succinic acid can be formed by the reversed actions of malic and succinic dehydrogenases, together with that of fumarase. In this case, however, the formation of α-ketoglutaric acid is left unexplained. Krebs pointed out that if this latter route were followed it should, since it involves succinic dehydrogenase, be inhibited by malonate. He therefore incubated pyruvate with liver tissue in the presence of malonate and found that even larger yields of succinate were obtained. Hence the synthesis must proceed by some route that does not involve succinic dehydrogenase. This, of course, is entirely in keeping with Krebs's cyclical hypothesis, and the evidence was further strengthened by the later demonstration that, in addition to succinate, substantial amounts of α-ketoglutarate and traces of citrate are formed at the same time.

Much illuminating evidence regarding the Krebs cycle was later obtained by employing radioactive carbon as a 'tracer'. If pyruvate is incubated with liver in the presence of radioactive carbon dioxide, radioactive intermediates including citrate and α-ketoglutarate can subsequently be isolated. This and other similar evidence again argues in favour of the cycle, and more precise information has been obtained by finding out precisely where, in the α-ketoglutarate molecule, the radioactive carbon was located.

There is now good evidence in favour of every step in the cycle, with an exception in the case of the supposed 7-C intermediate. Critical experiments designed to detect the formation of such a compound have failed and, indeed, there has never at any time been evidence that such a substance is formed. If a 7-carbon compound is produced it must lose one carbon atom, most probably by oxidative decarboxylation, to yield citric acid:

$$
\begin{array}{ccc}
\text{COOH} & \text{COOH} & \text{COOH} \\
| & | & | \\
\text{CH} & \text{CH}_2 & \text{CH}_2 \\
\| & | & | \\
\text{C(OH)COOH} & \text{C(OH)COOH} & \text{C(OH)COOH} \\
+ & \longrightarrow \quad\quad\quad & \rightarrow \\
\text{CH}_3 & \text{CH}_2 & \text{CH}_2 \\
| & | & | \\
\text{CO} & \text{CO} & \text{COOH} \\
| & | & \\
\text{COOH} & \text{COOH} & +\text{CO}_2 \\
\end{array}
$$

Now arsenite is known to be a powerful inhibitor of oxidative decarboxylation and it would therefore be anticipated that the formation of oxalocitraconic acid, the most probable 7-carbon intermediary, would readily be demonstrated by working in the presence of arsenite. Actually, however, experiments carried out in the presence of arsenite have led invariably to the isolation of the 5-carbon compound, α-ketoglutarate, together with traces of citrate, but with no trace of any 7-carbon substance. Moreover, oxalocitraconic acid itself is not metabolized. It seems very unlikely therefore that such a compound is formed.

Probably, therefore, citric acid must arise directly, presumably by a reaction between oxaloacetate and some 2-carbon substance, rather than the 3-carbon compound pyruvic acid. It is known that pyruvate readily undergoes oxidative decarboxylation to yield 'active acetate'. It has also been found that the aerobic oxidation of acetate itself is inhibited by malonate, a feature which indicates that acetate is probably oxidized by way of the catalytic cycle. Moreover, isotopically labelled acetate can be incorporated into the cycle and yields correspondingly labelled products. Present opinion therefore inclines towards the view that pyruvate first undergoes oxidative decarboxylation to yield 'active acetate', the latter then reacting with oxaloacetate to yield citric acid directly. The pyruvate may in fact be said to undergo its oxidative decarboxylation before, rather than after, it combines with oxaloacetate.

We have already considered some of the evidence for the occurrence of the reactions leading from citric acid to oxaloacetate (summarized on p. 437) and the enzymes concerned have been dealt with in some detail in Part I of this book. Special consideration must now be given to the synthetic reaction which leads to the formation of citrate. The formation of citrate from acetate and oxaloacetate has been demonstrated many times in tissue minces and homogenates, but only very recently has such a synthesis been demonstrated by means of a purified enzyme. Until this was achieved it was open to question whether citrate itself is the first product to be formed. Citrate could arise by an addition reaction between acetate and oxaloacetate; condensation, on the other hand, would yield aconitate, from which citrate could arise indirectly through the action of aconitase:

Addition:

$$
\begin{array}{c}
COOH \\
| \\
CH \\
\| \\
CH(OH)COOH \quad \text{Co A} \\
+ \quad \xrightarrow{\quad ATP \quad} \\
CH_3 \\
| \\
COOH
\end{array}
\qquad
\begin{array}{c}
COOH \\
| \\
CH_2 \\
| \\
C(OH)COOH \\
| \\
CH_2 \\
| \\
COOH
\end{array}
$$

Condensation:

$$
\begin{array}{c}
COOH \\
| \\
CH \\
\| \\
CH(OH)COOH \quad \text{Co A} \\
+ \quad \xrightarrow{\quad ATP \quad} \\
CH_3 \\
| \\
COOH
\end{array}
\qquad
\begin{array}{c}
COOH \\
| \\
CH \\
\| \\
C.COOH + H_2O \\
| \\
CH_2 \\
| \\
COOH
\end{array}
$$

Ochoa was able to prepare from pigeon liver an enzyme, the so-called 'condensing enzyme', which was virtually free from aconitase and which, under suitable conditions, formed citrate in large yield from added acetate and oxaloacetate, thus demonstrating for the first time that *citrate arises directly* and not by way of aconitate. The precise mechanism of the reaction was still at the time unknown, but the achievement of the synthesis of citrate from acetate and oxaloacetate set the final seal of acceptance upon the citric acid cycle itself.

To achieve this synthesis, ATP and Co A must be present. That ATP is involved reawakened the long-standing suspicion that 'active acetate' is none other than acetyl phosphate. Acetyl phosphate itself cannot however replace free acetate plus ATP, but clearly enough some form of 'active acetate' was generated under the conditions of Ochoa's experiments. The subsequent discovery of acetyl-Co A finally resolved the problem, for Ochoa has found that this product can react with oxaloacetate in the presence of the 'condensing enzyme' to give almost quantitative yields of citrate, this time without the participation of ATP. Since Co A is now known to be an indispensable factor in most of the biological processes in which 'active acetate' is involved, it seems very probable indeed that it can act as an acceptor, carrier and donator of 'active' acetate radicals in much the same way as ATP behaves with respect to 'high-energy' or 'active' phosphate radicals. It seems, in fact, that the nature and identity of 'active acetate' have at last found their solution, and that 'active acetate', in the form of acetyl-Co A, arises from free acetate through the following reactions, with ATP as the eventual energy-source for its synthesis:

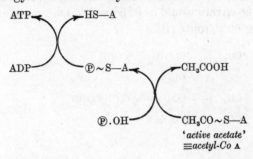

In the meantime the next reaction in the cycle had been studied extensively. *Citrate is a symmetrical substance* and as such would be expected to undergo dehydration equally at either of two points, one in that portion of the molecule which arises from oxaloacetate and the second in that part which arises from acetate:

Oxalo-acetate:	COOH | CH || CH(OH)COOH	COOH | CH_2 | CH(OH)COOH	COOH | CH || C.COOH	COOH | CH_2 | C.COOH
	+	$\longrightarrow$	$-H_2O \longrightarrow$	*and*
Acetate:	CH_3 | COOH	CH_2 | COOH	CH_2 | COOH 50 %	CH | COOH 50 %

However, as Ogston was the first to point out, it does not follow that because citrate is a symmetrical substance it will necessarily *behave* in a symmetrical manner when combined with its enzyme, if only because the enzyme-substrate complex is exceedingly unlikely to be symmetrical. Indeed, there is now evidence which proves conclusively that citrate does not, in fact, behave as a symmetrical compound.

If radioactive carbon dioxide and pyruvate are incubated together with liver tissue, terminally labelled citric acid is formed and has been isolated. If it behaved symmetrically, this citrate would be expected to go on round the cycle to give an α-keto-glutarate carrying radioactive carbon in both its carboxyl radicals. This is shown by the following equations, in which 50 % of the citrate would be expected to follow route (A) and the remaining 50 % route (B):

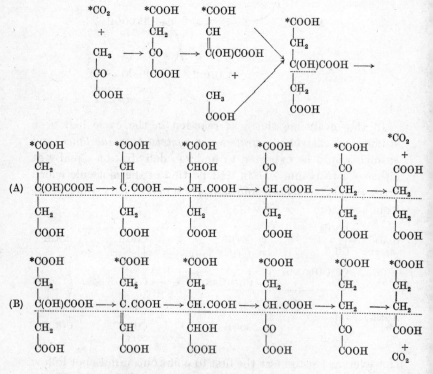

α-Ketoglutarate was accordingly isolated from liver tissue previously incubated with pyruvate and radioactive carbon dioxide in the presence of arsenite, and examined. By decarboxylating the product with permanganate it was shown that all the radioactive carbon was present in the α-carboxyl group, for the carbon dioxide released was radioactive while the residual succinic acid was not. As an additional check, succinic acid also was isolated from the liver preparations and found not to contain radioactive carbon. These results show that *citrate does not react symmetrically* and that only route (A) is followed. This means that the dehydration of citrate by aconitase takes place in that part of the molecule that arises from oxaloacetate; or, to be more precise, between the α and β atoms of the original oxaloacetate.

The same conclusion also follows from experiments in which citrate was formed from oxaloacetate and carboxyl-labelled acetate. In this case the succinate is radioactive and the carbon dioxide inert; again only route (A) is followed:

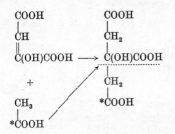

We have travelled some way since the first hypothetical scheme was suggested by Szent-Györgyi, and there is little doubt that many details remain even yet to be established. For the moment, however, it will be convenient to recapitulate and summarize the reactions of the 'tricarboxylic acid cycle' as they are now believed to take place. A schematic summary is presented in Fig. 35 and the individual stages will now be briefly reviewed.

(1) Pyruvic acid undergoes oxidative decarboxylation, yielding 'active acetate' which (2) reacts with the *enol*-form of oxalo-acetic acid. The product of this reaction is citric acid which (3) loses water in the manner we have described to yield aconitic

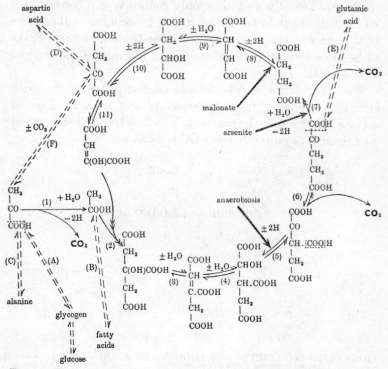

Fig. 35. The citric acid cycle, showing some important side-reactions and the effects of some inhibitors. For list of enzymes involved see Table 36.

Note that acetate reacts as acetyl-coenzyme A.

acid, which (4) takes up water and yields *iso*-citric acid under the influence of aconitase. (5) *iso*-Citric acid is now dehydrogenated by its dehydrogenase, giving rise to oxalosuccinic acid which, in turn, (6) is decarboxylated by oxalosuccinic decarboxylase and yields α-ketoglutaric acid. Oxidative decarboxylation of the latter (7) gives rise to succinic acid. This is dehydrogenated (8) to give fumaric acid, which, under the influence of fumarase, is hydrated (9) to yield malic acid. A further dehydrogenation (10) converts this into oxaloacetic acid which (11) enolizes and re-enters the cycle.

TABLE 36. ENZYMES INVOLVED IN THE CITRIC ACID CYCLE (*see* Fig. 35)

Reaction no.	Enzymes and coenzymes
1	Oxidative decarboxylation system*
2	'Condensing enzyme'; Co A, ATP
3	Aconitase
4	Aconitase
5	*iso*-Citric dehydrogenase; Co II
6	Oxalosuccinic decarboxylase; Mn^{++}
7	Oxidative decarboxylation system*
8	Succinic dehydrogenase
9	Fumarase
10	Malic dehydrogenase; Co I
11	Spontaneous isomerization
A	Glycolytic systems†
B	Unnamed fat-synthesizing enzyme systems
C	Transaminase‡
D	Transaminase‡
E	L-Glutamic dehydrogenase + Co I
F	Oxaloacetic decarboxylase

* See p. 427.   † See pp. 406, 409.   ‡ See p. 136 et seq.

Pairs of hydrogen atoms are transferred to the appropriate hydrogen acceptors in reactions (1), (5), (7), (8) and (10), and pass on through the cytochrome system. In all, therefore, five pairs of H atoms are removed with each turn of the wheel, and three molecules of carbon dioxide are removed at the same time, one molecule of pyruvic acid being used up. These quantities fit the theoretical equation for the complete oxidation of pyruvic acid:

$$C_3H_4O_3 + 5O = 3CO_2 + 2H_2O.$$

The five atoms of oxygen figured in this equation correspond to the five pairs of hydrogen atoms which, transferred through the cytochrome system, require five atoms of oxygen for their eventual conversion to water, three molecules of which are consumed in the cycle.

Although it is certain that most of the reactions are reversible it is probable that the cycle is unidirectional in actual operation, since the reactions involving oxidative decarboxylation (1, 7) are in all probability irreversible. This scheme, every step of which is now well established, provides us with an explanation for the complete oxidation of pyruvate itself, of acetate, and of any substance that gives rise to pyruvate or to acetate. As we have already pointed out, acetate only reacts in the form of 'active acetate', but this can be generated from free acetate if ATP and Co A are present, as they may be presumed to be in the tissues. The cycle accounts also for the complete oxidation of any substance lying on the cycle and for the complete oxidation of any substance that gives rise to a compound lying on the cycle. If, for example, a large amount of succinate is added, only a catalytic amount remains in the cycle itself; the remainder passes round the usual reactions until it is converted into oxalo-acetate, which breaks down to yield carbon dioxide and pyruvate by β-decarboxylation. The pyruvate is then oxidatively decarb-oxylated and oxidized through the cycle. It follows that we have, in this catalytic system, a machine that can accomplish or complete the metabolic oxidation of a great diversity of important primary foodstuffs and the intermediary products of their metabolism.

Citric acid itself tends to accumulate if the later reactions of the sequence are inhibited, e.g. by anaerobiosis, by arsenite or by malonate. It also accumulates in large quantities in the presence of fluoroacetate. The latter has no action upon the 'condensing enzyme' but is itself taken up by reacting with oxaloacetate to form a fluorocitrate, which has a powerful inhibitory action upon aconitase and so checks the further metabolism of citrate, but not its synthesis. Practically quantitative yields of citrate have also been obtained by incubating liver tissue with pyruvic, or acetic, and oxaloacetic acids under strictly anaerobic condi-tions, suggesting that anaerobiosis retards or suppresses the dehydrogenation of iso-citric acid (reaction (5)). This may be because iso-citric dehydrogenase requires Co II for its action and, once the available Co II has been reduced, no system can be found to reoxidize it with appreciable velocity, for relatively few of the known dehydrogenases can collaborate with this coenzyme. The next oxidative reaction in the sequence (7) is an oxidative de-carboxylation and, as such, is inhibited by arsenite, so that α-ketoglutaric acid accumulates, but small amounts of citric acid are found at the same time. Malonate inhibits the next reaction (8), in which succinic dehydrogenase is the responsible catalyst, and leads to the accumulation of succinate, together with small amounts of α-ketoglutaric acid and traces of citrate.

Recent work has shown that the complex system of enzymes and co-factors involved in the cycle, called 'cyclophorase' by D. E. Green, are associated mainly with the mitochondria. Suspensions of washed, intact mitochondria can catalyse all the events which compose the cycle, but the particles can be dis-integrated to some extent, e.g. by treatment with fat solvents, liberating some of the enzymes. Several of the enzymic com-ponents have now been obtained in individual form, including Ochoa's 'condensing enzyme', which has recently been crystal-lised.

In addition to the reactions composing the cycle proper, atten-tion may now be paid to a number of important side reactions. Most important among these is the glycolytic reaction sequence (A) which leads from glucose and glycogen to pyruvate and hence to 'active acetate'. The cycle allows us now to account for the complete oxidation of glucose, glycogen, and all the known inter-mediates involved in glycolysis. Furthermore, if, as there is reason to believe, the breakdown of fatty acids also culminates in the production of acetic acid in some highly reactive form (B), we can account for the complete oxidation of fat and its inter-mediary metabolites also.

This remarkable mechanism also provides a link between the metabolism of carbohydrates and that of proteins. Among the amino-acids that enter into the composition of proteins there are some that are non-essential and can be synthesized in the animal body in seemingly unlimited amounts. Three such are alanine (C), aspartic acid (D) and glutamic acid (E). The corre-sponding α-keto-acids, pyruvic, oxaloacetic and α-ketoglutaric acids, arise, according to this scheme, as intermediary pro-ducts in the course of carbohydrate metabolism, and would only require to be aminated or transaminated to yield the amino-acids in question.

Particularly important among the side reactions is the β-carboxylation of pyruvate to yield oxaloacetate (F). In muscle, which contains no oxaloacetic decarboxylase, oxaloacetate drifts slowly out of the system by spontaneous β-decarboxylation, so that the rate of respiration of minced muscle slowly declines. Presumably the maintenance of a high rate of respiration in intact muscle also requires the provision of a constant supply of some one or other of the catalytic dicarboxylic acids. In liver, by contrast with muscle, oxaloacetic decarboxylase is present, and here oxaloacetate will rapidly drift out of the system if the concentration of pyruvate is low. But if pyruvate is suddenly produced, e.g. by the administration of pyruvate to the intact animal or, again, by a sudden burst of glycolysis, oxaloacetate will be formed and the oxidation of pyruvate by way of 'active acetate' can be initiated. Oxidation will continue so long as the concentration of pyruvate remains high, but when it falls again to a low level, oxaloacetate will once more drift out of the system and, as the catalytic carriers fall in concentration, respiration will again slow up. But oxidation will not be the only process tending to reduce the concentration of pyruvate: some will be converted into glycogen, in all probability, some will be oxidatively decarboxylated and give rise to 'active acetate' and hence to ketone bodies or fat instead of being immediately oxidized, while some may even be transaminated and converted into alanine.

Fixation of carbon dioxide leading to the formation of oxaloacetate can also take place through an indirect route (not shown in Fig. 35) with malate as an intermediate. The enzyme, which requires reduced Co II and Mn^{++}, catalyses a reductive carboxylation of malate from pyruvate and carbon dioxide:

$$
\begin{array}{lcl}
CO_2 & & COOH \\
+ & & | \\
CH_3 & & CH_2 \\
| & & | \\
CO & + \text{Co II}.2H \rightleftharpoons & CHOH + \text{Co II} \\
| & & | \\
COOH & & COOH
\end{array}
$$

This enzyme, malic decarboxylase, is particularly abundant in pigeon liver and is not identical with malic dehydrogenase, but the latter can oxidize malate produced in this way to yield oxaloacetate. Here, therefore, we have a second mechanism, again involving pyruvate and CO_2-fixation, through which the catalytic reactants of the citric cycle can be built up and maintained, but again their formation depends upon the production and presence of pyruvate.

While it is probable in the extreme that a great deal still remains to be discovered about this catalytic cycle and its various side reactions, there can be little doubt of the great and fundamental importance of the system as a whole, both as a clearing-house for the oxidation of the many products formed on the metabolic lines which converge upon it and as a meeting-place for the main metabolic pathways of carbohydrate, fat and protein. As has already been pointed out, there is evidence that this cycle, in the form envisaged by Szent-Györgyi, is as widely distributed as are cytochrome and cytochrome oxidase. The cells of animals, plants and micro-organisms appear, with very few exceptions, to contain succinic and malic dehydrogenases, together with fumarase, while *iso*-citric dehydrogenase and aconitase, which together correspond to the citric dehydrogenase originally described by Thunberg, seem likewise to have a very wide occurrence. Again, there is reason to believe that most cells have the ability to accomplish the oxidative decarboxylation of α-keto-acids. It seems not by any means impossible, therefore, that further work will show that the carbohydrate metabolism of many living cells is organized on the same fundamental lines, glycolysis leading to the formation of pyruvate from glycogen, the pyruvate being metabolized in its turn through 'active acetate' and the tricarboxylic acid cycle under aerobic conditions, and linking up, as it does in mammalian liver, with the metabolism of protein and of fat.

That we shall find variations on the general, fundamental theme we may be sure, and, indeed, we have already discovered in the phosphagen of muscular tissues a specialized chemical adaptation which admirably subserves the highly specific functions

29-2

which muscle is called upon to discharge. Similarly, we may consider that the carboxylase of yeast is a specialization which permits that organism to live on carbohydrate even in the total absence of oxygen. It might, of course, be argued that fermentation is a simpler operation than respiration, and that the simpler must logically be the more primitive but, at the same time, there is evidence that evolutionary advancement and specialization may be attended by the loss of old enzymes, as well as by the acquisition of new, as is the case of the enzymes concerned with purine metabolism (p. 361).

But, beneath all the secondary and specific adaptations that we are likely to meet in the future, there is every reason to think that we shall discover evidence of the existence of a common metabolic ground-plan to which living cells in general conform.

Evidence already available indicates that the citric acid cycle is present in living organisms of many different kinds. Primarily perhaps, its function is that of providing supplies of citrate, α-ketoglutarate, succinate and the other components of the cycle. From these, other substances such as glutamate, glutamine and other side products, many of which are of enormous importance in intermediary metabolism, can then be produced. But, in animal tissues at any rate, the main function of the cycle is apparently that of energy production, for here, quite apart from producing many substances of metabolic importance and dealing with the oxidative disposal of many more, the cycle operates fast enough to be capable of supplying the greater part of the free-energy requirements of animal cells and tissues. We shall accordingly proceed next to consider the energetic aspects of the cycle.

ENERGETICS OF CARBOHYDRATE OXIDATION

The loss of free energy entailed by complete oxidation of glucose to carbon dioxide and water amounts to about 686,000 cal. per g.mol. The corresponding figure for the glycolysis of glucose, yielding lactic acid, is about 36,000 cal. per g.mol., and we know that a balance of 2 new energy-rich phosphate bonds arises in the process (p. 396). In complete oxidation, therefore, we might expect a maximal yield of the order of $2 \times \frac{686}{36}$ ($\sim$), i.e. somewhere about 40 ($\sim$) per g.mol. if we assume that free energy can be transferred from carbohydrate to ATP with about equal efficiency under aerobic and anaerobic conditions alike.

It has been found in experiments with kidney, brain and other tissues that, under suitable conditions, ATP can be synthesized when the tissue is oxidizing added succinate to fumarate, for example, and it now seems probable that every oxidative step in the cycle can give rise to new energy-rich bonds. These new bonds arise mainly in the oxido-reduction chains through which pairs of hydrogen atoms, or electrons, are transmitted from the substrates of oxidation to molecular oxygen itself, and data are available which allow us to calculate the approximate number of new bonds formed during the complete oxidation of one g.mol. of glucose.

Under anaerobic conditions the glycolysis of 1 g.mol. of glucose gives a net yield of 2 ($\sim$) (p. 396). Under these conditions, it will be remembered, triosephosphate is oxidized at the expense of the reduction of Co I and the reduced Co I is then re-oxidized by the reduction of pyruvate to lactate. Aerobically, however, no lactate need be formed; instead the reduced Co I will pass on its 2H to oxygen through the diaphorase-cytochrome system, yielding 3 ($\sim$) per molecule (see p. 214), i.e. 6 ($\sim$) in all, since 2 molecules of triosephosphate arise from 1 molecule of glucose and reduce 2 molecules of the coenzyme. Under these circumstances pyruvate is not reduced to lactate. Thus the overall yield of ($\sim$) in the aerobic formation of 2 molecules of pyruvate from one of glucose will amount to 8 ($\sim$) in all:

$$C_6H_{12}O_6 + O_2 \rightarrow 2CH_3COCOOH + 2H_2O + 8(\sim)$$

The subsequent energy-yielding stages may be summarized as follows (see p. 216):

Reaction	Primary H-acceptor	Estimated yield of ($\sim$)
Pyruvate $\rightarrow$ acetate + CO_2	Co I	4
iso-Citrate $\rightarrow$ oxalosuccinate	Co II	3
α-Ketoglutarate $\rightarrow$ succinate	Co I	4
Succinate $\rightarrow$ fumarate	Cytochrome b	2
Malate $\rightarrow$ oxaloacetate	Co I	3
	Total	16

Since glucose yields 2 molecules of pyruvate the total bond yield from this part of the process will be 32, making a grand total of 40 ($\sim$) per g.mol. of glucose oxidized. These, of course, are imperfect calculations and the knowledge upon which they are based is still imperfect, but there is good agreement between this and the estimate arrived at in the first paragraphs of this section.

Many experiments have been carried out in order to determine directly the energy-yields of oxidative processes in various tissues. If, for example, dialysed kidney extracts are incubated with succinic acid in the presence of ADP, inorganic phosphate and Mg ions, the system as a whole takes up oxygen, and ATP is synthesized. The amount of ATP formed can be determined and compared with the oxygen consumption of the preparation, and in this way an estimate can be made of the energy-yield of the oxidative metabolism taking place. In one such series of experiments carried out on pigeon-breast muscle, the tissue was previously chopped and exhaustively washed. On incubation in the presence of glucose, with addition of ADP, inorganic phosphate and other essential coenzymes, the yields of ATP recorded ranged from 1 to 3 molecules of ATP for each atom of oxygen consumed. Since the oxidation of one molecule of glucose requires 12 atoms of oxygen, these results indicate an energy-yield of 12–36 ($\sim$) per molecule of glucose oxidized. Bearing in mind the probability that some ATP must have been broken down in the course of incubation we may assume that *at least* 36 ($\sim$) are formed for each molecule of glucose undergoing oxidation and that, given ideal experimental conditions, the yields might conceivably be greater even than this.

This again is in reasonable agreement with the estimate of 40 ($\sim$) reached by calculation and for which we can account by experimental data. We may therefore assume for the present that the true yield is probably not less than 40 ($\sim$) for each g.mol. of glucose oxidized, and this allows us to calculate the minimal efficiency of the oxidative process as a whole. A bond-yield of 40 ($\sim$) corresponds to an energy-capture of $40 \times 11,500$ cal., i.e. 460,000 cal. out of the 686,000 cal. to which the cell gains access by oxidizing one g.mol. of glucose. This corresponds to an energy-capture efficiency of about 67 %. This figure may be compared with the 46 % efficiency calculated for the alcoholic fermentation (p. 379) and that of 64 % for the glycolysis of glucose (p. 396), and suggests that aerobic metabolism is not much more efficient, from the point of view of energy-capture than anaerobic. Even so, these considerations provide a further striking demonstration of the remarkable efficiency of the organism in capturing and diverting to its own uses the intrinsic free energy of its food materials.

CHAPTER XVIII

THE METABOLISM OF FATS

TRANSPORT AND STORAGE OF FATS

ACCORDING to modern opinion a large proportion of the food fat is absorbed in finely emulsified form from the small intestine by way of the lymphatic system and hence, through the thoracic duct, into the blood, where it appears in the form of minute droplets of neutral fat. The remainder undergoes hydrolysis to yield free fatty acids which also pass into the lymphatic stream.

The immediate fate of ingested fatty material has been studied with the aid of deuterated fats, i.e. fats containing heavy hydrogen. Heavy hydrogen gives rise to heavy water when burned and, on account of the numerous and very marked differences between heavy water and 'ordinary' water, heavy hydrogen can readily be detected and estimated by suitable physical methods. Deuterated fats may be prepared by catalytic hydrogenation of unsaturated fats, such as linseed oil, with hydrogen containing a high proportion of heavy hydrogen. Deuterated fat was fed to mice for several days and the animals were then killed. The fats from different parts of the body were extracted from the carcasses, the water formed by their combustion being carefully collected and analysed for heavy water. The results showed quite clearly that the bulk of the deuterium administered had found its way into the depot fats, and only small amounts into the other tissues. We must therefore suppose that the first fate of ingested food fat after absorption is its deposition in the fat depots of the body. Of these the most important are the mesenteries and the intramuscular and subcutaneous connective tissues.

Generally speaking, the kind of fat present in the fat depots of a given animal is fairly characteristic of the species. Beef fat is always much the same in composition, while mutton fat is always characteristically mutton fat. But it is not difficult to alter the composition of the depot fat considerably by feeding fats of a kind which the animal does not ordinarily consume. If, for instance, a dog is given large amounts of linseed oil it will lay down a softer and much more unsaturated depot fat than is characteristic of dogs as a whole. But it is none the less true that, in the ordinary way, each species lays down its own kind of fat, just as each species lays down its own kind of tissue proteins. The reason for this constancy is only partly covered by the tendency of animals to select a diet which is fairly constant in composition; not all the fat found in the depots is merely food fat that has been transported thither from the alimentary canal, but fat which has been synthesized from non-fat sources. As every stock-breeder knows, animals can be fattened cheaply by feeding them an abundance of carbohydrates, and fat can also be synthesized from protein to some extent. It seems likely that the nature of the fat formed from these sources will depend upon the metabolic make-up of the particular species concerned, different animals starting from much the same raw materials but each manufacturing its own kind of fat.

The synthesis of fats from non-fat sources is particularly important in cattle, sheep and other herbivorous animals, for here cellulose bulks large as a foodstuff. In these animals, cellulose is digested by symbiotic micro-organisms which produce from it high yields of short-chain fatty acids, among which acetic and propionic acids predominate, together with some butyric and small amounts of other acids. Acetic and butyric acids are fat-formers, propionic acid yielding glycogen. In animals of this kind, therefore, it is probable that the main reserves of fat and carbohydrate are built up almost entirely from short-chain fatty acids.

The average animal is capable of laying down almost unlimited amounts of fat and, in point of fact, fat has certain definite advantages over proteins and carbohydrates as a form of reserve fuel. Fat is far richer in carbon and hydrogen than the other primary foodstuffs, so that there is more combustible material in a gram of fat than in a gram of either protein or carbohydrate. From the point of view of energy, therefore, fat allows the greatest storage per gram of reserve material. If a gram of each of the three main types of food is burned in a bomb calorimeter the heat produced is approximately as follows:

1 g. protein	...	...	...	5600 cal.
1 g. carbohydrate	...	...		4200 cal.
1 g. fat ...	...	...	...	9300 cal.

Closely bound up with this is the fact that fat, when burned, gives rise to about twice as much water as the other foodstuffs on account of its high content of hydrogen:

1 g. protein	...	...	...	0·41 g. water
1 g. carbohydrate	...	...		0·55 g. water
1 g. fat ...	...	...	...	1·07 g. water

This is an important feature of fat metabolism, especially among terrestrial animals, many of which live under conditions of acute water shortage. In such cases there is commonly a heavy emphasis on the oxidation of fat; in this way the organism is better able to eke out its external supplies of water with metabolic water formed in its own tissues. As an example of this phenomenon we may refer to the developing chick embryo. At laying, the hen's egg is provided with a definite and limited amount of water, an amount which, by itself, would be insufficient to see the embryo through development. But during the 3 weeks of incubation, rather more than 90 % of all the material oxidized by the embryo consists of fat. Again, the mealworm, a larval insect that can live for long periods under the most arid conditions, metabolizes during starvation about 2½ parts of carbohydrate for every part of protein, and no less than 8 parts of fat. The almost legendary ability of the camel to travel for days in the desert without a drink is similarly attributable to heavy fat metabolism with proportionately large-scale production of metabolic water.

Fat which is on its way from the gut to the fat depots is carried mainly in the form of droplets of neutral fat, and a pronounced condition of lipaemia is regularly to be observed after the consumption of a fatty meal. A small proportion of the total fat apparently travels in the form of phospholipids, for the concentration of phospholipid materials in the blood shows a pronounced rise during absorption. When fat is being withdrawn from the depots to be metabolized elsewhere there is no lipaemia, however, and it seems that most of the fat being transported must travel in the form of phospholipids which, unlike the other lipids, are appreciably soluble in water. Phospholipids are normally present in the blood in small quantities, together with a certain amount of cholesterol and cholesterol esters, but neutral fat is only present as such while the condition of post-absorptive lipaemia persists.

The mobilization of depot fat can conveniently be studied in starving animals. After a short period of starvation the glycogen reserves of the liver are used up, and no more glycogen is forthcoming except through glyconeogenesis. Presumably because of the shortage of carbohydrate, large amounts of fat appear in the liver. This condition, which is known as 'fatty liver', can also be observed in a variety of conditions other than starvation and it seems certain that the accumulation of fat in the liver represents the first step towards its metabolic breakdown.

The fat which appears in a fatty liver arises from the fat depots. As has been pointed out, the administration of deuterated fat to mice leads first to the deposition of most of the heavy hydrogen in the fat depots. But if the animals are allowed to starve for several days before being killed and the body fats are then worked up for heavy hydrogen, it is found that the fat content of the liver is greater than at the beginning of starvation and, moreover, that the liver fat contains twice or three times as much deuterium as that in the depots. After its absorption, therefore, most of the ingested fat goes first to the fat depots, from which it is withdrawn and transported to the liver as and when the need arises.

The condition of fatty liver can be established by any treatment that tends seriously to diminish the power of the liver to store, produce or metabolize carbohydrate. In diabetes, for instance, the storage powers of the liver are impaired, and fatty liver is one of the features of this disease. Furthermore, in severe cases, the blood may contain three or four times as much fat as normal. In the pseudo-diabetic condition induced by phlorrhizin the glycogen reserves of the liver are broken down and the glucose thus set free is excreted by way of the urine. Here again fatty liver is to be observed. Small doses of liver poisons such, for instance, as carbon tetrachloride, chloroform, phosphorus and diphtheria toxin, also lead to fatty liver because they disturb the normal functions of the liver with respect to carbohydrate metabolism. In all these cases the establishment of a fatty liver is' encouraged by feeding cholesterol and discouraged by the administration of choline or ethanolamine. How the cholesterol effect is produced we do not know, but when choline or ethanolamine is given it seems not unlikely that their arrival in the liver encourages the formation of phospholipids which, being soluble in water, tend to be carried away.

FUNCTIONS OF FAT: CONSTANT AND VARIABLE ELEMENTS

It will be clear from what has been said that the fat content of the depot tissues and of the liver—and the same is true of other organs—varies very widely with the nutritional condition of the organism. If an animal is allowed to starve for a long time, the amount of reserve fat in the body becomes very small, but, even at death from starvation, the tissues still contain large amounts of lipid material which, apparently, forms a part of the structural material of the tissues and is not available for use as fuel. This part of the total body lipids is referred to as the 'constant element'; constant because, being a part of the actual fabric of the organism, it is always present and always must be present. The remainder of the lipids comprise the 'variable element', so-called because they vary in amount with the nutritional state of the organism and the demands made upon them for energy production.

The contrast between the constant and variable elements can be appreciated by comparing the effects of different doses of liver poisons upon the lipid content of the liver. Small amounts of carbon tetrachloride, for example, lead to the mobilization of fat from the depots and its deposition in the liver. Here we observe the movement of a part of the variable element from one place to another. If larger doses of the same poison are administered, the liver cells suffer serious damage and we observe the condition known as fatty degeneration. Again the cells are rich in lipid materials, but mainly because the other cell constituents have been broken down and dispersed. Indeed, the lipids present in fatty degeneration are all that remains of the structural materials of the cell, and represent the constant or structural element of the tissue lipids.

Fats, then, have two main functions. They act as fuel reserves, and they form an important part of the structure of living tissues. In addition, there are indications that certain fatty acids have special and specific functions, for it is known that rats kept on fat-free diets, or on diets from which particular fatty acids have been carefully removed, become ill and suffer from caudal necrosis, but we shall return presently to consider this condition and its metabolic implications.

METABOLISM OF FATS: GENERAL

Our knowledge of the mechanisms whereby fats are metabolized is far from being complete and the complexion of the whole subject is changing rapidly. The evidence available regarding fat metabolism has in the past been so contradictory and speculation so rife that almost any statement made might be contradicted by as many facts and arguments as could be produced in its support. In what follows, therefore, the author will attempt to give what appears to him to be the most reasonable account of fat metabolism, aware though he is that the picture may have changed considerably by the time it is printed.

It is generally believed that the liver plays a predominant role in the metabolism of fat, for it is to this organ above all that fat is transported when carbohydrate metabolism is subnormal and an alternative energy source is required. It has usually been assumed, though never proved, that fats are hydrolytically split into glycerol and free fatty acids before any oxidation takes place. This is not entirely an unreasonable supposition, for cells of most kinds seem to be furnished with lipolytic enzymes, the action of which is freely reversible.

Glycerol, if administered to a diabetic or phlorrhizinized animal, is converted almost quantitatively to glucose. It also leads to the deposition of glycogen in the liver if administered to a starving animal. The most probable pathway for its conversion into carbohydrate is through phosphoglycerol, oxidation of the latter to triosephosphate and hence, through the normal glycolytic reaction sequence, back to glycogen or glucose.

Fatty acids are normally completely oxidized to carbon dioxide and water. There is an abundance of evidence, which we shall presently review, that fatty chains are split into 2-carbon units consisting of some form of 'active acetate'. Acetate itself can be totally oxidized, e.g. by washed kidney-cortex homogenates in the presence of oxaloacetate, and its oxidation is inhibited by malonate and other inhibitors of the citric acid cycle, whence we may conclude that it enters and is oxidized by way of this cycle. Confirmation of this is found in the fact that isotopically labelled acetate can be incorporated into the cycle and gives rise to correspondingly labelled intermediates in the presence of the usual inhibitors (p. 445). Long-chain fatty acids also can be completely oxidized by a variety of tissue preparations, including slices, breis, homogenates and mitochondrial suspensions, and here again oxidation is dependent upon the presence of oxaloacetate or some other intermediate of the citric cycle, and here too the oxidation is inhibited by malonate. These facts indicate that acetate and longer chains alike are probably metabolized through the same route and that acetate, and the 2-carbon units arising in the breakdown of longer chains, enter the cycle through a probably common intermediary.

Now the entry of acetate itself into the cycle depends upon the presence of ATP and Co A and there is evidence (p. 443) that these substances react together in the presence of acetate to yield acetyl-Co A. The latter, we know, can react directly with oxaloacetate to yield citrate (p. 442), from which oxaloacetate is subsequently regenerated with formation of two molecules of carbon dioxide, corresponding to the two carbon atoms of the acetate entering the cycle (p. 446). Since no form of 'active acetate' other than acetyl-Co A has so far been discovered we may tentatively assume that the 2-carbon units formed from fatty acids arise in this form. In confirmation of this we have the further fact that fatty acids can be synthesized from acetate, presumably by way of the same common 2-carbon intermediate. These points may be summarized:

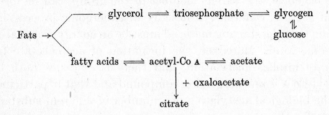

Until these facts came to light it was considered that glycollic and glyoxylic acids might be intermediates in the oxidation of acetate on account of the structural relationships between these substances:

$$\begin{array}{ccc}
\text{CH}_3 & \text{CH}_2\text{OH} & \text{CHO} \\
| & | & | \\
\text{COOH} & \text{COOH} & \text{COOH} \\
\textit{acetic acid} & \textit{glycollic acid} & \textit{glyoxylic acid}
\end{array}$$

Glycollic acid, however, has been found not to be appreciably oxidized, while glyoxylic acid strongly inhibits the oxidation of acetic acid itself.

Now, in some tissues and under certain circumstances, fatty acids give rise to large amounts of other compounds, the ketone or acetone bodies. These are *acetoacetic acid*, together with *β-hydroxybutyric acid* and small amounts of *acetone*. It is generally agreed that the parent substance of this group is acetoacetic acid. Under the influence of the widely distributed β-hydroxybutyric dehydrogenase and Co I, acetoacetic acid and β-hydroxybutyric acids are freely interconvertible. Acetone arises from acetoacetic acid by spontaneous decarboxylation, a process which takes place at an appreciable speed under

physiological conditions of temperature and pH. The relationships between these three substances can briefly be summarized
as follows:

$$CH_3COCH_2COOH$$
acetoacetic acid

$\pm 2H$

$$CH_3CH(OH)CH_2COOH \qquad CH_3COCH_3 + CO_2$$
β-hydroxybutyric acid   *acetone*

Acetoacetate, the parent member of the group, can be formed
from acetate, but the synthesis is an endergonic process, indicating that the starting material must be an energy-rich material
of some kind. Moreover, the formation of acetoacetate from
acetate implies acetylation, and there is evidence both that
acetyl-Co A is an energy-rich compound and that it participates
in the biological acetylation of a number of different substances
(p. 423). Hence we may suppose that acetoacetate arises from
acetate and from acids with longer chains by way of acetyl-Co A.
Now acetoacetate, like acetate itself and like the long-chain
fatty acids, can be completely oxidized by various tissue preparations in the presence of oxaloacetate and other intermediates of
the citric cycle, and once again oxidation is inhibited by malonate.
Furthermore, isotopically labelled acetoacetate can gain admis-
sion to the cycle, yielding correspondingly labelled intermediates.
Once again, therefore, we must suppose that acetyl-Co A is
involved as an intermediate, and again we may summarize our
conclusions:

Acetoacetate $\rightleftharpoons$ acetyl-Co A $\rightleftharpoons$ acetate

$\downarrow$ + oxaloacetate

citrate

These considerations lead us to suspect that fatty acids and
carbohydrates alike undergo final oxidation by way of a common
2-carbon intermediate, in the form of acetyl-Co A, and by
a common mechanism, in the citric acid cycle. We may therefore
summarize our summaries in a united form as shown in Fig. 36.

Small quantities of ketone bodies are formed from ketogenic
amino-acids when these are administered to diabetic or phlor-

rhizinized animals, but that they arise mainly from fat cannot be doubted. Their genesis from fatty acids might be attributable to one of two processes: they might be normal intermediate products of fatty acid metabolism, or they might on the other hand arise as side-products from intermediary metabolites formed during the breakdown of fatty acids.

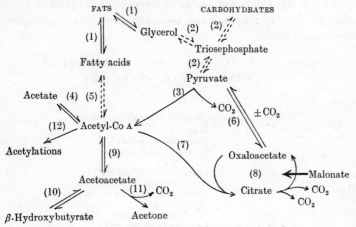

Fig. 36. Outlines of metabolism of fats and carbohydrates.

Traces of ketone bodies can be detected in the blood of normal animals, but the amounts present are greatly increased when there is a heavy emphasis upon fat metabolism. The energy requirements of a typical animal are normally met by metabolizing fat and carbohydrate together, but if, for any reason, carbohydrate metabolism is subnormal, correspondingly more fat has to be metabolized. Thus ketone bodies tend to accumulate when the food contains disproportionately large amounts of fat. They also accumulate in starvation, once the glycogen reserves of the liver have been exhausted. These reserves can be experimentally drained in fed animals by injecting phlorrhizin, when ketone bodies again make their appearance. They are also formed if the liver's power to store and metabolize glycogen is seriously impaired, as it is in diabetes and in cases of poisoning by chloroform, carbon tetrachloride, phosphorus and other liver poisons.

There is a similar dependence upon carbohydrate metabolism in isolated, perfused livers. The blood leaving a perfused liver ordinarily contains small amounts of ketone bodies, but the amounts are greatly increased if members of the naturally occurring fatty acids are added to the ingoing blood. The yield of ketone bodies is particularly high when butyric acid is used, but in all cases the yields are higher in livers that are poor in carbohydrate. Similar results have been reported from experiments with liver slices.

TABLE 37. ENZYMES INVOLVED IN BREAKDOWN
OF FATS AND CARBOHYDRATES

(*see* Fig. 36)

Reaction	Enzyme or catalytic system
1	Lipase
2	Glycolytic enzymes
3	Oxidative decarboxylase
4	See p. 464
5	Enzymes of β-oxidation
6	Oxaloacetic decarboxylase; also malic decarboxylase + malic dehydrogenase
7	'Condensing enzyme'
8	Enzymes of citric cycle ('cyclophorase')
9	Transacetylase
10	β-Hydroxybutyric dehydrogenase
11	None (spontaneous)
12	Transacetylase

Note that there are at least two transacetylases in the scheme: each is probably specific for a particular substrate.

So intimate is the relationship between fat metabolism and that of the ketone bodies that any theory of fat metabolism which fails to explain the production of ketone bodies is doomed in advance. Whether we regard the ketone bodies as direct or as secondary products of fatty acid metabolism, it is evident that the organism's ability to oxidize fatty acids is limited and in some way linked with its carbohydrate metabolism, so that the intermediate products fail to be completely oxidized when carbohydrate metabolism is subnormal. But this is not equally true of all animals. It is more difficult to induce starvation ketosis in rats than in men, for example, while the chick embryo, which metabolizes fat almost to the exclusion of other materials during the period of its incubation, contains not a trace of ketone bodies at the time of hatching. Even among the human species, Eskimos can tolerate diets so rich in fats that the average European on the same diet develops intense ketosis.

Since it seems certain that acetyl-Co A is a common metabolite between fatty acids and ketone bodies alike and is able to enter and undergo metabolism by way of the citric cycle, it appears that five possible fates are open to it. It may enter the cycle and be oxidized: it may yield acetoacetate, it may revert to acetate or fatty acids, or it may participate in acetylation reactions.

We know that the entry of acetyl-Co A into the citric cycle depends upon the availability of oxaloacetate with which it can react to form citrate. Now oxaloacetate can arise in the liver, by the direct carboxylation of pyruvate or by oxidizing malate, formed by the reductive carboxylation of pyruvate, by malic decarboxylase; but in both cases the equilibrium conditions are heavily weighted in favour of pyruvate. Pyruvate in turn is in equilibrium with glycogen through the long chain of equilibria involved in the reactions of glycolysis, and it follows that, if carbohydrate is in short supply, the concentration of pyruvate will tend to be low and that of oxaloacetate low also as a result. Under these conditions, i.e. conditions in which carbohydrate metabolism is subnormal or suppressed, acetyl-Co A will be able to enter the cycle only slowly and can be only slowly metabolized.

Now when carbohydrate metabolism is subnormal there is usually a heavy emphasis on that of fat, the alternative source of energy production, leading to a proportionately heavy production of 2-carbon materials. It follows, therefore, that in the deficiency or absence of carbohydrate metabolites there will be not only a tendency for acetyl-Co A to accumulate for lack of oxaloacetate with which to combine, but a simultaneous increase in its rate of formation. Under these conditions, therefore, 2-carbon units tend to accumulate and pairs begin to combine, yielding acetoacetate, from which the other members of the group of ketone bodies can then arise, so that ketosis is a more or less inevitable consequence of subnormality of carbohydrate metabolism.

It may be remarked, however, that these arguments probably do not apply to tissues other than liver, for here oxaloacetate undergoes only a slow and spontaneous breakdown to pyruvate as opposed to the rapid breakdown catalysed by the oxaloacetic decarboxylase of liver, and therefore does not depend so intimately upon the supply of carbohydrate metabolites. These extrahepatic tissues can and do metabolize acetoacetate and β-hydroxybutyrate much more readily than does the liver and, even when the liver is producing significant quantities of ketone bodies, these may pass into the blood and undergo oxidation in the extrahepatic tissues; no actual ketosis develops until the rate of formation of acetoacetate and the other ketone bodies in the liver outstrips that at which they can be oxidized by the other tissues.

Having now dealt in outline with the main features of fat metabolism as we know them at present, it is time to give more detailed evidence in favour of and against the conclusions so far summarized.

DESATURATION

It has been known for many years that if fatty acids are incubated with liver tissue there is an increase in the iodine number of the sample, indicating that the liver is capable of introducing double bonds into the fatty chain. Leathes pointed out that the liver normally contains rather a high proportion of unsaturated fatty acids, and suggested that fat might be broken down by the introduction of double bonds at more or less arbitrary points along the chain, the latter then being broken into fragments at the 'weak' linkages thus introduced.

That the liver can dehydrogenate fats is certain, but the notion that double bonds can be introduced *anywhere* in the chain is disproved by the following facts. If rats are given a diet from which all traces of fatty acids with a double bond at $C_{12:13}$ have been carefully removed, they develop a condition known as fat-deficiency disease, characterized by a scaly condition of the tail (caudal necrosis). If the liver were able to introduce double bonds at *any* point in the fatty chain, this condition could hardly exist at all: the disorder is curable by the administration of linoleic acid, for example, and this could be made from oleic acid by desaturation in the 12 : 13 position. This the liver clearly cannot do, at any rate in rats.

Attempts have been made to discover precisely where double bonds can be inserted, by incubating liver tissue with fatty acids already containing double bonds in known positions. When this was done, desaturation still took place except in acids containing a double bond at the α:β position. This indicates that desaturation can be accomplished in the α:β position. Evidence has been obtained in other ways to show that the liver also contains an enzyme capable of introducing a double bond in the middle (9:10) of the stearic acid chain, giving rise to oleic acid.

β-Oxidation

The introduction of an α:β double bond is perhaps the first step in the process known as β-oxidation, first postulated many years ago by Knoop. Knoop prepared a series of ω-phenyl fatty acids, i.e. fatty acids which had been 'labelled' by the introduction of a phenyl radical at the carbon atom most remote from the carboxyl radical. These acids were administered to dogs, the urine being collected and worked up for substances containing the phenyl group. In every case a phenylated compound was isolated, the products being benzoic and phenylacetic acids respectively. Both acids were actually eliminated in the form of their glycine conjugates, hippuric and phenaceturic acids, but for our present purposes the conjugation can be neglected. The important feature of Knoop's discoveries was the fact that administration of an acid with an even number of carbon atoms in the side-chain led always and only to the formation of phenylacetic acid, odd-numbered chains giving rise always and only to benzoic acid, e.g.

even: $C_6H_5CH_2CH_2\!:\!CH_2COOH \rightarrow C_6H_5CH_2COOH \rightarrow (C_6H_5CH_2CO.HN.CH_2COOH)$
phenylbutyric acid   *phenylacetic acid*   (*phenaceturic acid*)

odd: $C_6H_5CH_2\!:\!CH_2COOH \rightarrow C_6H_5COOH \rightarrow (C_6H_5CO.HN.CH_2COOH)$
phenylpropionic acid   *benzoic acid*   (*hippuric acid*)

This must mean that the organism is unable to remove carbon atoms one at a time from the chain: if it could do so, phenylacetic acid would be expected to be converted into benzoic acid, while the administration of either an odd- or an even-numbered chain would be expected to give either benzoic acid alone, or else a mixture of benzoic and phenylacetic acids. Presumably, then, *the carbon atoms must be split off in even numbers, most probably in pairs.* Knoop accordingly suggested the following scheme to account for the breakdown of the normal fatty chain, the process involved being one of repetitive β-oxidation and hydrolysis:

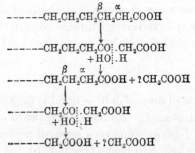

Now it happens that the naturally occurring fatty acids are, almost without exception, members of the even-numbered series. Any such acid, by losing two carbon atoms at a time, would pass eventually through the stage of butyric acid which, undergoing β-oxidation in its turn, would give rise to acetoacetic acid, an important point in favour of Knoop's scheme. This is especially apposite when fat is being extensively metabolized and, in fact, if butyric acid is given to a diabetic or phlorrhizinized animal, or perfused through an isolated liver, it is largely or even quantitatively converted into acetoacetate and the other ketone bodies.

The theory of β-oxidation received much support from Embden's experiments on perfused livers and on diabetic and phlorrhizinized animals. If a fatty acid containing an even number of carbon atoms were perfused or fed as the case might be, there was invariably an increase in the amount of ketone bodies formed by the preparation. If, on the other hand, acids with an odd number of carbon atoms were administered, there was no appreciable increase in ketone-body formation. These results are in excellent agreement with the notion that aceto-acetic acid arises by the β-oxidation of butyric acid, which must necessarily be formed by repetitive β-oxidation of the natural fatty acids. In the case of the odd-numbered acids there would be no 4-carbon stage, and propionic acid would be formed in-stead. Propionic acid is known to be a glucose-former and, as has been pointed out, ketone body formation is always less marked when carbohydrate material is being metabolized.

The general validity of the hypothesis of β-oxidation has been well confirmed, for example, by experiments in which the phenyl 'markers' used by Knoop were replaced by cyclohexane rings. When the resulting compounds were administered to dogs it was found that derivatives of the even-numbered acids were completely oxidized, those of odd-numbered acids giving rise to benzoic acid. Still more recently it has been shown that if deuterostearic acid, with 18 carbon atoms, is fed to animals, heavy hydrogen can later be found in the palmitic acid (C_{16}) fraction of the body lipids. Further evidence has been obtained in other experiments to which we shall refer presently and, taken all in all, the evidence in favour of β-oxidation appears to be overwhelming.

Various objections to and criticisms of the work so far de-scribed must now be considered. One evident criticism of work in which fatty acids are substituted by abnormal 'markers' is that new and abnormal reactions may take place as a result of the modification of the chemical structure of the fatty acids. This seems improbable, however, since the use of unsubstituted fatty acids in liver perfusion experiments and in feeding experi-ments on phlorrhizinized and diabetic animals give results which conform so precisely with expectations based on the hypothesis of β-oxidation. So also do experiments with deuterated fats. It may also be objected that Knoop and Embden worked almost exclusively with fatty acids containing 6–7 carbon atoms at most, and these are so much shorter than the 14–18 carbon chains which predominate among natural fatty acids that they might conceivably be metabolized in a different manner. This objection however loses much of its weight when it is realized that the metabolic behaviour even of acetic acid closely resembles that of the long-chain acids, as we shall see. The possibility nevertheless remains that other types of oxidation might apply when the longer natural chains are being metabolized. A little evidence has been obtained for the occurrence of α-, γ- and even δ-oxidation, but little of it carries much conviction. In more recent times, however, evidence has been brought forward to show that fatty chains can be oxidized at the ω-position. Such a process could not have been detected in Knoop's experiments because the ω-carbon had been protected against oxidation by the introduction of a phenyl radical.

ω-OXIDATION

Evidence in favour of the ω-oxidation of fatty acids was first brought forward by Verkade who, with his colleagues, prepared the triglycerides of octanoic (C_8), nonanoic (C_9), decanoic (C_{10}), undecanoic (C_{11}), dodecanoic (C_{12}) and terdecanoic (C_{13}) acids. These compounds were fed to dogs and to the investigators themselves, the urines being collected and worked up for dicarboxylic acids. The C_{11} derivative, for example, was found to give rise to dibasic acids with 11, 9 and 7 carbon atoms respectively:

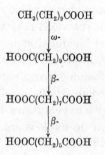

$$CH_3(CH_2)_9COOH$$
$$\downarrow \omega\text{-}$$
$$HOOC(CH_2)_9COOH$$
$$\downarrow \beta\text{-}$$
$$HOOC(CH_2)_7COOH$$
$$\downarrow \beta\text{-}$$
$$HOOC(CH_2)_5COOH$$

Acids containing more than 12 or less than 8 carbon atoms invoked little or no diaciduria however. Verkade concluded that free fatty acids can be oxidized in the ω-position to yield the corresponding dicarboxylic acids, and that the latter can then undergo repetitive β-oxidation from both ends.

That dicarboxylic acids can be formed from fatty acids in the animal body is evident enough from the results of Verkade's experiments. Other workers have administered dibasic acids to dogs and recovered them in part from the urine, together with other dicarboxylic acids with 2 or 4 carbon atoms less. Thus undecandioic acid (C_{11}) gave rise to azelaic (C_9) and pimelic (C_7) acids, while sebacic (C_{10}) yielded suberic (C_8) and adipic (C_6) acids. Dibasic acids with 12–18 carbon atoms were completely oxidized and the same was true of acids with less than 8 carbon atoms. That the acids between these two extremes are excreted presumably means that they are more resistant to oxidation than those with longer or shorter chains.

In view of these results it seems difficult to believe, as many authorities do, that ω-oxidation plays no part in the oxidation of fatty acids. It should be remembered, moreover, that in Verkade's experiments and those of his followers, the fatty chains used approximated fairly closely to the natural occurring chains, among which C_{14}–C_{18} acids predominate. In the work of Knoop, Embden and others, in which ω-oxidation was not detected, the acids employed usually contained from 1 to 7 carbon atoms only, and longer chains were rarely used.

Verkade's conclusions cannot be accepted without reserve, however. With chains of 6 or 8 carbon atoms we should expect that ω- and β-oxidation together would yield one or two 2-carbon fragments together with succinic acid, e.g.

$$CH_3(CH_2)_6COOH$$
$$\downarrow \omega\text{-}$$
$$HOOC(CH_2)_6COOH$$
$$\downarrow \beta\text{-}$$
$$HOOC(CH_2)_4COOH + ?\, CH_3COOH$$
$$\downarrow \beta\text{-}$$
$$HOOC(CH_2)_2COOH + ?\, CH_3COOH$$

Succinic acid is known to be a glucose-former, while the 2-carbon fragments could perhaps react together and produce one molecule of acetoacetic acid, though in the presence of succinate it is likely that ketone bodies would not appear. Yet there is incontrovertible evidence (p. 481) that octanoic acid can give rise to *two* molecules of acetoacetic acid, and that hexanoic acid, which would be expected to give one 2-carbon fragment and one molecule of succinate, is able to yield $1\frac{1}{2}$ molecules of acetoacetate. Finally, in the case of butyric acid, ω-oxidation would lead directly to the production of one molecule of succinic acid whereas, in fact, the product is acetoacetic acid, often in quantitative yield. There cannot be much doubt therefore that ω-oxidation does not take effect unless the fatty acid chain contains more than 8 carbon atoms or thereabouts, a conclusion that explains why no diaciduria was observable when the triglycerides of acids with less than 8 carbon atoms were used in Verkade's original experiments.

How the oxidation of the terminal methyl radical is accomplished we do not know, but that such a group can be oxidized to a carboxyl radical is well established and had, indeed, been demonstrated before Verkade's results were published. *n*-Propylbenzene has been injected intraperitoneally into dogs and found to give rise to benzoic acid in the urine, while *n*-butyl and *n*-amylbenzenes yielded phenylacetic and benzoic acids respectively. These results are completely in accord with the supposition that the side chains of these compounds undergo first ω- and then β-oxidation, exactly as though they were typical fatty acids:

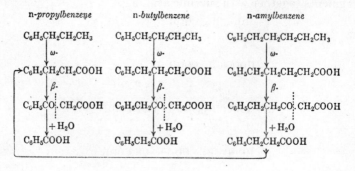

It has been urged against the hypothesis of ω-oxidation that the 4-carbon product arising from combined ω- and β-oxidation of fatty acids of the naturally occurring series would be, not butyric, but succinic acid, so that no explanation would remain for the production of acetoacetic acid and the other ketone bodies to which the latter gives rise. Succinic acid, indeed, is a glycogenic compound and, as such, would diminish rather than encourage the production of the ketone bodies. But this perhaps is not a very serious objection. The majority of the experiments in which massive production of ketone bodies has been demonstrated at the expense of fatty acids involved the use of short-chain acids, usually with 7–8 carbon atoms or less, and to these, as we have seen, it is probable that ω-oxidation does not apply.

Whether ω-oxidation is or is not a normal mode of oxidation for fatty acid chains, there is no doubt whatsoever that the main mechanism of degradation is that of β-oxidation and that the predominant product consists of highly reactive 2-carbon units.

MECHANISMS OF FATTY ACID METABOLISM

There is now abundant evidence that fatty acids undergo oxidation by mechanisms involving the citric acid cycle. Many experiments with a wide range of tissue preparations, including slices, breis, homogenates and even washed suspensions of mitochondria, have shown that the oxidation of acetate and higher fatty acids alike depends upon the presence of one or other of the reactants of the citric cycle, and that the oxidation is powerfully inhibited by malonate and other reagents known to inhibit the cyclic mechanism. We know that fatty chains undergo degradation to 2-carbon fragments, and that 2-carbon fragments in the form of acetyl-Co A can react directly with oxaloacetate to form citrate, and it is now incumbent upon us to consider the possibility that the products of β-oxidation may consist of acetyl-Co A.

The oxidation of fatty acids in tissue preparations can be considerably accelerated by the addition of ATP and can also

be facilitated by the addition of one or other of the reactants
of the citric acid cycle. The operation of the citric cycle leads,
of course, to the production of ATP and might be thought to
facilitate fatty acid oxidation for that reason. The effect of ATP
has led to the suggestion that the first step in the metabolic
breakdown of fatty acids must probably consist in their phosphorylation by ATP, a supposition that found some support in
the fact that acyl phosphates are more rapidly oxidized than
the corresponding fatty acids. But in the case of acetic acid,
such a reaction would lead to the formation of acetyl phosphate
which, as we now know, cannot enter the citric cycle. Nor is
there any good evidence that acetyl phosphate arises in animal
tissues. In the case of longer chains an acyl phosphate might,
by virtue of the presence of its energy-rich phosphate bond, be
more susceptible to oxidation than the free acid, but on β-oxida-
tion such an acyl phosphate would yield its first two carbon
atoms in the form of acetyl phosphate again.

There is a more satisfactory explanation of the effect of ATP.
In the case of acetic acid, ATP and Co A are known to be required
before the acid can react with oxaloacetate and enter the citric
cycle (p. 442), and it now appears that ATP, Co A and free
acetate first react together to yield acetyl-Co A, probably as
follows:

(i) $ATP + HS—A \rightleftharpoons ADP + \textcircled{P} \sim S—A,$

(ii) $\textcircled{P} \sim S—A + CH_3COOH \rightleftharpoons HO . \textcircled{P} + CH_3CO \sim S—A.$

Similar reactions, since they would introduce an energy-rich
bond, might well account for the facilitation of fatty acid oxidation by ATP, provided always that Co A is available in the tissue
preparation employed. In general, and especially in tissue slices,
breis and homogenates, this condition is likely to be fulfilled. We
may therefore conclude that the first step probably consists in
the formation of an acyl-Co A complex from the free fatty acid.

Very little is known about the intermediate reactions that lead
to the formation of the β-keto-acids which figure in Knoop's
original formulation (p. 470). Indeed, it has often been doubted
whether β-keto-acids are produced on any significant scale since,
apart from acetoacetic acid, the simplest member of the series,

no such acids have been isolated from animal tissues. This, admittedly, does not prove that such acids are not formed, for it is always possible that they are transitory products, being removed as fast as they are formed. There is now evidence that if β-keto-acids are incubated anaerobically with oxaloacetate in the presence of enzyme preparations obtained from liver, citrate is formed in large yields, together with fatty acids containing two carbon atoms less than the parent keto-acid. There is clear evidence here that the two terminal carbon atoms leave the chain and are incorporated into the citric system.

There is a little evidence, as we have seen, that the first stage in the process of β-oxidation consists in the introduction of an $\alpha{:}\beta$ double bond, and by analogy with the reactions involved in the conversion of succinate to oxaloacetate the following reactions might be suggested:

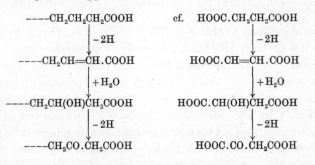

If these reactions correspond to reality it would be expected that the unsaturated, hydroxy- and β-keto-acids would all react similarly in the tissues. These possibilities were first considered by Dakin, who prepared β-ketohexanoic, β-hydroxy-hexanoic, and $\alpha{:}\beta$-hexanenic acids, viz. $CH_3CH_2CH_2CO.CH_2COOH$, $CH_3CH_2CH_2CH(OH)CH_2COOH$ and $CH_3CH_2CH_2CH{=}CH.COOH$. When these compounds were perfused through surviving livers, all three behaved similarly and gave similar yields of acetoacetic acid. More recently, studies of the metabolism of acids up to and including terdecanoic (C_{13}) acid have been made with the aid of washed suspensions of mitochondria. Apart from propionic acid, which is known to be glycogenic, all these were oxidized in the presence of added succinate, and the $\alpha:\beta$-unsaturated, β-hydroxy- and β-ketonic acids behaved in exactly the same manner as the unsubstituted parent acids. While these results are in agreement with the sequence of reactions suggested above they do not in any way prove that, even if the unsaturated, β-hydroxy- and β-ketonic acids do arise in the course of metabolism, they necessarily arise in that order. In any case it now seems probable that the compounds react in the form of their energy-rich Co A derivatives, rather than in the free condition.

If now we assume that in some way or other β-ketonic acids are indeed formed, we may enquire how they are split into a 2-carbon fragment and the fatty acid with 2 carbon atoms less. Here the classical view was in favour of simple hydrolysis to liberate acetic acid:

$$\text{----}CH_2CO\vdots CH_2COOH + H\vdots OH \longrightarrow \text{----}CH_2COOH + CH_3COOH$$

The objections to this hypothesis were, first, that β-keto-acids are not prone to this kind of hydrolysis at physiological pH, and second, that the biological formation of acetic acid from acetoacetic acid or any other β-ketonic acid in significant quantities had never been demonstrated. Knoop disposed of the latter difficulty by the supposition that acetate is removed as fast as it is formed, and, as we now know, acetate can indeed be rapidly incorporated into the citric cycle. It has in any case long been certain that acetic acid or some form of 'active acetate' does arise in the body because many substances containing $-NH_2$ groups, such as aniline and the sulphonamide drugs, are excreted in acetylated form after administration to experimental animals. Moreover, small amounts of acetic acid have been isolated from liver tissue in the form of the 2:4-dinitrophenylhydrazide.

If now the fatty acid-Co A derivative undergoes oxidation in the β-position, either by the reactions considered above or in some other way, the product could undergo fission, perhaps by hydrolysis, to yield acetyl-Co A:

$$\overset{\textstyle HO\vdots H}{\text{---}CO\vdots CH_2CO\sim S\text{---}A} \longrightarrow \text{---}COOH + CH_3CO\sim S\text{---}A$$

This product, as we know, is capable of direct reaction with oxaloacetate to yield citrate.

Now, if the β-oxidative split is hydrolytic in character, this reaction would lead to the dissipation of the free energy of the $\alpha:\beta$ bond in the form of heat. We have already learned that the splitting of α-keto-acids, in particular that of pyruvic acid, is mediated by Co A, and the suggestion may now be made that Co A is again involved in the fission of β-keto-acids, perhaps as follows:

$$\text{---CH}_2\text{CO}\vert.\text{CH}_2\text{CO}\sim\text{S---A} \longrightarrow \text{----CH}_2\text{CO}\sim\text{S---A} + \text{CH}_3\text{CO}\sim\text{S---A}$$
$$\text{S---A}\vert.\text{H}$$

This change may be formulated in the following manner (a) and compared with that of oxidative decarboxylation (b):

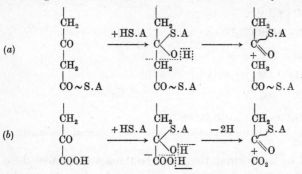

This is an interesting possibility since it means that the 'priming energy' originally provided from ATP through the mediation of coenzyme A would be recovered in the energy-rich bond of the acetyl-Co A unit split off, while the residual fatty chain would be left already 'primed' for the next step in its degradation. Such a mechanism would lead, moreover, to the eventually complete degradation of naturally occurring, even-numbered chains into 2-carbon units consisting of acetyl-Co A. If now we combine the ideas developed in the last few pages we can arrive at an interesting, if frankly speculative, picture of the process of β-oxidation as a whole. Such a picture is presented in Fig. 37. The 'active' acetyl-Co A units thus formed can, as we know, enter freely into and undergo rapid oxidation by the citric acid cycle and can enter freely into reactions of biological acetylation also. But under conditions in which oxaloacetate is in short supply, i.e. in conditions in which carbohydrate metabolism is

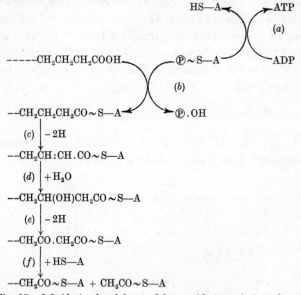

Fig. 37. β-Oxidative breakdown of fatty acids (speculative scheme).

suppressed or subnormal, there will be tendency for acetyl-Co A to accumulate for lack of oxaloacetate with which to combine and, moreover, there will be an increased production of this substance at the same time. Under such conditions as these ketone bodies make their appearance.

FORMATION OF ACETOACETIC ACID

It has already been emphasized that no theory of fat metabolism stands much chance of survival unless it can account adequately for the formation of ketone bodies, and a great deal of attention has been paid to the problem of ketone-body formation, especially in recent years. Jowett and Quastel, for example, used the liver-slice method, and with its aid confirmed in a general manner the results of earlier experiments carried out by the older techniques. They found that ketone bodies are formed from fatty acid chains containing an even number of carbon atoms, and that much smaller amounts are produced from odd-numbered chains. In particular they carried out quantitative determinations of the yields of ketone bodies (expressed in terms of acetoacetate) from a series of fatty acids, and discovered that some fatty acids give rise to more than one molecule of acetoacetic acid for each molecule of fatty acid metabolized. Other workers, using similar techniques, obtained rather different figures but nevertheless confirmed the observation that, in certain cases, one molecule of fatty acid can produce more than one molecule of acetoacetate. Feeding experiments carried out on starving rats have added further confirmation and, in the case of octanoic acid, which we may take as typical, two molecules of acetoacetate were obtained from each molecule of the C_8 acid. This corresponds to a complete conversion of fatty acid-carbon to ketone-body-carbon.

Now according to the theory of β-oxidation, as formulated by Knoop, a C_8 acid would lose two pairs of carbon atoms in the form of presumptive acetic acid, leaving butyric acid which, undergoing β-oxidation in its turn, could be converted into one molecule *and no more* of acetoacetate. On Verkade's theory of ω-oxidation a C_8 acid would similarly lose two pairs of carbon atoms and yield one molecule of succinate, so that no acetoacetate at all would be expected in this case. Thus neither of these theories could account for the observed behaviour of octanoic acid, and a new explanation had to be sought.

One way of accounting for the observed high yields of ketone bodies is to invoke the theory of multiple alternate oxidation. According to this scheme the fatty chain is supposed to undergo oxidation to form keto-groups at the β-carbon atom and at every alternate carbon atom along the chain, thus:

$$-----CH_2CH_2CH_2CH_2CH_2\overset{\beta}{CH_2}\overset{\alpha}{CH_2}COOH$$
$$\downarrow$$
$$-----\vdots CH_2CO.CH_2CO\vdots.\overset{\beta}{CH_2}CO.\overset{\alpha}{CH_2}COOH$$

The chain is supposed then to split into 4-carbon fragments, each fragment coming away in the form of a molecule of acetoacetic acid. From every molecule of octanoic acid therefore, we should expect to obtain two molecules of acetoacetic acid and this, of course, is what is actually observed. But to accept this hypothesis means totally ignoring and setting aside all the considerable mass of evidence in favour of β-oxidation: indeed, the only sound evidence in favour of multiple alternate oxidation seems to consist of precisely those facts which it sets out to explain. Furthermore, there is an alternative possibility which is entirely consistent with the theory of β-oxidation, i.e. that pairs of the 2-carbon products of β-oxidation react together to form acetoacetate.

It might, of course, be objected that β-oxidation applies as much to odd-numbered as it does to even-numbered chains, so that *all* fatty acids ought to give rise to acetoacetate if the latter is indeed formed from the 2-carbon units, whereas little ketone-body production has ever been observed from odd-numbered chains. In fact, however, most of the experiments on acids of this series were performed with chains containing only 7 carbon atoms or less. These would yield only one or two 2-carbon fragments and one molecule of propionic acid which, being a glucose-former, might be expected to prevent the formation of aceto-acetate. In any case it has now been found that valeric, heptanoic, nonanoic and undecanoic acids are all ketogenic in rabbits.

If now we consider the case of a fatty acid with less than 8 carbon atoms in the chain we shall expect that only β-oxidation will take place, for there are, as we have seen, sharp indications that ω-oxidation, if it takes place at all, does not assume significant proportions in chains of this length. In the case of a 6-carbon chain, for example, we should expect the following reactions:

$$\overset{\beta}{C}H_3CH_2CH_2\overset{\alpha}{C}H_2CH_2COOH$$
$$\downarrow$$
$$CH_3CH_2CH_2CO.CH_2COOH$$
$$\overset{\beta}{C}H_3CH_2\overset{\alpha}{C}H_2COOH + ?CH_3COOH$$
$$\downarrow$$
$$CH_3CO.CH_2COOH$$

Products: $CH_3CO.CH_2COOH + ?CH_3COOH$

The only possible source of acetoacetic acid here, over and above the single molecule accounted for by Knoop's theory, is the 2-carbon fragment. Even the theory of multiple alternate oxidation cannot account for the production of more than one molecule of acetoacetate in this particular case. Yet it has been shown that *all* the carbon of hexanoic acid can give rise to acetoacetate.

Experiment shows that butyric acid, with its 4 carbon atoms, yields a maximum of one molecule of acetoacetate. Hexanoic and octanoic acids can yield $1\frac{1}{2}$ and 2 molecules of acetoacetate respectively, but with decanoic and higher acids the amounts of ketone bodies formed are always less than the theoretical maximum. This, perhaps, is because ω-oxidation comes into play as longer chains are reached so that, in addition to the usual 2-carbon fragments, succinic acid also is formed and, being a glucose-former, tends to suppress the formation of ketone bodies.

Clearly it is important to consider the possibility that aceto-acetate may arise primarily from the 2-carbon units removed from the fatty chain by β-oxidation. These, as we have seen, probably consist of acetyl-Co A. Many experiments have been carried out in order to elucidate the fate of acetate itself when added to various tissue preparations. Feeding, perfusion, tissue-slice and brei experiments have all been used and, while different quantitative data have come out of different experiments, it has been established beyond reasonable doubt that acetic acid is at any rate partially converted into acetoacetate by liver and other tissues. That part which is not so converted disappears and is presumably oxidized. Moreover, the yields of acetoacetate are greatest in livers that are poor in glycogen and it therefore appears that two possible fates await acetic acid in the liver. Either (a) pairs of acetate molecules react together in some way and give rise to acetoacetate, from which the other ketone bodies subsequently arise, or else (b) acetate is completely oxidized. The factor determining the extent to which condensation and oxidation respectively shall take place appears to be the avail-ability of carbohydrate. With low-glycogen livers there is much condensation and little oxidation, while in high-glycogen livers there is much oxidation and little condensation. Here, therefore, as in fat metabolism generally, we find that the oxidation of fatty metabolites depends intimately upon the availability of carbohydrate or carbohydrate metabolites.

Convincing evidence for the formation of acetoacetate from acetate has been obtained by the use of isotopic carbon, for if isotopically labelled acetate is incubated with liver tissue and the resulting acetoacetate is isolated, it is found that the isotopic carbon has been transferred to the acetoacetate. The behaviour of octanoic acid in particular has been studied by the isotope method. Octanoic acid was prepared with C^{13} in the carboxyl radical, the product was incubated with rat liver tissue in the form of slices, and the acetoacetate formed was isolated and analysed for C^{13}. Now, according to the classical theory of β-oxidation, acetoacetate would be formed only from the butyrate left after two 2-carbon units had been removed, and the product should therefore contain no C^{13}. According to the theory of multiple alternate oxidation, the 8-carbon chain would give rise to two molecules of acetoacetate, of which only one would contain C^{13}, located in the carboxyl group. If, however, pairs of carbon atoms were removed in the form of acetic acid or some highly reactive derivative thereof, followed by random condensation of pairs of these 2-carbon units, C^{13} should be present both in the carboxyl and the ketonic groups of the product, but not in the methyl or $-CH_2-$ radicals:

$$CH_3C^{13}OOH + CH_3C^{13}OOH = CH_3C^{13}O.CH_3C^{13}OOH.$$

It was found that, in fact, isotopic carbon was present in the carboxylic and ketonic but not in the other two radicals, indicating that the acetoacetate formed must have been produced from the 2-carbon units split off from the molecules of octanoic acid by β-oxidation.

If, however, acetoacetate arises by purely random condensation of 2-C fragments, equal amounts of isotopic carbon would be expected to be present in the ketonic and carboxyl radicals. Actually, however, the carboxyl group is richer than the ketonic. This has been explained on the supposition that the free 2-C fragments can become (probably reversibly) attached to β-keto-acids, which subsequently lose *four* instead of only two carbon atoms, yielding acetoacetate directly, e.g.:

$$-CH_2CH_2CH_2CH_2\overset{*}{C}OOH$$
$$\downarrow$$
$$-CH_2CH_2CO.CH_2COOH$$
$$\downarrow$$
$$-CH_2CH_2COOH + CH_3\overset{*}{C}OOH$$
$$\downarrow \qquad\qquad \downarrow$$
$$-CO.CH_2\overset{*}{C}OOH + \overset{*}{C}H_3\overset{*}{C}OOH \longrightarrow -CO:CH_2CO.CH_2\overset{*}{C}OOH$$
$$\downarrow$$
$$-COOH + CH_3CO.CH_2\overset{*}{C}OOH$$

If this process, for which there is good evidence, takes place together with purely random condensation of pairs of 2-C units, the relatively low isotope content of the ketonic radical can be accounted for.

Krebs has produced evidence that acetoacetic acid may be formed from pyruvic and acetic acids together, thus emphasizing the relationship between the metabolism of acetate and that of a carbohydrate metabolite. His observations are consistent with the supposition that acetic and pyruvic acids condense together to form acetopyruvic acid. The latter, being an α-keto-acid, could then undergo oxidative decarboxylation and give rise to acetoacetate:

$$\begin{array}{ccccc}
CH_3 & & CH_3 & & CH_3 \\
| & & | & & | \\
COOH & & CO & & CO \\
+ & \xrightarrow{-H_2O} & | & \xrightarrow{+\frac{1}{2}O_2} & | \\
CH_3 & & CH_2 & & CH_2 \quad +CO_2 \\
| & & | & & | \\
CO & & CO & & COOH \\
| & & \cdots| \cdots & & \\
COOH & & COOH & &
\end{array}$$

Overall: $CH_3COOH + CH_3CO.COOH + \frac{1}{2}O_2 = CH_3CO.CH_2COOH + CO_2 + H_2O$

But the results are equally consistent with the supposition that pairs of acetate molecules condense together to form acetoacetate. It may be that in these experiments Krebs was in reality obtaining acetate in the form of acetyl-Co A by oxidative decarboxylation of the added pyruvate, and it is to be anticipated that this product, which we know to be a powerful biological acetylating reagent, would readily acetylate acetic acid itself:

$$CH_3CO \sim S—A + CH_3COOH \longrightarrow CH_3CO.CH_2COOH + HS—A.$$

The formation of ketone bodies from free acetate has, of course, been repeatedly demonstrated in tissue preparations of various kinds but is, nevertheless an endergonic process. We have reason to think that the 2-carbon product of β-oxidation probably consists of acetyl-Co A, an energy-rich compound and at the same time a natural acetylating agent, admirably qualified to serve as a source of acetoacetate. At the present time we can do little more than speculate, but the following reactions may be suggested:

(i) $CH_3CO \sim S—A + CH_3CO \sim S—A \longrightarrow CH_3CO.CH_2CO \sim S—A + HS—A,$

(ii) $CH_3CO.CH_2CO \sim S—A + HO.\textcircled{P} \longrightarrow CH_3CO.CH_2COOH + \textcircled{P} \sim S—A,$

(iii) $\textcircled{P} \sim S—A + ADP \longrightarrow HS—A + ATP.$

None of these reactions is essentially different from those already suggested as intermediate steps in β-oxidation (p. 480). Reaction (i) corresponds to reaction (f) in reverse, reaction (ii) to reaction (b) in reverse, and reaction (iii) to reaction (a) in reverse. Whatever criticism may be raised against this scheme it has at least the virtue of economy of hypotheses.

OXIDATION OF ACETOACETIC AND β-HYDROXYBUTYRIC ACIDS

Much attention has been given to the problem of the oxidative metabolism of acetoacetic and β-hydroxybutyric acids, and it is now well established that they are interconvertible through the action of β-hydroxybutyric dehydrogenase together with Co I, both of which are widely distributed in animal tissues.

Many tissues are able to oxidize added acetoacetate and β-hydroxybutyrate. Among the more recent contributions to this subject is the work of Kleinzeller, who studied the behaviour of a group of 4-carbon acids related to the ketone bodies, in the presence of sliced kidney tissue, a material that was selected because of its known ability to oxidize acetoacetate to carbon dioxide and water. The compounds examined included the following:

Butyric acid	$CH_3CH_2CH_2COOH$
Crotonic acid	$CH_3CH=CH\ COOH$
β-Hydroxybutyric acid	$CH_3CH(OH)CH_2COOH$
γ-Hydroxybutyric acid	$CH_2(OH)CH_2CH_2COOH$
α-γ-Dihydroxybutyric acid	$CH_2(OH)CH_2CH(OH)COOH$
Vinylacetic acid	$CH_2=CH.CH_2COOH$

All these substances were rapidly oxidized to carbon dioxide and in every case the oxidation was inhibited by malonate, which suggests that the oxidation of these substances, like that of the fatty acids themselves, takes place by way of the citric acid cycle.

Now if isotopically carboxyl-labelled acetoacetate is incubated with oxaloacetate in tissue homogenates, correspondingly labelled citrate can be formed, and similarly labelled derivatives can be obtained by the use of the usual inhibitors of the cycle. In this respect acetoacetate behaves like other β-keto-acids (p. 477), the two terminal carbon atoms being split off and incorporated into citric acid. Presumably, therefore, acetoacetate enters the cycle by way of acetyl-Co A once again, indicating that, since it can apparently arise from *and* give rise to acetyl-Co A, the reactions leading to its formation must be reversible, perhaps as follows:

(i) $CH_3CO\sim S—A + CH_3CO\sim S—A \rightleftharpoons CH_3CO.CH_2CO\sim S—A + HS—A$,

(ii) $CH_3CO.CH_2CO\sim S—A + HO℗ \rightleftharpoons CH_3CO.CH_2COOH + ℗\sim S—A$,

(iii) $℗\sim S—A + ADP \rightleftharpoons HS—A + ATP$.

If these reactions correspond to reality it follows that the formation of acetoacetate must be numbered among the reactions which lead to the generation of new energy-rich phosphate bonds.

If the reversibility of these reactions is accepted—and at present there is little evidence that they are in animal tissues, though they certainly are in bacteria—it follows that the oxidation of substances which, like butyrate, crotonate and β-hydroxybutyrate, are known to give rise to acetoacetate, can also be accounted for.

It remains to be explained why acetoacetate, β-hydroxy-butyrate and related compounds are freely oxidizable in certain tissues other than liver, even when carbohydrate is in short supply. Unlike the liver, kidney and muscle contain no oxalo-acetic decarboxylase, so that oxaloacetate is only spontaneously (as opposed to catalytically) degraded to pyruvate and carbon dioxide, and its concentration in these tissues is not immediately dependent upon the availability of carbohydrate. How these tissues maintain their stocks of oxaloacetate is not known; some oxaloacetate could arise by transdeamination of aspartic acid, and α-ketoglutaric, another reactant in the cycle, could be formed by the deamination of glutamate. In this connexion it is perhaps significant that L-glutamic aspartic transaminase and L-glutamic dehydrogenase are present in the tissues generally.

If we accept the scheme just proposed to account for the formation of acetoacetate, together with that proposed for the intermediate stages of β-oxidation (Fig. 37, p. 480), we have a hypothesis that can account for the complete oxidative de-gradation of fatty acids by way of the citric acid cycle, for the formation of ketone bodies by way of acetoacetate, and for the oxidative breakdown of any substance that can give rise either to fatty acids or to members of the group of ketone bodies. These are the salient features that have to be taken into account in any theory of fat metabolism.

It must be emphasized that our ideas here are as yet hardly out of the speculative phase. We have evidence enough only to be suggestive. In the last few pages we have taken what evidence is available at the time of writing and used it in a frankly speculative manner, trying, nevertheless, only to frame hypotheses that are reasonably consistent with the evidence and with general principles, and thus to gain a coherent idea of the way in which the intimate business of fatty acid metabolism is perhaps con-ducted. The field is being studied intensively at the present time and important advances may be expected in the very near future, perhaps even before these words appear in print. Evi-dence is accumulating that the oxidative degradation of the fatty acids is coupled up to the generation of new energy-rich bonds and the synthesis thereby of ATP, perhaps at each successive stage of β-oxidation, and certainly in the subsequent oxidative metabolism of the 2-carbon, acetyl-Co A units to which each such stage gives rise.

METABOLISM OF ACETATE IN MICRO-ORGANISMS

Although the citric acid cycle appears to be present in most and perhaps all kinds of cells and tissues, there is reason to think that it cannot account for more than a small fraction of the total energy output of yeast and a variety of other micro-organisms. Pyruvate and acetate can nevertheless be metabolized in such organisms, though by mechanisms of other kinds. In some cases, acetate, and the corresponding alcohol, ethanol, give rise to succinate and fumarate. Isotopic labelling at the α-carbon atom of these substances shows that succinate and fumarate probably originate in the following manner:

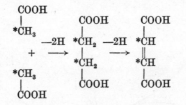

Here the presumptive 'active acetate' radicals react through the methyl group, as they do in citrate formation, and not through the carboxyl, as they do in acetylation.

Perhaps we have here an indication that the tricarboxylic, citric acid cycle is replaced in these micro-organisms by a dicarboxylic acid cycle, for most micro-organisms possess succinic dehydrogenase, fumarase, malic dehydrogenase, oxaloacetic decarboxylase and oxidative decarboxylation systems. These enzymes together could catalyse the oxidative cycle pictured in Fig. 38. Evidence for reaction (1) has already been quoted. The enzymes required for reactions (2), (3) and (4), viz. succinic dehydrogenase, fumarase and malic dehydrogenase, are known to occur in micro-organisms of many kinds, while reaction (5) is the Wood-Werkman reaction, catalysed by an oxaloacetic decarboxylase, which is well known among bacteria. Finally, the oxidative decarboxylation of pyruvate (6) certainly takes place in many micro-organisms, as witness the case of *B. delbrückii* and *Esch. coli*, already mentioned in these pages (p. 425).

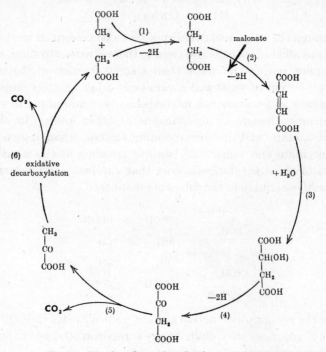

Fig. 38. Dicarboxylic acid cycle of micro-organisms.

This cycle, like its citric counterpart, involves succinic dehydrogenase, so that the respiration of the cells which utilize it would be expected to be stimulated by succinate, fumarate, malate and oxaloacetate, but inhibited by malonate. There is, in fact, evidence to this effect, evidence which was obtained in earlier studies of Szent-Györgyi's (p. 432) forerunner of Krebs's citric acid cycle.

SYNTHESIS OF FATTY ACIDS

It has long been known that fat can be synthesized from fatty metabolites such as acetoacetate, and also from carbohydrate sources. The naturally occurring fatty acids contain an even number of carbon atoms, practically without exception, and it follows that the starting materials for their synthesis must probably also contain even numbers of carbon atoms. It has from time to time been suggested that the raw material for the synthesis might be acetoacetate itself, with 4 carbon atoms, but in this case it might be anticipated that fatty acids with 4, 8, 12, 16 and 20 carbon atoms would predominate in nature. In fact, however, the 14-, 16- and 18-carbon acids are the most common, and all occur in similar proportions. It therefore seems probable that fatty acids must be synthesized from 2-carbon units.

The usual explanation in the past has been that fatty acids arise from acetetaldehyde by multiple aldol condensation, a reaction which readily takes place *in vitro*, followed by β-reduction, according to some scheme such as the following:

$$CH_3CHO + CH_3CHO = CH_3CH(OH)CH_2CHO$$

β-reduction

$$CH_3CH_2CH_2CHO + CH_3CHO = CH_3CH_2CH_2CH(OH)CH_2CHO$$

β-reduction

$$CH_3CH_2CH_2CH_2CH_2CHO + CH_3CHO = CH_3CH_2CH_2CH_2CH_2CH(OH)CH_2CHO$$

etc.

This hypothesis, at best, has always been purely speculative and with no factual basis, apart from the fact that aldehydes readily undergo aldol condensation under *in vitro* conditions. There is no reason to believe that acetaldehyde arises in quantity in the tissues of animals. Despite a complete lack of evidence it has often been suggested that acetaldehyde might arise, as it does in yeast, by the action of carboxylase upon pyruvic acid; this latter suggestion, indeed, has been thought to provide an explanation for the synthesis of fats from carbohydrate sources.

Recent developments in our ideas about fat metabolism suggest an alternative hypothesis which, if it is at present hardly less speculative than the aldol mechanism, has at least the virtue of being reasonable. It may be suggested that the starting material is not acetaldehyde but acetyl-Co A, i.e. 'active acetate'. The latter is known to be derivable from pyruvic acid by oxidative decarboxylation and, in addition, is probably the predominant product of the β-oxidative fission of fatty acid chains. It can also arise from free acetate by reacting with phosphorylated Co A formed at the expense of ATP in the manner suggested on p. 443. Recent work bears out the truth of the supposition that fatty acids can be synthesized from 2-carbon units in the form of acetate, though without giving any indication of the intermediate processes. Acetic acid, containing deuterium in the methyl group and C^{13} in the carboxyl radical, was fed to rats for 8 days. The liver fats were then collected and analysed, with the result that deuterium and C^{13} were found alternately in $-CH_2-$ radicals throughout the chain, while C^{13} also appeared in the terminal carboxyl group.

Pairs of acetyl-Co A molecules might react together to give β-keto-compounds which, by β-reduction (i.e. reversal of β-oxidation) would yield corresponding derivatives of Co A, thus:

$$CH_3CO\sim S-A + CH_3CO\sim S-A \rightarrow CH_3CO.CH_2CO\sim S-A + HS-A$$

β-reduction

$$CH_3CH_2CH_2CO\sim S-A + CH_3CO\sim S-A \rightarrow CH_3CH_2CH_2CO.CH_2CO\sim S-A + HS-A$$

β-reduction

$$CH_3CH_2CH_2CH_2CH_2CO\sim S-A + CH_3CO\sim S-A \rightarrow CH_3CH_2CH_2CH_2CH_2CO.CH_2CO\sim S-A + HS-$$

β-reduction

$$CH_3CH_2CH_2CH_2CH_2CH_2CH_2CO\sim S-A, \text{ etc.}$$

Every addition of 2 carbon atoms to the chain in this scheme consists in an acetylation reaction and, as we know, acetyl-Co A is capable of performing certain biological acetylations. Further, the scheme as a whole postulates no reactions other than the reversal of those already suspected of taking place in β-oxidative degradation (Fig. 37). Certainly this scheme is much more in keeping with facts and probabilities than is the older hypothesis of aldol condensation.

CONVERSION OF FAT TO CARBOHYDRATE

While there can be no doubt whatever that fats can be synthesized from carbohydrate sources, the reverse process takes place to a very limited extent and, in fact, it has been denied that the conversion of fat into carbohydrate can take place at all. Much of the earlier work on this problem gave results which were somewhat vague, and some of it has actually been discredited. Inasmuch as they yield glycerol on hydrolysis, and may possibly yield succinic acid as a result of ω- and repetitive β-oxidation, fats certainly are potential sources of glycogen, for glycerol and succinate alike are quantitatively converted into glucose when administered to diabetic or phlorrhizinized animals. Apart from glycerol and, if ω-oxidation is a normal process, a certain amount of succinate, fats are not known to give rise to anything but 'active acetate' and the free acetate and ketone bodies which can be derived from it.

Experiments have been performed in which the incubation of sliced rat liver with butyric acid gave small but apparently significant increases in the glycogen content of the tissue. But, as we now know, glycogen and fat alike are oxidized through a common metabolite in the form of 'active acetate' and it may well be that the addition of butyrate merely spares the oxidation of glycogen by giving rise to this common metabolite.

Since 'active acetate' can be formed by the oxidative decarboxylation of pyruvate and can itself give rise to the synthesis of fat, there is not much doubt that this is an important route for the production of fat from carbohydrate sources. It may be asked whether this process is reversible. There is, however, no evidence that the stage of oxidative decarboxylation can be reversed, at any rate in animal tissues, so that, while pyruvate freely gives rise to 'active acetate', the latter is not convertible back into pyruvate. Buchanan has shown that, if lactate or pyruvate containing isotopic carbon is administered to animals, the carbon isotope can be partly recovered in the liver glycogen. If acetate similarly 'labelled' is used instead, however, very little transference of the isotope to the liver glycogen can be detected. It may therefore reasonably be assumed that the conversion of acetate to pyruvate takes place to a limited extent at most if, indeed, it takes place at all.

In short, there is no convincing evidence for any large-scale production of carbohydrate from fatty sources and, in so far as such a conversion takes place at all, it must probably be attributed to the formation of glycerol, and perhaps succinate to some extent, as intermediary metabolites of fat katabolism.

BIBLIOGRAPHY

The list of references that follows makes no claim to be exhaustive. It is designed only as an introduction to the literature, but a wealth of further references will be found in the books (marked with an asterisk) and articles listed here. Preference has in general been given to recent publications, but for the most recent work the *Annual Review of Biochemistry* should be consulted: here will be found many valuable and critical appraisals of the newest work, together with exhaustive lists of references to recent papers. Short but useful reviews of specific subjects will be found annually in *Federation Proceedings*, the *Annual Reports of the Chemical Society* and elsewhere.

REFERENCES

	Chapters
ARNON, D. I. & HOAGLAND, D. R. (1944). Plant nutrition. *Biol. Rev.* **19**, 55.	IX
BACH, S. J. (1945). Biological methylation. *Biol. Rev.* **20**, 158.	V
BALDWIN, E. (1936). Arginase. *Biol. Rev.* **11**, 247.	XII
*BALDWIN, E. (1949). *An Introduction to Comparative Biochemistry* (3rd ed.). Cambridge.	XII, XIII
BARRON, E. S. G. (1943). Mechanisms of carbohydrate metabolism. *Adv. Enzymol.* **3**, 149.	XV–XVII
BELL, D. J. (1948). The structure of glycogens. *Biol. Rev.* **23**, 256.	IV, XVI
BERGMANN, M. (1942). A classification of proteolytic enzymes. *Adv. Enzymol.* **2**, 49.	IV
BERGMANN, M. & FRUTON, J. S. (1941). The specificity of proteinases. *Adv. Enzymol.* **1**, 63.	IV
BLASCHKO, H. (1945). The amino-acid decarboxylases of animal tissues. *Adv. Enzymol.* **5**, 67.	IV, XVII
BLOCH, K. (1947). The metabolism of acetic acid in animal tissues. *Physiol. Rev.* **27**, 574.	XVII, XVIII
*BLOOR, W. R. (1943). *Biochemistry of the Fatty Acids and their Compounds, the Lipids.* New York.	XVIII
BRADFIELD, J. R. G. (1950). The localization of enzymes in cells. *Biol. Rev.* **25**, 113.	General
*BRAND, T. VON (1946). *Anaerobiosis in Invertebrates.* Normandy, Miss.	XV, XVI
BREUSCH, F. L. (1948). The biochemistry of fatty acid catabolism. *Adv. Enzymol.* **8**, 343.	XVIII
BUCHANAN, J. M. & HASTINGS, A. B. (1946). The use of isotopically marked carbon in the study of intermediary metabolism. *Physiol. Rev.* **26**, 120.	General, VIII

Chapters

CHIBNALL, A. C. (1939). *Protein Metabolism in the plant.*
New Haven.   X, XI

DAVIES, R. E. (1951). The mechanism of hydrochloric
acid production by the stomach. *Biol. Rev.* **26**,
87.   IX

DIXON, M. (1949). *Multi-enzyme Systems.* Cambridge.   General

DOYLE, W. L. (1943). Nutrition of the Protozoa. *Biol.
Rev.* **18**, 119.   IX

DUBUISSON, M. (1950). Muscle activity and muscle
proteins. *Biol. Rev.* **25**, 46.   XVI

ENGELHARDT, V. A. (1946). Adenosinetriphosphatase
properties of myosin. *Adv. Enzymol.* **6**, 147.   XVI

FOLLEY, S. J. & KAY, H. D. (1936). The phosphatases.
Ergebn. Enzymforsch. **5**, 159.   IV

FRAZER, A. C. (1946). The absorption of triglyceride fat
from the intestine. *Physiol. Rev.* **26**, 103.   IX

GALE, E. F. (1946). The bacterial amino-acid decarboxylases. *Adv. Enzymol.* **6**, 1.   IV, XI

GALE, E. F. (1947). *The Chemical Activities of Bacteria.*
London.   General

GREEN, D. E. (1940). *Mechanisms of Biological Oxidations.* Cambridge.   VI, VII

GREEN, D. E. (1941). Enzymes and trace substances.
Adv. Enzymol. **1**, 177.   General

GREEN, D. E. (editor) (1946). *Currents in Biochemical
Research.* New York.   General

GREEN, D. E. (1951). The cyclophorase complex of
enzymes. *Biol. Rev.* **26**, 410.   XVII, XVIII

GUNSALUS, I. C. (1950). Decarboxylation and transamination. *Fed. Proc.* **9**, 556.   IV, V, X

HALDANE, J. B. S. (1930). *Enzymes.* London.   I, II

HASSID, W. Z. & DOUDOROFF, M. (1950). Synthesis of
disaccharides with bacterial enzymes. *Adv. Enzymol.*
10, 123.   V

HEHRE, E. J. (1951). Enzymic synthesis of polysaccharides; a biological type of polymerization. *Adv.
Enzymol.* **11**, 297.   V

HERBST, R. M. (1944). The transamination reaction.
Adv. Enzymol. **4**, 75.   V, X

HEVESY, G. (1947). Some applications of radioactive
indicators in turnover studies. *Adv. Enzymol.* **7**,   General
111.   VIII

HILDEBRANDT, F. M. (1947). Recent progress in industrial
fermentation. *Adv. Enzymol.* **7**, 557.   XV

HOPKINS, R. H. (1946). The actions of the amylases.
Adv. Enzymol. **6**, 389.   IV

Chapters

JENSEN, H. & TENENBAUM, L. E. (1944). The influence of hormones on enzymatic reactions. *Adv. Enzymol.* **4**, 257. — General

JOHNSON, M. J. & BERGER, J. (1942). The enzymatic properties of peptidases. *Adv. Enzymol.* **2**, 69. — IV

KALCKAR, H. M. (1941). The nature of energetic coupling in biological systems. *Chem. Rev.* **28**, 7. — III

KALCKAR, H. M. (1942). Function of phosphate in cellular assimilations. *Biol. Rev.* **17**, 28. — III

KLEINZELLER, A. (1948). Synthesis of lipides. *Adv. Enzymol.* **8**, 299. — XVIII

KNIGHT, B. C. J. G. (1945). Growth factors in microbiology. *Vitam. & Horm.* **3**, 108. — IX

KREBS, H. A. (1934). Urea formation in the animal body. *Ergebn. Enzymforsch.* **3**, 247. — XII

KREBS, H. A. (1943). The intermediary stages in the biological oxidation of carbohydrate. *Adv. Enzymol.* **3**, 191. — XVI, XVII

*LARDY, H. A. (editor) (1949). *Respiratory Enzymes* (2nd ed.). Minneapolis. — VI, VII

LAUFFER, M. A., PRICE, W. C. & PETRE, A. W. (1949). The nature of viruses. *Adv. Enzymol.* **9**, 171. — XIV

LEHNINGER, A. L. (1951). The organized respiratory activity of isolated rat-liver mitochondria. In *Enzymes and Enzyme Systems*. Cambridge, Mass. — XVII, XVIII

LEIBOWITZ, J. & HESTRIN, S. (1945). Alcoholic fermentation of the oligosaccharides. *Adv. Enzymol.* **5**, 87. — XV

LIPMANN, F. (1941). Metabolic generation and utilization of phosphate bond energy. *Adv. Enzymol.* **1**, 99. — III

LIPMANN, F. (1946). Acetyl phosphate. *Adv. Enzymol.* **6**, 231. — III, XVII, XVIII

LIPMANN, F. (1949). Mechanism of peptide bond formation. *Fed. Proc.* **8**, 597. — V

McANALLY, R. A. & PHILLIPSON, A. T. (1944). Digestion in the ruminant. *Biol. Rev.* **19**, 41. — IX

MARTIUS, C. & LYNEN, F. (1950). Probleme des Citronensäurecyklus. *Adv. Enzymol.* **10**, 167. — XVII, XVIII

MEYER, K. (1943). The chemistry of glycogen. *Adv. Enzymol.* **3**, 109. — IV, XVI

MOOG, F. (1946). The physiological significance of the phosphomonoesterases. *Biol. Rev.* **21**, 41. — IV

*NACHMANSOHN, D. (editor) (1950). *Metabolism and Function*. (Articles by A. V. Hill, H. H. Weber, M. Dubuisson, A. Szent-Györgyi, D. M. Needham and others.) New York. — XVI

Chapters

Needham, J. & *Green*, D. E. (editors) (1937). *Perspectives in Biochemistry*. Cambridge.   General

Neurath, H. & *Schwert*, G. W. (1950). The mode of action of the crystalline pancreatic enzymes. *Chem. Rev.* 46, 69.   IV

Nord, F. F. & *Vitucci*, J. C. (1948). Certain aspects of the microbiological degradation of cellulose. *Adv. Enzymol.* 8, 253.   IX

Ochoa, S. (1951). Biological mechanisms of carboxylation and decarboxylation. *Physiol. Rev.* 31, 56.   XV–XVII

Peat, S. (1951). The biological transformations of starch. *Adv. Enzymol.* 11, 339.   IV, V

Petrie, A. H. K. (1943). Protein synthesis in plants. *Biol. Rev.* 18, 105.   X

Pigman, W. W. (1944). Specificity, classification and mechanism of action of the glycosidases. *Adv. Enzymol.* 4, 41.   IV

Pirie, N. W. (1940). The criteria of purity used in the study of large molecules of biological origin. *Biol. Rev.* 15, 377.   General

Potter, V. R. (1944). Biological transformations of energy and the cancer problem. *Adv. Enzymol.* 4, 201.   III

Ratner, S. (1949). Mechanism of urea synthesis. *Fed. Proc.* 8, 603.   XII

Roche, J. & *Thoai*, N. (1950). Phosphatase alcalin. *Adv. Enzymol.* 10, 83.   IV

Rose, W. C. (1938). The nutritive significance of the amino-acids. *Physiol. Rev.* 18, 109.   IX

Rose, W. C. (1949). Amino-acid requirements of man. *Fed. Proc.* 8, 546.   IX

Schlenck, F. (1945). Enzymatic reactions involving nicotinamide and its related compounds. *Adv. Enzymol.* 5, 207.   VII, XIV

Schlenck, F. (1949). Chemistry and enzymology of nucleic acids. *Adv. Enzymol.* 9, 455.   XIV

Schoenheimer, R. (1949). *The Dynamic State of Body Constituents*. Cambridge, Mass.   General

Sizer, I. W. (1943). Effects of temperature on enzyme kinetics. *Adv. Enzymol.* 3, 35.   I, II

Slyke, D. D. van (1942). The kinetics of hydrolytic enzymes and their bearing on methods for measuring enzyme activity. *Adv. Enzymol.* 2, 33.   I, II

Smith, E. L. (1951). Aspects of the specificity and mode of action of some peptidases. In *Enzymes and Enzyme Systems*. Cambridge, Mass.   IV

Chapters

SMITH, H. W. (1936). Retention and physiological role of urea in Elasmobranchii. *Biol. Rev.* **11**, 49.   XII

*SOSKIN, S. & LEVINE, R. (1946). *Carbohydrate Metabolism*. Chicago.   XVI, XVII

STEARN, A. E. (1949). Kinetics of biological reactions, with special reference to enzymic processes. *Adv. Enzymol.* **9**, 25.   I, II

*STEPHENSON, M. (1949). *Bacterial Metabolism* (3rd ed.). London.   General

STOTZ, E. (1945). Pyruvate metabolism. *Adv. Enzymol.* **5**, 129.   XVII

STREET, H. E. (1949). Nitrogen metabolism in higher plants. *Adv. Enzymol.* **9**, 391.   X–XI

STREET, H. E. (1950). The role of high energy phosphate bonds in biosynthesis. *Sci. Progress*, **38**, 43.   III

*SUMNER, J. B. & MYRBÄCK, K. (1951–2). *The Enzymes*. New York.   General

*SYMPOSIUM (1950) of the Biochemical Society (ed. R. T. Williams), No. 4. *Biochemical Aspects of Genetics*. Cambridge.   General

SYMPOSIUM (1950) on *Chemical Transformations in Photosynthesis*. *Fed. Proc.* **9**, 524.   IX

*SYMPOSIUM (1948) of the Biochemical Society (Ed. R. T. Williams), No. 1, p. 90. *The Nomenclature of Amino-acids*. Cambridge.   XI

*SYMPOSIUM (1947) of the Society for Experimental Biology, No. 1. *Nucleic Acid*. Cambridge.   XIV

*SYMPOSIUM (1951) on *Isotopes in Biochemistry* (CIBA Foundation). London.   General

*SYMPOSIUM (1942) on *Respiratory Enzymes*. Wisconsin.   VI, VII

*SZENT-GYÖRGYI, A. VON (1951). *Chemistry of Muscular Contraction* (2nd Ed.). New York.   XVI

TRÄGER, W. (1941). The nutrition of invertebrates. *Physiol. Rev.* **21**, 1.   IX

TRÄGER, W. (1947). Insect nutrition. *Biol. Rev.* **22**, 148.   IX

VONK, H. J. (1937). The specificity and collaboration of digestive enzymes in Metazoa. *Biol. Rev.* **12**, 245.   IX

WILLIAMS, R. J. (1941). Growth-promoting nutrilites for yeasts. *Biol. Rev.* **16**, 49.   IX

*WILLIAMS, R. T. (1947). *Detoxication Mechanisms*. London.   XI

WOOD, H. G. (1946). The fixation of carbon dioxide and the inter-relationships of the tricarboxylic acid cycle. *Physiol. Rev.* **26**, 198.   XVII

Brain, metabolism in thiamine deficiency, 420–1
— — of pyruvate in, 420–1
— oxidative decarboxylation in, 420–1
Branching factor, 130–2, 408–9
Branching points (of polysaccharides), 96–7
Brassica, 161
Brei, use in metabolic studies, 230–1
British antilewisite (BAL), 286
Bromelin, 93
Bromobenzene, 287
Bromogorgoic acid, *see* Dibromotyrosine
p-**Bromophenyl mercapturic acid,** 287
iso-**Butyl alcohol,** 387
n-**Butylbenzene,** 474
Butyric acid, formation from cellulose, 99, 457
— ketone bodies from, 224, 466, 470, 474, 481, 483–7
— oxidation of, 487
— synthesis of fatty acids from, 457
γ-**Butyrobetaine,** 334

Cadaverine, detoxication, 166, 294
— formation by bacteria, 114, 294
Caffein, 352
Calcium, 38, 108, 370
Calorific value, of foodstuffs, 60, 457–8
Calorimetry, animal, 60–1
Camel, 458
Cannizzaro reaction, 165, 210
Carbamyl glutamic acid, 142, 292–3, 322
Carbobenzoxy compounds, 82, 83
Carbobenzoxyglycylanilide, enzymic synthesis, 20
Carbohydrases, 94–104
Carbohydrate, absorption from gut, 246–8
— alcoholic fermentation of, 363–86
— amino-acids from, 268–9, 274, 446, 449–50
— calorific value of, 457–8
— digestion of, 244–6
— fat from, 410, 457, 491, 493
— from amino-acids, 259–60, 273–5, 408, 410

— from fat, 493–4
— from fatty acids, *see* Propionic acid
— from non-carbohydrate material, *see* Glyconeogenesis
— glycolysis, in liver, 403–12
— — in muscle, 394–403
— oxidation, 430–55
Carbohydrate metabolism, aerobic, 430–55
— anaerobic, *see* Fermentation, Glycolysis
— energy-yield of fermentation, 364–5, 378–81
— — of glycolysis, 364–5, 395–6
— — of oxidation, 212–16, 452–5
— linkage with fat metabolism, 410, 429, 449, 464–8, 484
— — with protein metabolism, 223–4, 259–60, 429, 436, 449
— relationship to fatty liver, 459–61
— — to ketogenesis, 465–8, 483–4
Carbon dioxide, fixation in liver, 429, 444, 450–1
— from citric cycle, 446
— from dicarboxylic cycle, 490
— from fermentation, 376, 378, 418
— from oxidative decarboxylation, 43, 116, 419–27, 434, 446, 490
— from respiration, 418–20, 446, 490
— from 'straight' decarboxylation, 42–3, 115, 370, 418–20
Carbon, isotopic, *see* Isotopic carbon
Carbon monoxide, inhibition of *Atmungsferment,* 171–3, 179–82
— — of cellular respiration, 171–3
— — of cytochrome oxidase, 40, 179–82
— — of indophenol oxidase, 179–82
— — influence of light on, 40, 171–3, 179–82
— reaction with *Atmungsferment,* 171–3
— — with chlorocruorin, 174
— — with cytochrome a_3, 179–82
— — with cytochrome oxidase, 40, 179–82
Carbonic anhydrase, 114–15
Carboxylase, coenzyme requirement of, 43, 115, 370, 376, 379, 418
— in yeast, 42–3, 370, 376, 379, 418
— production of acetaldehyde by, 42, 115, 370, 376, 379, 418, 491

[**Carboxylase,**] properties of, 115

β-Carboxylase, see Oxaloacetic decarboxylase

β-Carboxylation, see Oxaloacetic decarboxylase

Carboxypeptidase, activation, 85
— esterase activity of, 92
— in digestion, 83, 90–1, 243
— in pancreatic juice, 83, 243
— properties, 90–1
— specificity, 90–1

Carnitine, 334

Carnosinase, 94, 345

Carnosine, β-alanine in, 282, 297, 345
— histidine in, 282, 297, 345
— in vertebrate muscle, 297, 345
— methylation of, 297, 345
— replacement of histidine by, 345

Carriers, as true catalysts, 44–5, 157, 183, 208
— of amidine groups, see Arginine
— of amino-groups, see Aspartic acid, Glutamic acid
— of hydrogen, see Accessory carriers, Coenzymes I and II, Cytochromes, Flavoproteins, Prosthetic groups
— of methyl groups, see Methionine
— of phosphate, see Adenosine diphosphate, Adenosine triphosphate
— of sulphydryl groups, see Homocysteine

Cartilage, ossification of, 108

Casein, action of rennin on, 92
— phosphoserine in, 283

'Caseinogen', see Casein

Catalase, absorption spectrum of, 27
— compared with haemoglobin, 37
— inhibition, 27, 168
— peroxidase activity of, 168–9
— properties, 168–9

Catalase-azide, 27, 168

Catalase-azide-peroxide, 27

Catalyst, amount required, 3, 4, 29
— definition, 2
— directive effect of, 5
— effect on reaction velocity, 2–3
— heavy metals as, 2, 40
— inhibition, 3–4
— initiation of new reactions by, 4, 57

— reversibility of action, 3
— specificity, 5
— thermostable, see Activators, Coenzymes, Myokinase
— water as, 2
— see also Enzymes

Catechol, action of polyphenol oxidase on, 156
— as hydrogen-carrier, 157
— in 'browning' of plant tissues, 158

Caudal necrosis, 461, 468

Cellobiase, 102

Cellobiose, 102

Cellular respiration (enzymes), 148–216

Cellulase, 99–100

Cellulose, digestion of, 99–100, 237, 244, 411, 457

Cephalins, ethanolamine in, 253, 331

Cephalochorda, 340–1

Cephalopods, agmatine in, 342
— octopine in, 138, 293, 343

Charcoal 'models', see Blood charcoal 'models'

Chelation, 85

Chelonia, eggs of, 312
— nitrogen excretion of, 311–12, 315

Chemosynthesis, 233

Chick embryo, 313–14, 458, 466–7

Chitin, 100

Chitinase, 100

Chloral, 148–9

Chloral hydrate, 149

Chlorella, 184

Chloride, activation of amylases by, 41–2, 49, 98

Chlorocruorin, 172, 174

Chlorophyll, bacterial counterparts of, 233
— in photosynthesis, 233

Cholamine, see Ethanolamine

Cholesterol, action of bile salts on, 250
— in blood, 459
— production of fatty liver by, 460

Cholesterol esters, in blood, 459

Cholic acid, in bile salts, 249

Choline, acetylation of, 143, 331, 423
— as source of methyl groups, 143, 288, 330–1, 334
— as vitamin, 331

[Fats,] desaturation of, by liver, 468–9, 477–8
— digestion of, 106–7, 248–54
— emulsification of, in gut, 248–50
— first fate after absorption, 356
— from carbohydrate, 410, 457, 491, 493
— from cellulose, 457
— from protein, 259, 274
— functions, 460–1
— 'labelled', in absorption studies, 253–4
— — in metabolic studies, 456, 459, 471, 484, 492
— metabolic water from, 458
— metabolism, 456–94
— — linkage of, with carbohydrate, 410, 429, 449, 464–8, 484
— mobilization of, 459
— specific nature of, 456–7
— storage, 456–60
— synthesis, 106, 457
— tolerance, 466–7
— transport, 253–4, 456–60
— see also Fatty acids
Fatty acids, absorption of, 250–54
— acetate from, 462–3, 478
— acetylcoenzyme A from, 462–3, 475–6, 478–80
— 'active acetate' from, 449, 462, 478–86
— carbohydrate from, 457
— dicarboxylic acids from, 472–5
— desaturation of, in liver, 468–9, 477–8
— emulsification by, 250
— from acetate, 457, 491–2
— from butyrate, 457
— from carbohydrate, 410, 457, 491, 493
— from cellulose, by micro-organisms, 99, 244, 411, 457
— ketone bodies from, 224, 463–8, 470–1, 480–6
— multiple alternate oxidation of, 481–2, 484
— oxidation by citric cycle, 462–3, 475–6
— β-oxidation of, 469–72, 476–80
— ω-oxidation of, 472–5
— synthesis of, 457, 491–3
Fatty liver, 459–61

Feeding experiments, in metabolic studies, 219–22
Fermentation, alcoholic, adenosine phosphates in, 370–2, 374–81
— arsenate effect on, 383
— by yeast cells, 368, 381–4
— — juice, 366–81
— coenzymes of, 38, 370, 378–9
— energetics of, 364–6, 378–81
— enzymes (summary), 378–9
— formation of acetic acid in, 385–6
— — of fusel oil in, 363, 386–7
— generation of energy-rich bonds in, 375–6, 378–81
— glycerol as product of, 368, 383–6
— influence of pH on, 385–6
— — of phosphate on, 368, 374–5, 378–9, 382
— inhibition by arsenate, 383
— — by bisulphite, 371, 376, 379, 384–5
— — by dialysis, 369, 371, 375–7, 379
— — by fluoride, 371, 373–5, 379, 383
— — by iodoacetate, 371–2, 375, 377, 379
— inhibitors (summary), 378–9
— Neuberg's three forms of, 384–6
— overall reactions of, 377–9
— reactions (summary), 378–9
— selective inhibitors of, 371, 379
Fermentation, lactic, 4, 5, 10, 192
Ficin, 93
Fig, 93
Firefly, 75
Fishes, nitrogen excretion of, 307–10, 315, 332–3, 362
Flavin mononucleotide, see Riboflavin phosphate
Flavokinase, 122
Flavoproteins, as reduced-coenzyme dehydrogenases, 201–7
— functions, 206–7
— properties, 169, 201–7
Fluoride, inhibition of catalase by, 168
— — of enolase by, 112, 375, 379
— — of fermentation by, 371, 373–5, 379, 383
— — of glyolysis by, 394, 407
Fluoroacetate, 448

[**Glutathione,**] glycine in, 280–1
— oxidation by oxygen, 285
— –SH groups of, 40, 285
— structure, 281
— synthesis of, 134–6
Glyceraldehyde, optical activity of, 277–8
Glycerides, di- and mono-, 106–7, 250
Glycerol, fermentative manufacture, 384–6
— in absorption of fatty acids, 252–3
— in glycogenesis, 224, 273, 408, 410, 462, 493–4
— in normal fermentation, 368, 383–4
Glycerol-α-phosphate, see α-Glycerophosphate
α-Glycerophosphate, action of phosphatase on, 108, 384
— free energy of phosphate bond, 71
— in absorption of fatty acids, 252–3
— in fermentation, 373–4, 384
— in glyconeogenesis, 410, 462
α-Glycerophosphate dehydrogenase (soluble), in fermentation, 373, 383
— insoluble, 190–1
— properties, 190–1, 193
— soluble, 193, 373, 383
Glycine, creatine from, 141–2, 288, 337–8
— deamination of, 163, 264, 275, 280
— ethanolamine from, 280
— glycogenic, 260, 280
— glyoxylic acid from, 280
— in association with betaine, 280, 334
— — with sarcosine, 280, 334
— in bile salts, 249, 280
— in detoxication, 281, 292, 335, 469
— in glutathione, 280–1
— in glycocholic acid, 249, 280
— in purine synthesis, 327
— methylation of, 280, 333–4
— non-essential, 256
— special metabolism of, 280–1
— transamidination of, 141, 337–8
Glycine betaine, demethylation of, 143, 288, 334

— formation of, 280, 331, 333–4
— in association with glycine, 334
— in transmethylation, 143, 288, 334
— occurrence, 328, 333–4, 346
Glycine oxidase, 163, 264, 275, 280
Glycocholic acid, 249, 280; see also Bile salts
Glycocyamine, creatine from, 142, 288, 337–8
— formation, 141, 337–8
— transmethylation of, 142, 288, 337–8
Glycogen, action of amylases on, 95–8, 245
— constitution, 97
— digestion of, 95–8, 245–6
— enzymic synthesis of, 65, 72–4, 80, 129–33; see also Glycogenesis, Glyconeogenesis
— in diabetes, 224, 413–14, 465
— in starvation, 273, 410, 462, 465
— metabolism of, aerobic, 430–52
— — anaerobic, 388–414
— occurrence, 411
— phosphorolysis, 73, 129–33, 394–5, 406–9, 411–13
— see also Glycogenolysis, Glycolysis
Glycogenesis, in liver, 65, 73, 129–33, 273–4, 405–7, 408–12, 417, 462
— in muscle, 73, 129–33, 405–7, 411–12
— see also Glucogenesis
Glycogenolysis, 65, 129–33, 411–12
Glycollic acid, 463
Glycolysis, coenzymes of (summary), 407
— definition, 408
— energetics, 364–6, 395–6
— enzymes (summary), 407
— inhibitors (summary), 407
— in muscle, 388–403, 406
— in other tissues, 403–14
— reactions (summary), 406
— reversibility, 405–7
Glyconeogenesis, definition, 408
— from amino-acids, 260, 273–4, 408, 410
— from fatty acids, 411, 457, 493–4
— from glycerol, 224, 273–4, 408, 462, 493–4
— from lactate, 224, 273–4, 405–7, 410, 416–17

521

Phospho-*enol*-pyruvic acid, action of enolase on, 76, 112, 375, 378, 381, 406
— energy-rich bond of, 76, 112, 381
— in fermentation, 375, 378, 381
— in glycolysis, 406
— in transphosphorylation, 122, 376, 378, 406
— reversible reaction with ADP, 405–6
Phosphoriboisomerase, 145, 353
Phosphoric acid, as coenzyme, 38, 370, 374–5, 379, 407
— in absorption of fatty acids, 252–3
— — of sugars, 247–8
— in coenzymes I and II, 185–6
— in fermentation, 368, 370, 374–5, 378–9, 382
— in glycolysis, 129–33, 391–2, 394, 406–7, 412
— in muscle, 391–2, 394, 396–403, 406–7
— in nucleotides, 350
— in ossification, 108
— in phosphorolysis, 73, 126–33, 353–4, 394–5, 406–7, 408–13
Phosphorolysis, *see* Phosphorylases
Phosphorylases, in glycogenesis, 73, 126–33, 408–12
— in glycogenolysis, 408–12
— in glycolysis, 394–5, 406–7, 411–12
— in liver, 73, 129–33, 408–9, 412
— in muscle, 129–33, 394, 407, 411–12
— in peas, 129
— in potatoes, 129, 131
— in synthesis of nucleosides, 133, 353–4
— inhibition by glucose, 413
— properties, 79, 125–33
— synthetic action, 73, 125–33, 353–4, 405–6, 408–9
— *see also* Amylophosphorylase, Nucleoside phosphorylase, Sucrose phosphorylase
Phosphorylation, in absorption of fatty acids, 252–3
— in absorption of sugars, 247–8
— magnesium in, 40
— of nucleosides, 354–9
— of sugars, in fermentation, 368–9, 371–2, 378
— — in glycogenesis, 408–9

— — in glycolysis, 406
— *see also* Transphosphorylation
Phosphoserine, 283
Phosphotriose isomerase, in fermentation, 372, 373
— in glycolysis, 407
— properties, 144
Photinus pyralis, 75
Photosynthesis, 233, 271
Physiological salines, 227–8
Pigeon, uricogenesis in, 326–7
Pimelic acid, 473
Pineapple, 93
pK values, of enzymes, as quantitative characteristic, 47–9
Plant, amylases, 95–8
— asparaginase in, 111, 271–2
— L-aspartic transaminase in, 140, 266, 271–2
— 'browning' of, 158
— cytochromes, 179
— L-glutamic dehydrogenase in, 195
— — transaminase in, 266
— intracellular peptidases in, 93
— nutrition of, 233
— peroxidase, 167–8
— phenol oxidases, 155–60
— phosphatases, 123–5
— phosphorylases, 129–32
— respiration, 157–8, 184
— storage of nitrogen in, 271–2
— triosephosphate dehydrogenase of, 197
— viruses, 347–8
Platyhelminths, 239
Polyfructofuranosides, 100
Polyphenol oxidases, 156–8, 160
Polyphosphatases, 107–8; *see also* Adenosinetriphosphatase, Pyrophosphatase
Polysaccharases, 95–100
Polysaccharides, bacterial, 127–8
— digestion, 94–100, 244–5
— synthesis, 127–33; *see also* Glycogenesis, Glyconeogenesis
Porphyropsin, 46
Portal blood stream, amino-acids in, 243
— fatty acids in, 254
Potassium, as coenzyme, 38, 370, 406
— in phosphorylation of pyruvic acid, 406

Potato, aldehyde oxidase of, 165
— 'browning' of, 158
— phosphorylase of, 129–33
— polyphenol oxidase of, 156–8
Pre-mortal rise, of nitrogen excretion, 258
Primates, detoxication by glutamine in, 292
— excretion of purines by, 162, 361–2
Priming reactions (general), 64–5, 72
Pro-enzymes, see Enzyme precursors
Prolidase, 91
Proline, glucogenic, 260
— imino-acid, 299
— non-essential, 256
— special metabolism, 299–300
Proline oxidase, 299–300
Propionic acid, formation from cellulose, 99, 410–11, 457
— glycogenesis from, 273–4, 408, 410–11, 457, 471, 477
n-Propyl benzene, 474
Pro-rennin, 92
Prosthetic groups, activation of, 46, 169–70, 203
— adenineflavin dinucleotide in, 155, 163–5, 169–70, 201–7, 355
— as hydrogen acceptors, 46, 169–70, 201–7
— — carriers, 169–70
— compared with coenzymes, 45–6, 169–70
— — with substrates, 45–6, 146
— copper in, 155–6, 159, 161, 170
— 2:3-diphosphoglyceric acid as, 147, 407
— flavin mononucleotide in, 201–7, 355
— general properties, 45–7
— glucose-1:6-diphosphate as, 146, 379, 407
— iron in, 155, 162, 167–8, 178–81
— metallic, 85
— mode of action of, 146, 169–70
— of oxidases, 155
— pyridoxal, pyridoxamine in, 114, 137–40, 268
— riboflavin in, 201–7
— zinc in, 41, 115, 155, 162
— see also Activation, Coenzymes

Protective synthesis, see Detoxication
Proteinases, see Peptidases
Proteins, absorption, 243–4
— as enzymes, 14–23, 398–9
— biological value of, 259
— calorific value of, 457–8
— contractile, 389, 398–9
— denaturation of, 19–22, 242
— deprivation of, 258
— digestion of, 86–92, 242–4
— excess, metabolism of, 259–60
— excretory metabolism of, 301–29
— fat from, 259, 274
— functions of, 255–60
— general metabolism of, 255–72
— in glycogenesis, 259–60
— in ketogenesis, 259–60
— linkage with carbohydrate metabolism, 223–4, 259–60, 429, 436, 449
— minimum requirement of, 258–9
— nitrogenous end-products of, 301–29
— replacement of, by amino-acids, 244
— storage of, 260
— synthesis of, 135–6
Protocatechuic acid, 158
Protochordata, 340–1
Protozoa, 234, 239
Pseudomonas saccharophila, 126
Pterocera, 99
Purines, deamination of, 111, 301, 359–61
— end-products of metabolism of, 162, 361–2
— formation, 280, 297, 324–8
— in nucleoside formation, 353–4
— metabolism, 161–5, 327, 359–62
— methylated, 352
— occurrence, 329, 346, 350–2
— structure, 352, 360
— tautomerism, 352, 360
— urico-oxidase in metabolism of, 161–2, 326, 361–2
— xanthine oxidase in metabolism of, 163–5, 327, 359–61
Purpurogallin, 168
Putrescine, bacterial formation, 114, 294
— detoxication, 166, 294
Pyocyanine, 152, 184, 209

535

Sodium fluoride, *see* Fluoride

Sodium glycocholate, hydrotropic action of, 251–2

— in digestion, 248–53

— *see also* Bile salts

Sodium iodoacetate, *see* Iodoacetate

Sodium taurocholate, hydrotropic action of, 251–2

— in digestion, 248–53

— *see also* Bile salts

L-Sorbose, 127

Soya bean, 110

Spinach, 157

Specificity, of active groups in enzymes, 23, 35, 51

— of adsorption, 26

— of biological catalysts, 5

— of enzymes, absolute, 12

— — general, 9–14

— — group, 12

— — homo-, 93, 239

— — low, 11

— — optical, 9–12, 282

— — stereochemical, 9–12, 282

— of inorganic catalysts, 5

Specific inhibitors, *see* Selective inhibitors

Spermatozoa, creatine phosphate in, 405

— nucleoproteins in, 347

Spiders, excretion of guanine by, 329, 359

Spirogyra, 100

Spleen, 93

Sponge, agmatine in, 342

— digestion in, 239

Squash, 161

Squid, 'ink' of, 159

Stachydrine, 334–5

Starch, action of amylases on, 95–98, 245

— constitution, 95–6

— digestion of, 95–8, 245

— enzymic synthesis of, 129–33

— phosphorolysis of, 129, 412

Starfish, 344

Starvation, fatty liver in, 459

— glycogenesis in, 224, 273–4, 410

— ketogenesis in, 465–6, 481

— protein metabolism in, 258

Stearic acid, conversion to palmitic, 471

— desaturation in liver, 469

Stereochemical specificity, *see* Specificity

Stereoisomerism, of amino-acids and sugars, 277–80

Streptococcus faecalis, lactic fermentation by, 4

Strombus, 99

Suberic acid, 473

Substrates, activation of, 36–7, 51–2, 56

— compared with coenzymes, 46–7, 189–90

— — with prosthetic groups, 46–7

— union of, with enzyme, 23–37, 51

Succinic acid, as respiratory catalyst, 431–6

— formation of, from acetate, 489

— — from ethanol, 489

— — from α-ketoglutarate, 291, 434–5, 437–440, 447

— in citric cycle, 436–8, 444–7

— in dicarboxylic cycle, 489–90

— in fat metabolism, 473–5

— oxidation of, 448

— — and energy-rich bonds, 216

— synthesis from pyruvate, 428, 439–400

— *see also* Succinic dehydrogenase

Succinic dehydrogenase, coupling with lactic dehydrogenase, 209–10

— inhibition by iodoacetate, 191–2

— — by malonate, 13, 34, 191, 432–8, 440–1, 446

— inhibition by oxidation, 40, 192

— in citric cycle, 437–8, 447

— in dicarboxylic cycle, 489–90

— in tissue respiration, 148, 364–6, 430–6

— properties of, 190–2

— -SH groups of, 40, 191–2

— specificity of, 19, 121, 191

Sucrose, digestion of, 103, 245

— fermentation of, 367

— phosphorolysis of, 126–7

— synthesis of, 104, 126–7

Sucrose phosphorylase, 126–7

Sudan III, 253

Sugar-beet residues, 328

Sugars, stereoisomerism of, 277–80

Sulphatases, 104